적중100

영어 기출 문제집

중3

비상 | 김진완

Best Collection

구성과 특징

교과서의 주요 학습 내용을 중심으로 학습 영역별 특성에 맞춰 단계별로 다양한 학습 기회를 제공하여
단원별 학습능력 평가는 물론 중간 및 기말고사 시험 등에 완벽하게 대비할 수 있도록 내용을 구성

Words & Expressions

Step1   Key Words 단원별 핵심 단어 설명 및 풀이
            Key Expression 단원별 핵심 숙어 및 관용어 설명
            Word Power 반대 또는 비슷한 뜻 단어 배우기
            English Dictionary 영어로 배우는 영어 단어

Step2   실력평가 단원별 수시평가 대비 주관식, 객관식 문제풀이

Step3   서술형 대비 학업성취도 및 수행능력평가 대비 서술형 문제풀이

Conversation

Step1   핵심 의사소통 소통에 필요한 주요 표현 방법 요약
            핵심 Check 기본적인 표현 방법 및 활용능력 확인

Step2   대화문 익히기 교과서 대화문 심층 분석 및 확인

Step3   교과서 확인학습 빈칸 채우기를 통한 문장 완성 능력 확인

Step4   기본평가 시험대비 기초 학습 능력 평가

Step5   실력평가 단원별 수시평가 대비 주관식, 객관식 문제풀이

Step6   서술형 대비 학업성취도 및 수행능력평가 대비 서술형 문제풀이

Grammar

Step1   주요 문법 단원별 주요 문법 사항과 예문을 알기 쉽게 설명
            핵심 Check 기본 문법사항에 대한 이해 여부 확인

Step2   기본평가 시험대비 기초 학습 능력 평가

Step3   실력평가 단원별 수시평가 대비 주관식, 객관식 문제풀이

Step4   서술형 대비 학업성취도 및 수행능력평가 대비 서술형 문제풀이

Reading

Step1   구문 분석 단원별로 제시된 문장에 대한 구문별 분석과 내용 설명
            확인문제 문장에 대한 기본적인 이해와 인지능력 확인

Step2   확인학습A 빈칸 채우기를 통한 문장 완성 능력 확인

Step3   확인학습B 제시된 우리말을 영어로 완성하여 작문 능력 키우기

Step4   실력평가 단원별 수시평가 대비 주관식, 객관식 문제풀이

Step5   서술형 대비 학업성취도 및 수행능력평가 대비 서술형 문제풀이
            교과서 구석구석 교과서에 나오는 기타 문장까지 완벽 학습

Composition

|영역별 핵심문제|

단어 및 어휘, 대화문, 문법, 독해 등 각 영역별 기출문제의 출제 유형을 분석하여 실전에 대비하고 연습할 수 있도록 문제를 배열

|단원별 예상문제|

기출문제를 분석한 후 새로운 시험 출제 경향을 더하여 새롭게 출제될 수 있는 문제를 포함하여 시험에 완벽하게 대비할 수 있도록 준비

|서술형 실전 및 창의사고력 문제|

학교 시험에서 점차 늘어나는 서술형 시험에 집중 대비하고 고득점을 취득하는데 만전을 기하기 위한 학습 코너

|단원별 모의고사|

영역별, 단계별 학습을 모두 마친 후 실전 연습을 위한 모의고사

교과서 파헤치기

- **단어Test1~3** 영어 단어 우리말 쓰기, 우리말을 영어 단어로 쓰기, 영영풀이에 해당하는 단어와 우리말 쓰기
- **대화문Test1~2** 대화문 빈칸 완성 및 전체 대화문 쓰기
- **본문Test1~5** 빈칸 완성, 우리말 쓰기, 문장 배열연습, 영어 작문하기 복습 등 단계별 반복 학습을 통해 교과서 지문에 대한 완벽한 습득
- **구석구석지문Test1~2** 지문 빈칸 완성 및 전문 영어로 쓰기

이책의 차례

Contents

Lesson ① **The Art of Communication** 5

Lesson ② **Wonderful Nature** 59

Lesson ③ **For the Love of Our Country** 115

〈Insight on the textbook〉 교과서 파헤치기 01~64

〈책 속의 책〉 정답 및 해설 01~48

The Art of Communication

 의사소통 기능

- 화가 난 감정 표현하기
  A: How come you don't talk much with Anna these days?
  B: Well, I'm upset about an argument we had.
- 오해 지적하기
  A: I got cold feet.
  B: That's too bad. How did you get a cold?
  A: No. That's not what I meant. I meant I got scared.

 언어 형식

- 관계대명사 what
  Starting a sentence with "I" can help him focus on **what** he feels.

- 관계부사
  Calli should pick a time **when** her mom is ready to listen.

Words & Expressions

Key Words

- **actually** [ǽktʃuəli] 부 사실은
- **argue** [ɑ́ːrgjuː] 동 말다툼하다, 언쟁하다
- **argument** [ɑ́ːrgjumənt] 명 주장, 논쟁
- **careless** [kɛ́ərlis] 형 부주의한, 조심성 없는
- **clip** [klip] 명 동영상
- **concentrate** [kɑ́nsəntrèit] 동 집중하다
- **consider** [kənsídər] 동 배려하다, 고려하다
- **copy** [kɑ́pi] 동 복사하다, 모방하다
- **demand** [dimǽnd] 명 요구
- **detail** [ditéil] 명 구체적 내용, 자세한 내용
- **direct** [dirékt] 형 직접적인, 단도직입적인
- **disappointed** [dìsəpɔ́intid] 형 실망한, 낙담한
- **diving** [dáiviŋ] 명 다이빙, 잠수
- **effectively** [iféktivli] 부 효과적으로
- **exam** [igzǽm] 명 시험
- **express** [ikspés] 동 표현하다, 나타내다
- **feeling** [fíːliŋ] 명 감정, 느낌
- **finish** [fíniʃ] 동 마치다, 끝나다
- **focus** [fóukəs] 동 집중하다
- **go** [gou] 동 (일의 진행이 어떻게) 되어가다, 진전되다
- **hairstyle** [hɛ́ərstàil] 명 머리 모양, 헤어 스타일
- **helpful** [hélpəl] 형 도움이 되는, 유용한
- **hide** [haid] 동 숨기다, 감추다
- **instead** [instéd] 부 그 대신에

- **long face** 우울한 얼굴
- **loudly** [láudi] 부 크게, 큰 소리로
- **mad** [mæd] 형 화난
- **mean** [miːn] 형 못된, 심술궂은 동 의미하다
- **pick** [pik] 동 선택하다, 고르다
- **prepare** [pripɛ́ər] 동 준비하다
- **prevent** [privént] 동 막다, 예방하다
- **probably** [prɑ́bəbli] 부 아마도
- **quiet** [kwáiət] 형 조용한, 소리 없는
- **reason** [ríːzn] 명 이유
- **relationship** [riléiʃənʃip] 명 관계
- **request** [rikwést] 명 요청
- **scared** [skɛərd] 형 두려워하는, 겁먹은
- **seem** [siːm] 동 (~처럼) 보이다, ~인 듯하다
- **simply** [símpli] 부 단순히
- **solve** [sɑlv] 동 해결하다
- **somewhere** [sʌ́mhwɛər] 부 어딘가에
- **text message** 문자 메세지
- **tired** [taiərd] 형 피곤한
- **trouble** [trʌ́bl] 명 고민, 문제
- **uncomfortable** [ʌnkʌ́mfərtbəl] 형 불편한
- **unhappy** [ʌnhǽpi] 형 불만스러운, 불행한
- **upset** [ʌ́pset] 형 화난, 기분 나쁜

Key Expressions

- **be busy 동사ing** ~하느라 바쁘다
- **be ready to 동사원형** ~할 준비가 되다
- **be upset about ~** ~에 대해서 화가 나다
- **cut ~ off** ~을 중단시키다, ~을 잘라내다
- **end up 동사ing** 결국 ~하게 되다
- **find out** 발견하다, 알아보다
- **first of all** 먼저, 무엇보다도
- **focus on** ~에 집중하다
- **free from** ~이 없는
- **get a good grade** 좋은 성적을 얻다
- **get cold feet** 긴장하다, 겁을 먹다
- **go on a trip** 여행가다
- **have a look** (한번) 보다
- **have one's head in the clouds** 공상에 잠겨 있다
- **hit the books** 공부하다
- **how come** 어찌하여, 왜
- **in class** 수업 중에
- **in the middle of** ~의 도중에, ~의 중간에

- **keep ~ in mind** ~을 명심하다, 마음에 담아 두다
- **keep 동사ing** ~을 계속하다, 반복하다
- **let one's hair down** 느긋하게 쉬다
- **let the cat out of the bag** 비밀을 누설하다
- **make a demand** 요구하다
- **on time** 정시에, 제때에
- **order+사람+around** ~에게 자꾸 이래라저래라 하다
- **point the finger at** ~을 비난하다
- **put on** 입다
- **B rather than A** A라기보다는 B
- **stop 동사ing** ~을 그만두다, ~하지 않게 되다
- **stressed out** 스트레스로 지친, 스트레스가 쌓인
- **such as** ~와 같은
- **take a look at** ~을 보다
- **tend to 동사원형** ~하는 경향이 있다
- **these days** 요즘
- **try to 동사원형** ~을 노력하다
- **work out** 해결하다

Word Power

※ 접두사 pre-, un-

- **pre**-는 '미리, 먼저(**before**, **beforehand**)'의 의미가 있는 접두사이다.
  - □ **pre**(= **before**) + **vent** → **prevent**(막다, 예방하다)
  - □ **pre**(= **before**) + **pare** → **prepare**(준비하다)
  - □ **pre**(= **before**) + **view**(보다) → **preview**(미리 보기; (시사, 시연 등을) 보다)
  - □ **pre**(= **before**) + **caution**(주의) → **precaution**(조심, 예방책)

- **un**-은 '부정(**not**)'의 의미가 있는 접두사이다.
  - □ **un**(= **not**) + **comfortable**(편안한) → **uncomfortable**(불편한)
  - □ **un**(= **not**) + **certain**(확실한) → **uncertain**(불확실한)
  - □ **un**(= **not**) + **friendly**(친절한) → **unfriendly**(불친절한)
  - □ **un**(= **not**) + **fortunate**(운이 좋은) → **unfortunate**(불운한, 불행한)
  - □ **un**(= **not**) + **fair**(공평한) → **unfair**(불공평한)
  - □ **un**(= **not**) + **likely**(~할 것 같은) → **unlikely**(~할 것 같지 않은)

English Dictionary

□ **argument** 주장, 논쟁
  → an angry disagreement between people
  사람들 간에 격심한 의견의 불일치

□ **concentrate** 집중하다
  → to give all your attention to the thing you are doing
  지금 하고 있는 일에 모든 주의를 기울이다

□ **consider** 배려하다, 고려하다
  → to think about someone's feelings or reactions
  어떤 사람의 감정이나 반응을 생각하다

□ **detail** 구체적 내용, 자세한 내용
  → one of many small facts or pieces of information relating to a situation
  어떤 상황에 관계된 많은 사소한 사실들이나 정보 중의 하나

□ **disappointed** 실망한, 낙담한
  → unhappy because something that you hoped for or expected did not happen or because someone or something was not as good as you expected
  바라거나 예상했던 것이 일어나지 않았거나, 예상했던 누군가나 어떤 것이 예상만큼 좋지 않아 행복하지 않은

□ **express** 표현하다, 나타내다
  → to tell someone about a feeling, opinion, or goal by speaking or writing about something
  어떤 것에 관해 말하거나 써서 감정, 의견 또는 목표를 말하다

□ **helpful** 도움이 되는, 유용한
  → useful, or providing help
  유용한 또는 도움을 제공하는

□ **hide** 숨기다, 감추다
  → to put something in a place so that no one can find or see it
  아무도 어떤 것을 찾거나 볼 수 없게 그것을 어떤 장소에 놓다

□ **long face** 우울한 얼굴
  → a sad, disappointed, or serious expression on someone's face 슬프거나, 실망한 또는 심각한 누군가의 얼굴 표정

□ **mad** 화난
  → angry 화난

□ **mean** 못된, 심술궂은
  → cruel or not kind 잔인한 또는 친절하지 않은

□ **reason** 이유
  → a fact, situation, or intention that explains why something happened, why someone did something, or why something is true
  왜 어떤 일이 발생했는지, 왜 누군가가 그것을 행했는지, 또는 왜 그것이 진짜인지 등에 대해 설명하는 사실이나 상황 또는 의도

□ **scared** 두려워하는, 겁먹은
  → frightened, or worried
  겁먹은, 또는 걱정하는

□ **solve** 해결하다
  → to find a solution to something that is causing difficulties
  어려움을 유발하는 어떤 것에 대한 해결책을 찾다

□ **unhappy** 불만스러운, 불행한
  → feeling sad or upset
  슬프거나 속상한

□ **upset** 화난, 기분 나쁜
  → very sad, worried, or angry about something
  무언가에 대해 매우 슬프거나, 걱정하는, 또는 화가 나는

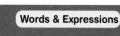
[01~02] 다음 밑줄 친 부분과 의미가 가장 가까운 것을 고르시오.

01

Why are you so upset?

① tired ② scared ③ angry
④ serious ⑤ disappointed

02

Stop talking and concentrate on your work.

① try ② bring ③ make
④ focus ⑤ enjoy

03 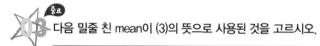 다음 밑줄 친 mean이 (3)의 뜻으로 사용된 것을 고르시오.

(1) to have a particular meaning
(2) to intend to do something or intend that someone else should do something
(3) cruel or not kind

① I didn't mean to upset you.
② It's a mean trick to play on a friend.
③ What I mean is that I don't feel alone anymore.
④ I've been meaning to ask you if you want to come for a meal next week.
⑤ Oh, yeah! I see what you mean.

04 다음 빈칸에 공통으로 들어갈 말을 고르시오.

• By the end of the semester I was totally stressed _____.
• I'm glad everything worked _____ fine.

① on ② in ③ out
④ off ⑤ for

05 다음 주어진 표현과 이에 대한 뜻이 바르게 연결되지 않은 것을 고르시오.

① get cold feet – become too nervous and worried to do something
② have one's head in the clouds – very happy because something very good has happened
③ hit the books – study
④ let one's hair down – relax and enjoy and do not worry about behaving correctly
⑤ let the cat out of the bag – reveal something secret or private

06 다음 빈칸 (A)~(C)에 알맞은 말로 짝지어진 것을 고르시오.

• Mike is free (A)_____ cares.
• We may never find (B)_____ the truth about what happened.
• First (C)_____ all, clean the surface that you are going to paint.

(A) (B) (C)
① for – out – of
② for – of – to
③ from – out – of
④ from – of – for
⑤ from – out – to

07 다음 빈칸에 알맞은 단어를 고르시오. (2개)

This week, let's _____ a look at some of the characteristics of successful people.

① take ② do ③ give
④ bring ⑤ have

01 다음 밑줄 친 부분의 쓰임이 자연스럽지 <u>않은</u> 것을 찾아 고치시오.

> ⓐ I'm busy <u>studying</u> for the midterm exam.
> ⓑ We're not <u>ready leaving</u> yet!
> ⓒ Customers <u>end up to spend</u> more money than they should.

➡ _____

_____

[02~03] 두 문장이 같은 의미가 되도록 빈칸을 채우시오. (철자가 주어진 경우 주어진 철자로 시작할 것)

02

> Sally got scared at the last moment.
> = Sally got c_____ f_____ at the last moment.

03

> Remember that when you come to make your decision.
> = K_____ that _____ _____ when you come to make your decision.

04 다음 우리말에 맞도록 빈칸에 알맞은 말을 쓰시오. (철자가 주어진 경우 주어진 철자로 시작할 것)

(1) 그 시스템이 지역 사회에 서비스를 더 효과적으로 줄 수 있다.
➡ The system can deliver services to local communities more _____.

(2) 그녀는 Tom이 그녀의 편지에 답장을 하지 않아서 낙담했다.
➡ She was d_____ that Tom never replied to her letter.

(3) 그는 뛰어가서 덤불 뒤로 숨었다.
➡ He ran and _____ behind a bush.

(4) 왜 그토록 많은 사람이 병에 걸리는지에 대한 이유는 여전히 명확하지 않다.
➡ The r_____ why so many people caught the disease is still not clear.

05 다음 빈칸에 공통으로 들어갈 말을 쓰시오.

> • It has been a _____ cold winter this year.
> • He has had a _____ face ever since he failed the examination.

06 다음 우리말에 맞게 주어진 단어를 바르게 배열하시오.

(1) 많은 나무들은 홍수로부터 산사태를 막는 데 도움을 줄 수 있다.
(from, trees, prevent, flood, many, landslides, to, can, help)
➡ _____

(2) 그녀는 당신이 당신의 문제를 해결하도록 도와줄 수 있다.
(solve, she, problem, can, your, you, help)
➡ _____

(3) 이 코트는 입기에 불편하다.
(this, to, uncomfortable, is, wear, coat)
➡ _____

(4) 그 대신에 너의 노력이 중요하다.
(your, important, instead, is, effort)
➡ _____

교과서

Conversation

1 화가 난 감정 표현하기

> **A:** How come you don't talk much with Anna these days? 요즘 너는 왜 Anna와 별로 말을 하지 않니?
> **B:** Well, I'm upset about an argument we had. 음. 나는 우리가 한 논쟁에 화가 나.

■ 'be upset about ~'은 '~에 대해서 화가 난다'라는 의미로 화가 난 감정을 나타낼 때 사용하는 표현이다. 화남을 나타내는 또 다른 표현으로는 'be angry at[with] ~', 'be mad at ~', 'be upset with[because of] ~', 등이 있다. 그 외에도 'be annoyed with ~', 'can't stand ~', 'make me mad' 등을 이용해 화가 났음을 나타낼 수 있다.

화남을 나타내는 표현

- I am upset about[with, because of] ~. (나는 ~에 대해[~에게, ~ 때문에] 화가 나.)
- I am mad at ~.   • I am angry at[with] ~.
- I am annoyed with[by] ~.   • I can't stand ~. (나는 ~을 참을 수 없어.)
- ~ make(s) me mad. (~은 나를 화나게 해.)

핵심 Check

1. 다음 우리말과 일치하도록 주어진 단어를 배열하여 문장을 쓰시오.

   > **A:** _____ (friend, upset, I, with, am, my)
   > (나는 내 친구 때문에 화가 나.)
   > **B:** What's the matter?
   > **A:** She forgot my birthday.

2. 다음 대화의 순서를 바르게 배열하시오.

   > (A) She tore my book.
   > (B) What did she do?
   > (C) I'm upset with my dog.

   ➡ _____

3. 다음 문장과 같은 의미가 되도록 주어진 단어를 이용하여 쓰시오.

   > I'm very upset because of my sisters.

   ➡ _____ (angry)

2 오해 지적하기

A: I got cold feet. 난 겁이 났어.

B: That's too bad. How did you get a cold? 그거 안 됐구나. 어떻게 감기에 걸렸니?

A: No. That's not what I meant. I meant I got scared. 아니. 그런 뜻이 아니야. 내가 겁먹었다는 뜻이야.

■ That's not what I meant.는 '그런 뜻이 아니야.'라는 의미이며, 상대방이 자신의 말의 의도를 오해할 때 정정하기 위해 쓰는 표현이다. 'That's not what I meant to say.', 'I didn't mean to say that.', 'I hope there is no misunderstanding.' 등도 비슷한 표현이다.

■ 오해를 지적하는 말을 하고, 이어서 'I mean[meant] ~.'을 이용해서 자신이 의도했던 바를 얘기할 수 있다.

오해 지적하기

- That's not what I meant. (내가 의미한 것은 그게 아니야.)
- I didn't mean to say that. (그 말을 하려던 것이 아니었어.)
- I'm afraid you don't understand what I'm saying. (제가 하는 말을 이해 못 하시는 것 같군요.)

핵심 Check

4. 다음 우리말과 일치하도록 빈칸에 알맞은 말을 쓰시오.

> **A:** Let's hit the road!
> **B:** Why do you want to hit the road?
> **A:** _____ _____ let's start our trip.
> (그런 뜻이 아니야. 그건 여행을 시작하자는 말이야.)

5. 다음 대화의 순서를 바르게 배열하시오.

> (A) That's not what I meant to say. I mean you should eat more vegetables.
> (B) You are eating too much meat.
> (C) Do you think I should not eat meat?

➡ _____

Listen & Talk 1 A-1

M: Sally, ❶how come you don't talk much with Anna these days?

W: Well, ❷I'm upset about an argument we had.

M: Why are you upset?

W: She ❸kept cutting me off ❹in the middle of my sentences, so I ❺got mad. We ❻argued and I ❼stopped talking to her.

M: Oh, ❽I'm sorry to hear that.

M: Sally야, 요즘에 왜 Anna와 많이 대화를 하지 않니?
W: 음, 나는 우리가 한 논쟁 때문에 화가 나.
M: 왜 화가 난 거야?
W: 그녀가 계속해서 내가 말을 하고 있는 도중에 끊어서 화가 났어. 우리는 논쟁을 했고, 나는 그녀와 이야기를 하지 않았어.
M: 오, 그거 유감이구나.

❶ how come을 이용해서 상대방에게 이유를 물을 수 있다. 이때 그 다음에 '주어+동사'의 어순이 이어지는 것에 주의해야 한다. talk with ~: ~와 대화를 나누다 much는 '많이'의 뜻인 부사로 talk를 수식하고 있다. these days: 요즘

❷ upset: 화난, 기분 나쁜 'an argument'와 'we had' 사이에는 목적격 관계대명사 which 또는 that이 생략되어 있다.

❸ keep은 동명사를 목적어로 가지는 동사이다. cut ~ off: ~을 중단시키다, ~을 잘라내다

❹ in the middle of: ~ 도중에, ~ 중간에

❺ got 대신에 was나 felt를 대신 사용할 수 있다.

❻ argue: 말다툼하다, 언쟁하다

❼ stop 동사ing: ~을 그만두다, ~하지 않게 되다

❽ 'I'm sorry to hear that.'은 '유감이구나.'란 의미로 상대방에게 유감이나 동정을 표현할 때 사용하는 표현이다.

Check(√) True or False

(1) Sally doesn't talk to Anna these days. T ☐ F ☐

(2) The man is asking why Sally is happy. T ☐ F ☐

Listen & Talk 2 A-2

W: Did you finally ❶go diving yesterday, Nick?

M: ❷Actually, I ❸got cold feet, Mina.

W: That's too bad. How did you get a cold?

M: No, Mina. ❹That's not what I meant. ❺I meant that I got scared, so I didn't dive.

W: Nick, 어제 드디어 다이빙하러 갔니?
M: 미나야, 사실 난 겁이 났어.
W: 그거 안 됐구나. 어떻게 감기에 걸렸니?
M: 아니, 미나야. 그건 그런 뜻이 아니야. 내가 겁을 먹어서 다이빙을 안 했다는 뜻이야.

❶ go diving: 다이빙하러 가다

❷ actually: 사실은

❸ 'get cold feet' 또는 'have cold feet'은 어떤 것에 대해 긴장하거나(nervous), 걱정하거나(worried), 겁이 날 때(scared) 쓰는 표현이다.

❹ 'That's not what I meant.'는 '그런 뜻이 아니야.'라는 의미이며, 상대방이 자신의 말을 오해할 때 이를 정정하기 위해 쓰는 표현이다.

❺ meant 다음의 that은 접속사로 meant의 목적어를 이끌어 주는 역할을 하고 있으며 생략할 수 있다.

Check(√) True or False

(3) Nick caught a cold. T ☐ F ☐

(4) Nick didn't dive yesterday. T ☐ F ☐

Listen & Talk 1 A-2

W: How is your science homework ❶going?

M: Not good. ❷I'm upset about my science group.

W: ❸What's wrong?

M: The group members only speak and never listen. I don't think that we can finish the homework ❹on time.

W: That's too bad.

W: 너의 과학 숙제는 어떻게 되어 가고 있니?

M: 좋지 않아. 나는 나의 과학 그룹에 화가 나.

W: 뭐가 문제인데?

M: 그룹 구성원들이 말만 하고 전혀 듣지 않아. 나는 우리가 숙제를 제시간에 끝낼 수 있을 거라고 생각하지 않아.

W: 그것 참 안 됐구나.

❶ go: (일의 진행이 어떻게) 되어가다, 진전되다

❷ upset: 화난, 기분 나쁜 어떤 상황에 대하여 화가 났음을 말할 때 'I'm upset about+명사'로 표현할 수 있다.

❸ 'What's wrong?'은 상대방의 슬픔이나 불만족, 실망의 원인에 관해 물을 때 사용되는 표현으로 'What's the matter to you?', 'What's the problem?', 'Is there anything wrong?', 'What happened to you?' 등으로 바꿔 쓸 수 있다.

❹ on time: 정시에, 제때에

Check(√) True or False

(5) The man is pleased with his science group.   T ☐ F ☐

(6) The man hopes that his science group can finish the homework on time.   T ☐ F ☐

Listen & Talk 1 B

M: ❶Why the long face, Julie?

W: I ❷got angry at my sister yesterday and said some mean things to her.

M: Oh, why were you angry?

W: I was really tired and I wanted to sleep. But she ❸was talking loudly on the phone. I was really upset about that.

M: I see. And you two ❹haven't worked it out yet?

W: No, not yet. I want to say I'm sorry that I was mean to her, but I don't know ❺how.

M: ❻Why don't you write her a note or send her a text message?

W: Hmm, that's a good idea. Thanks.

M: 왜 그렇게 우울한 얼굴이니, Julie?

W: 어제 내 여동생한테 화가 나서 그녀에게 심술궂은 말을 했어.

M: 오, 왜 화가 났니?

W: 정말 피곤해서 자고 싶었어. 하지만 여동생은 전화로 큰 소리로 이야기하고 있었어. 나는 그것에 대해 정말 화가 났어.

M: 그렇구나. 그리고 너희 둘은 아직 화해하지 않았니?

W: 아니, 아직이야. 내가 여동생에게 심술궂게 굴어서 미안하다고 말하고 싶지만, 방법을 모르겠어.

M: 그녀에게 편지를 쓰거나 문자 메시지를 보내는 게 어때?

W: 음, 좋은 생각이야. 고마워.

❶ the long face: 우울한 얼굴

❷ 'get angry at'을 이용해서 화남을 나타내고 있다. 같은 의미의 표현들로 'be upset at[with, because of]', 'be mad at', 'be angry at[with]', 'be annoyed with[by]' 등이 있다.

❸ talk on the phone: 전화로 얘기하다 loudly는 동사인 talk를 수식하고 있다.

❹ work out: 해결하다 'you two haven't worked it out yet?'의 문장에서 동사는 현재완료의 '완료 용법'으로 사용되고 있다.

❺ how 다음에 'to say I'm sorry that I was mean to her'가 생략되어 있다.

❻ 'Why don't you ~?'는 '~하는 건 어때?'의 의미로 상대방에게 충고할 때 쓰는 표현이다. 'You'd better ~.', 'I advice you to ~.' 등으로 바꿔 쓸 수 있다.

Check(√) True or False

(7) Julie said some mean things to her sister yesterday.   T ☐ F ☐

(8) Julie and her sister have worked it out already.   T ☐ F ☐

Listen & Talk 1 Get Ready

A: Why do you ❶look so unhappy?

B: I'm upset about Roy. He always copies me.

A: ❷Don't take it so hard.

❶ look+형용사: ～하게 보이다 unhappy: 불만스러운, 불행한
❷ 'Don't take it so hard.'는 상대방의 안 좋은 상황을 위로하는 표현으로 'Don't feel so bad.'로 사용할 수 있다.

Listen & Talk 2 Get Ready

A: Don't ❶let the cat out of the bag about Clara's surprise party.

B: A cat? I don't have a cat.

A: ❷That's not what I meant. ❸Keep her party a secret.

❶ "let the cat out of the bag: 비밀을 누설하다
❷ That's not what I meant.: 그건 그런 뜻이 아니야.
❸ keep이 5형식으로 사용되어 her party가 목적어, a secret이 목적격 보어이다.

Listen & Talk 2 A-1

W: Mr. Brown, I want to ❶get a good grade in English. What should I do?

M: Well, Sujin, ❷you should concentrate in class, ❸first of all. I see you often ❹have your head in the clouds.

W: Clouds? I can't see the sky from inside the classroom.

M: ❺That's not what I meant. I meant you don't ❻focus in class.

❶ get a good grade: 좋은 성적을 얻다.
❷ 충고를 할 때는 'You should ～'로 말할 수 있다. 이외에 'You'd better ～.', 'Why don't you ～?', 'What[How] about ～?', 'I advise you to ～.' 등을 이용해 충고할 수 있다. concentrate: 집중하다
❸ first of all: 먼저, 무엇보다도
❹ have one's head in the clouds: 공상에 잠겨 있다
❺ 'That's not what I meant.'는 '그런 뜻이 아니야.'라는 의미이며 상대방이 자신의 말의 의도를 오해할 때 정정하기 위해 쓰는 표현이다.
❻ focus: 집중하다 in class: 수업 중에

Listen & Talk 2 B

W: I'm so ❶stressed out about my exams, Jinsu.

M: Yeah, me, too. ❷We have two more to go.

W: After finishing my exams, ❸I want to go on a trip and just let my hair down.

M: You want to change your hair style?

W: No, that's not what I meant. I want to go somewhere and ❹feel free from all my troubles.

❶ stressed out: 스트레스로 지친, 스트레스가 쌓인
❷ two more 다음에 exams가 생략되어 있다.
❸ go on a trip: 여행가다 let one's hair down: 느긋하게 쉬다
❹ 접속사 and로 to go somewhere와 feel free from all my troubles가 병렬 관계를 이루고 있다. feel free from all my troubles 앞에 to가 생략되어 있다. free from: ～이 없는 trouble: 고민, 문제

Communication

W: Hey, Jason. You ❶seem upset. ❷Anything wrong?

M: People keep ❸telling me that I'm too direct. I'm upset about that.

W: Hmm.... ❹I kind of know what they're talking about.

M: What do you mean?

W: Well, ❺sometimes you tend to say what's on your mind too strongly.

M: Should I just keep quiet, then?

W: ❻That's not what I meant. You can ❼try to consider others' feelings.

M: I see. I'll try that.

❶ seem: ～처럼 보이다 upset: 화난, 기분 나쁜
❷ 'Anything wrong?'은 '무슨 문제 있니?'의 뜻으로 상대방의 슬픔이나 불만족, 실망의 원인에 대해 물을 때 사용되는 표현이다. 'What's wrong?', 'What's the problem?', 'Is there anything wrong?', 'What happened to you?', 'Why the long face?' 등으로 바꿔 쓸 수 있다.
❸ tell이 4형식 동사로 me가 간접목적어, that I'm too direct가 직접목적어이다. direct: 딱 부러지는, 단도직입적인
❹ kind of: 약간, 어느 정도
❺ tend to 동사원형: ～하는 경향이 있다 what's on your mind에서 what은 관계대명사로 '～하는 것'으로 해석한다. the thing(s) which[that]으로 바꿔 쓸 수 있다.
❻ That's not what I meant: 그건 그런 뜻이 아니야.
❼ try to 동사원형: ～하려고 노력하다 consider: 배려하다, 고려하다 other'=other people's

● 다음 우리말과 일치하도록 빈칸에 알맞은 말을 쓰시오.

Listen & Talk 1 Get Ready

A: _____ do you look so _____?

B: I'm upset _____ Roy. He always copies me.

A: Don't _____ _____ so hard.

해석

A: 너는 왜 침울해 보이니?
B: 나는 Roy한테 화가 나. 그는 항상 나를 따라 해.
A: 너무 속상해 하지 마.

Listen & Talk 1 A-1

M: Sally, how _____ you don't talk much _____ Anna _____ _____?

W: Well, I'm _____ _____ _____ _____ we had.

M: _____ are you upset?

W: She kept _____ _____ _____ _____ the middle of my sentences, so I got _____. We argued and I stopped _____ _____ her.

M: Oh, I'm sorry to hear that.

M: Sally야, 요즘에 왜 Anna와 별로 대화를 하지 않니?
W: 음, 나는 우리가 한 논쟁 때문에 화가 나.
M: 왜 화가 난 거야?
W: 그녀가 계속해서 내가 말을 하고 있는 도중에 끊어서 화가 났어. 우리는 논쟁을 했고, 나는 그녀와 이야기를 하지 않았어.
M: 오, 그거 유감이구나.

Listen & Talk 1 A-2

W: _____ is your science homework _____?

M: Not good. _____ _____ _____ my science group.

W: What's wrong?

M: The group members only speak and never listen. _____ _____ _____ _____ we can finish the homework _____ time.

W: That's too bad.

W: 너의 과학 숙제는 어떻게 되어 가고 있니?
M: 좋지 않아. 나는 나의 과학 그룹에 화가 나.
W: 뭐가 문제인데?
M: 그룹 구성원들이 말만 하고 전혀 듣지 않아. 나는 우리가 숙제를 제시간에 끝낼 수 있을 거라고 생각하지 않아.
W: 그것 참 안 되었구나.

Listen & Talk 1 B

M: _____ the _____ face, Julie?

W: I got _____ _____ my sister yesterday and _____ _____ _____ things to her.

M: Oh, why were you angry?

W: I was really tired and I wanted _____ _____. _____ she was _____ _____ _____ _____. I was really _____ about that.

M: 왜 그렇게 우울한 얼굴이니, Julie?
W: 어제 여동생한테 화가 나서 그녀에게 심술궂은 말을 했어.
M: 오, 왜 화가 났니?
W: 정말 피곤해서 자고 싶었어. 하지만 여동생은 전화로 큰 소리로 이야기하고 있었어. 나는 그것에 대해 정말 화가 났어.

M: I see. And you two _____ _____ _____ out yet?

W: No, not yet. I want to say I'm sorry _____ I was mean to her, _____ _____ _____ _____ _____ _____.

M: _____ don't you write her a note or _____ her a text message?

W: Hmm, that's a good idea. Thanks.

해석

M: 그렇구나. 그리고 너희 둘은 아직 화 해하지 않았니?

W: 아니, 아직이야. 내가 여동생에게 심 술궂게 굴어서 미안하다고 말하고 싶 지만, 방법을 모르겠어.

M: 그녀에게 편지를 쓰거나 문자 메시 지를 보내는 게 어때?

W: 음, 좋은 생각이야. 고마워.

Listen & Talk 2 Get Ready

A: Don't _____ _____ _____ _____ _____ _____ _____ about Clara's surprise party.

B: A cat? I don't have a cat.

A: _____ _____ _____ I meant. Keep her party _____ _____.

A: Clara의 깜짝 파티에 대해 비밀을 누 설하지 마.

B: 고양이? 나는 고양이가 없어.

A: 그건 그런 뜻이 아니야. 그녀의 파티 를 비밀로 해.

Listen & Talk 2 A-1

W: Mr. Brown, I want to _____ a good grade _____ English. What _____ I do?

M: Well, Sujin, you should _____ in class, _____ _____ _____. I see you often _____ _____ _____ _____ _____ _____.

W: Clouds? I can't _____ _____ _____ from inside the classroom.

M: _____ _____ _____ _____ _____ _____. I _____ you don't _____ in class.

W: Brown 선생님, 저는 영어에서 좋은 점수를 받고 싶어요. 어떻게 해야 하 죠?

M: 음, 수진아, 너는 우선 수업에 집중 해야 해. 난 네가 종종 공상에 잠겨 있는 것을 본단다.

W: 구름이요? 교실 안에서는 하늘을 볼 수 없어요.

M: 그건 그런 뜻이 아니야. 내 말은 네 가 수업에 집중하지 않는다는 거야.

Listen & Talk 2 A-2

W: Did you finally _____ _____ yesterday, Nick?

M: Actually, I _____ _____ _____, Mina.

W: That's too bad. How did you _____ _____ _____?

M: No, Mina. That's not what I meant. _____ _____ _____ I got _____, so I didn't dive.

Listen & Talk 2 B

W: I'm so _____ _____ _____ my exams, Jinsu.

M: Yeah, me, too. We have _____ _____ _____ _____.

W: After _____ my exams, I want to _____ _____ _____ trip and just let my _____ _____.

M: You want to change your _____ _____?

W: No, that's not _____ _____ _____. I want to go somewhere and _____ _____ all my troubles.

Communication

W: Hey, Jason. You _____ upset. Anything wrong?

M: People _____ _____ _____ _____ I'm too _____. I'm _____ about that.

W: Hmm…. I kind of know _____ _____ _____.

M: What do you mean?

W: Well, sometimes you _____ _____ _____ _____ _____ your mind too _____.

M: _____ I just keep quiet, then?

W: _____ _____ _____ _____ _____. You can _____ _____ _____ others' feelings.

M: I see. I'll _____ that.

01 다음 대화의 밑줄 친 문장과 같은 의미의 문장을 고르시오.

> A: I got cold feet.
> B: That's too bad. How did you get a cold?
> A: No. <u>That's not what I meant.</u> I meant I got scared.

① That's all right.

② I mean to say that.

③ I'm afraid you don't understand what I'm saying.

④ That's not my problem.

⑤ You got it.

02 다음 대화의 순서를 바르게 배열한 것을 고르시오.

> (A) She wears my clothes without asking me first.
> (B) I'm upset about my sister.
> (C) What's wrong?

① (A) – (C) – (B)　　　② (B) – (A) – (C)

③ (B) – (C) – (A)　　　④ (C) – (A) – (B)

⑤ (C) – (B) – (A)

[03~04] 다음 대화를 읽고 물음에 답하시오.

> W: Did you finally go diving yesterday, Nick?
> M: Actually, I got cold feet, Mina.
> W: That's too bad. (A)_____
> M: No, Mina. (B)(what, meant, that's, I, not). I meant that I got scared, so I didn't dive.

03 빈칸 (A)에 알맞은 말을 고르시오.

① How was the diving?

② Have you gotten cold feet?

③ How could you do that?

④ How did you get a cold?

⑤ Do you mean that you got scared?

04 괄호 (B) 안의 단어들을 순서대로 바르게 배열하시오.

➡ _____

01 다음 대화의 순서를 바르게 배열한 것을 고르시오.

(A) Well, Sujin, you should concentrate in class, first of all. I see you often have your head in the clouds.

(B) Clouds? I can't see the sky from inside the classroom.

(C) Mr. Brown, I want to get a good grade in English. What should I do?

(D) That's not what I meant. I meant you don't focus in class.

① (B) – (A) – (C) – (D)
② (B) – (C) – (A) – (D)
③ (C) – (A) – (B) – (D)
④ (C) – (B) – (A) – (D)
⑤ (C) – (D) – (B) – (A)

[02~04] 다음 대화를 읽고 물음에 답하시오.

W: Hey, Jason. You seem upset. (①) Anything wrong?

M: People keep telling me that I'm too direct. I'm upset about that. (②)

W: Hmm…. I kind of know what they're talking about.

M: (A)_____

W: Well, sometimes you tend to say what's on your mind too strongly. (③)

M: Should I just keep quiet, then? (④)

W: (⑤) You can try to consider others' feelings.

M: I see. I'll try that.

02 위 대화의 ①~⑤ 중 주어진 문장이 들어갈 알맞은 곳은?

That's not what I meant.

① ② ③ ④ ⑤

03 빈칸 (A)에 알맞은 말을 고르시오.

① What do you mean?
② Why are you upset?
③ Whom do you want to talk to?
④ What should I do?
⑤ Why don't you talk with them?

04 위 대화의 내용과 일치하지 <u>않는</u> 것은?

① 여자는 Jason이 가끔 말을 강하게 한다고 생각한다.
② 여자는 Jason이 다른 사람의 감정을 이해할 필요가 있다고 생각한다.
③ Jason은 사람들이 Jason에게 조용히 하라고 한 것에 대해 화가 났다.
④ 여자는 사람들이 Jason에 대해 이야기한 것을 어느 정도 이해하고 있다.
⑤ Jason은 단도직입적이라는 말을 사람들에게 들었다.

[05~06] 다음 대화를 읽고 물음에 답하시오.

A: Why do you look so (A)_____?
B: (B)I'm upset about Roy. He always copies me.
A: Don't take it so hard.

서답형
05 빈칸 (A)에 알맞은 말을 주어진 단어를 이용해서 채우시오.

➡ _____ (happy)

밑줄 친 (B)와 바꿔 쓸 수 있는 것을 고르시오.

① I don't care about Roy.

② Roy never makes me angry.

③ Roy seems to be angry.

④ I don't satisfied with Roy.

⑤ I can't stand Roy.

07 다음 대화의 빈칸에 들어갈 말을 〈보기〉에서 골라 순서대로 바르게 배열한 것은?

> M: Why the long face, Julie?
>
> W: _____
>
> M: _____
>
> W: _____
>
> M: _____
>
> W: No, not yet. I want to say I'm sorry that I was mean to her, but I don't know how.
>
> M: Why don't you write her a note or send her a text message?
>
> W: Hmm, that's a good idea. Thanks.

┌─ 보기 ─┐

(A) Oh, why were you angry?

(B) I got angry at my sister yesterday and said some mean things to her.

(C) I was really tired and I wanted to sleep. But she was talking loudly on the phone. I was really upset about that.

(D) I see. And you two haven't worked it out yet?

① (B) – (A) – (C) – (D)

② (B) – (C) – (A) – (D)

③ (C) – (A) – (B) – (D)

④ (C) – (B) – (A) – (D)

⑤ (C) – (D) – (B) – (A)

[08~09] 다음 대화를 읽고 물음에 답하시오.

> A: Don't let the cat out of the bag about Clara's surprise party.
>
> B: A cat? I don't have a cat.
>
> A: (A)_____ Keep her party a secret.

08 빈칸 (A)에 알맞은 말을 고르시오.

① I didn't hear you.

② That's not what I meant.

③ What you are saying is right.

④ I think so, too.

⑤ Don't misunderstand me.

09 According to the dialogue, what did A intend to say to B?

① A wants to go to Clara's birthday party.

② B wants to let the cat out of A's bag.

③ A wants B to bring Clara a cat.

④ A wants to keep Clara's surprise party a secret.

⑤ A wants to have a cat.

 다음 중 짝지어진 대화가 <u>어색한</u> 것은?

① A: I'm really angry at Jenmy.

　B: What did she do?

　A: She borrowed my English book, but I found some pages missing.

② A: You look so annoyed. What's wrong?

　B: One of the members in the science group doesn't do any work.

③ A: I'm angry at my brother.

　B: He didn't do well on the test.

④ A: What's the matter?

　B: I can't stand my older sister's behavior.

⑤ A: How come you are so upset?

　B: I'm angry with my best friend for forgetting my birthday.

[01~02] 다음 대화를 읽고 물음에 답하시오.

M: How come you don't talk much with Anna these days?

W: Well, (A)_____ (upset, an, we, I, argument, am, about, had)

M: Why are you upset?

W: She kept cutting me (B)_____ in the middle of my sentences, so I got mad. We argued and I stopped talking to her.

M: Oh, I'm sorry to hear that.

01 빈칸 (A)를 괄호 안에 주어진 단어를 알맞게 배열하여 채우시오.

➡ _____

02 빈칸 (B)에 알맞은 전치사를 쓰시오.

➡ _____

[03~04] 다음 대화를 읽고 물음에 답하시오.

M: You look upset, Anna. What's wrong?

W: Well, I'm upset about my sister, Elsa.

M: (A)왜 너는 그녀에게 화가 났니?

W: She keeps (B)_____ (order) me around.

M: Oh, maybe you should tell her how you feel.

03 밑줄 친 (A)의 우리말을 대화에 나온 단어를 이용해 영작하시오.

➡ _____

04 빈칸 (B)를 괄호 안에 주어진 단어를 이용하여 채우시오.

➡ _____

[05~07] 다음 대화를 읽고 물음에 답하시오.

W: I'm so stressed (A)_____ about my exams, Jinsu.

M: Yeah, me, too. We have two more to (B)_____.

W: After finishing my exams, I want to (C)_____ on a trip and just let my hair down.

M: You want to change your hair style?

W: No, (D)that's not what I meant. I want to go somewhere and feel free from all my troubles.

05 빈칸 (A)에 알맞은 단어를 쓰시오.

➡ _____

06 빈칸 (B)와 (C)에 공통으로 들어갈 단어를 쓰시오.

➡ _____

07 밑줄 친 문장 (D)와 같은 의미가 되도록 주어진 단어를 이용해 쓰시오. (say, mean, 6단어)

➡ _____

08 밑줄 친 ⓐ~ⓔ 중 어법상 어색한 것을 바르게 고치시오.

W: Mr. Brown, ⓐI want to get a good grade in English. ⓑWhat should I do?

M: Well, Sujin, ⓒyou should concentrate in class, first of all. I see you often have your head in the clouds.

W: Clouds? ⓓI can't see the sky from inside the classroom.

M: ⓔThat's not that I meant. I meant you don't focus in class.

➡ _____

Grammar

① 관계대명사 what

> • Starting a sentence with "I" can help him focus on **what** he feels.
> "I"로 문장을 시작하는 것은 그가 자신이 느끼는 것에 초점을 맞추도록 도울 수 있어.
>
> • That is **what** I was afraid of. 그것이 제가 우려했던 바예요.

■ 관계대명사 what은 다른 관계대명사와 다르게 선행사를 포함한 관계대명사로 '~하는 것'으로 해석하며, the thing(s) which[that]의 의미이다.

- Tell me **what** you think about Susie. Susie를 어떻게 생각하는지 말해 줘.
  (= Tell me the thing which[that] you think about Susie.)

■ 관계대명사 what이 이끄는 절은 명사절로 문장에서 주어, 보어, 목적어의 역할을 한다.

　(1) 주어 역할

- **What** he really wanted was revenge. 그가 정말 원했던 것은 복수였다.

　(2) 보어 역할

- It was **what** I should do. 그건 제가 해야 하는 것이었어요.

　(3) 목적어 역할

- Do you know **what** she said? 그녀가 뭐랬는지 알아? (동사의 목적어)
- You need to pay attention to **what** you eat. 여러분은 자신이 무엇을 먹는지에 대해 신경을 쓸 필요가 있습니다. (전치사의 목적어)

■ 관계대명사 what의 관용적인 표현

- He is **what is called** a young prince. 그는 소위 귀공자다.
- You should be satisfied with **what you** have. 당신은 당신이 가지고 있는 것에 만족해야 한다.
- **What is worse**, he lost his health. 설상가상으로 그는 건강까지 잃었다.

핵심 Check

1. 다음 우리말과 일치하도록 빈칸에 알맞은 말을 쓰시오.

　(1) 내가 하고 싶은 게 뭔지 아니?

　➡ Do you know _____ I want to do?

　(2) 나는 지난날의 내가 아니야.

　➡ I am not _____ I used to be.

　(3) 그녀가 말한 것은 위험한 것이었다.

　➡ _____ she said was dangerous.

② 관계부사

• Calli should pick a time **when** her mom is ready to listen.

Calli는 그녀의 엄마가 들을 준비가 되어 있는 때를 골라야 한다.

• It's a place **where** people can recharge. 그곳은 사람들이 재충전할 수 있는 곳이죠.

■ 관계부사는 두 문장을 연결하는 접속사의 역할과 부사의 역할을 동시에 한다. 관계부사 앞에 와서 수식을 받는 명사를 선행사라 하고, 그 선행사에 따라 관계부사 when(시간), where(장소), why(이유), how(방법)를 쓴다.

• There was a time **when** things were very different. 상황이 아주 달랐던 때가 있었다.

• This is the house **where** I was born. 이것이 내가 태어난 집이다.

• This is the reason **why** I'm here. 이것이 내가 여기 온 이유다.

• Scientists are studying **how** the birds find their food. 과학자들은 그 새들이 먹이를 찾는 방법을 연구하고 있다.

■ 관계부사 how는 선행사 the way와 함께 쓰지 않고 반드시 둘 중의 하나만 써야 하며 the way that이나 the way in which를 쓸 수 있다. 다른 관계부사의 경우 the time, the place, the reason과 같은 선행사가 나올 경우 선행사나 관계부사 중 하나를 생략할 수 있다.

• Do you know **the way how** the rain falls from the sky?　　(×)

• Do you know **the way**[또는 **how**] the rain falls from the sky? (○)

당신은 어떻게 하늘에서 비가 떨어지는지 아는가?

■ 선행사에 따른 관계부사

	선행사	관계부사	전치사+관계대명사
때	the time	when	in/on/at which
장소	the place	where	in/on/at which
이유	the reason	why	for which
방법	the way	how	in which

■ 주의: 관계대명사는 관계사절에서 주어나 목적어의 역할을 하므로 주어나 목적어가 빠진 불완전한 절이 오지만 관계부사는 부사 역할을 하므로 완전한 절이 온다.

핵심 Check

2. 다음 괄호 안에서 알맞은 말을 고르시오.

(1) The day (when / where) I start for my journey is drawing near.

(2) I remember the house (when / where) I grew up.

(3) The reason (why / how) he did it is complicated.

01 다음 빈칸에 알맞은 것을 고르시오.

> This is the house _____ I was born.

① when ② where ③ why
④ how ⑤ what

02 다음 중 어법상 어색한 문장은?

① The merchant paid customs on what he had bought in China.
② What he did to me was out of all knowledge.
③ I can't remember what I ate.
④ I want to know that you think of her music.
⑤ This is what I enjoy doing.

03 다음 주어진 두 문장을 한 문장으로 바꿀 때 옳지 않은 것은?

> • You have to admire the way.
> • He handled the situation in the way.

① You have to admire how he handled the situation.
② You have to admire the way he handled the situation.
③ You have to admire the way in which he handled the situation.
④ You have to admire the way that he handled the situation.
⑤ You have to admire the way how he handled the situation.

04 다음 우리말에 맞게 주어진 어휘를 알맞게 배열하시오.

(1) 봄은 꽃들이 피는 아름다운 때이다.
　　(the flowers, spring, time, bloom, is, beautiful, a, when)
　　➡ _____

(2) 여긴 왜 오셨죠?
　　(you, there, reason, here, any, is, are, why)
　　➡ _____

(3) 의사 없는 마을에서 살지 마라.
　　(a town, doctors, there, live, don't, are, no, in, where)
　　➡ _____

01 다음 중 어법상 올바른 것은?

① This is the house which Anne was born.
② Let's find out the reason why he has this problem.
③ This is the park how I met Sophie.
④ Tell me the way when you solved the problem.
⑤ I remember the day where I met her first.

02 다음 중 어법상 <u>어색한</u> 것은?

① What he says is not important.
② Lend me the book which you bought yesterday.
③ People believe that they want to believe.
④ This dress is what I wanted to buy.
⑤ You can eat what you like to eat on World Food Day.

03 다음 빈칸에 알맞은 말이 바르게 짝지어진 것은?

> • _____ he was doing would be considered as theft.
> • It is the hotel _____ we stayed when we traveled to Paris.

① Which – why ② That – where
③ That – when ④ What – where
⑤ What – when

서답형

04 다음 괄호 안에서 알맞은 말을 고르시오.

(1) This is the reason (how / why) I like bananas.
(2) That's the way (how / that) the system works.
(3) There are times (when / where) I feel depressed.
(4) The store doesn't sell (that / what) I am looking for.
(5) He was deprived of all (that / what) he owned.

05 다음 대화의 빈칸에 들어갈 말로 알맞은 것은?

> M: What did you have for lunch yesterday?
> W: Oh, _____ I had for lunch was some delicious spaghetti.

① it ② this ③ that
④ which ⑤ what

06 다음 문장의 빈칸에 들어갈 알맞은 것은?

> That is the place _____ my dog hides his food.

① where ② when
③ why ④ how
⑤ what

Grammar 25

07 다음 문장 중에서 어법상 **틀린** 것을 고르시오.

① Calli should pick a time when her mom is ready to listen.

② I will never forget the place where I met her.

③ It is the way how he proved the principle.

④ I don't know the reason why she left us.

⑤ This is the house which Sarah was born in.

08 다음 주어진 문장의 밑줄 친 <u>what</u>과 같은 용법으로 쓰인 것을 <u>모두</u> 고르시오.

Tell me <u>what</u> you know about Mars.

① <u>What</u> are you talking about?

② That's not <u>what</u> I meant.

③ He asked me <u>what</u> I wanted.

④ I guess that's <u>what</u> made me do it.

⑤ Please inform me <u>what</u> to do next.

09 주어진 어휘를 바르게 배열하여 다음 우리말을 영작하시오.

크리스마스는 우리가 가족과 함께 나누는 때이다.
(Christmas, a time, we, is, share, families, with, when)

➡ _____

10 다음 문장에서 어법상 **틀린** 부분을 찾아 바르게 고쳐 쓰시오.

The Sahara Desert is that is called "the sea of death."

➡ _____

11 다음 두 문장을 한 문장으로 바르게 연결한 것은?

• Every man had to gather to see the thing.
• It was happening.

① Every man had to gather to see happening.

② Every man had to gather to see it was happening.

③ Every man had to gather to see which was happening.

④ Every man had to gather to see that was happening.

⑤ Every man had to gather to see what was happening.

[12~13] 다음 빈칸에 들어갈 말이 나머지와 <u>다른</u> 하나는? (대 · 소문자 무시)

12 ① This is the house _____ Anne lives.

② 1921 is the year _____ Einstein received the Nobel Prize.

③ It was the day _____ we had your birthday party.

④ Do you know the time _____ TVs first appeared?

⑤ It's the month _____ Jesus was born.

13 ① Do you know _____ he is talking about?

② This is the bank _____ Marisol works at.

③ Let me know _____ you find out there.

④ _____ I want to do is playing computer games.

⑤ _____ you need is a good rest.

14 다음 두 문장을 한 문장으로 바르게 연결한 것을 고르시오.

> • Korea is the country.
> • The 1988 Olympic Games were held in the country.

① Korea is the country when the 1988 Olympic Games were held.

② Korea is the country why the 1988 Olympic Games were held.

③ Korea is the country how the 1988 Olympic Games were held.

④ Korea is the country which the 1988 Olympic Games were held.

⑤ Korea is the country in which the 1988 Olympic Games were held.

서답형

15 다음 우리말과 일치하도록 주어진 어휘에 한 단어를 추가하여 영작하시오.

> • 나는 현실이 내 예상과는 아주 다르다는 것을 알았다.
> (I, I, the reality, imagined, quite, had, different, found, from)

➡ _____

_____

중요

16 다음 중 어법상 어색한 것을 고르시오. (2개)

① I'm very sorry for that I did that night.

② What she says will sound like a request rather than a demand.

③ The birthday presents were the reason why I looked forward to my birthday.

④ May 1 is the day how workers celebrate the rights they have fought for.

⑤ This is the station where we met.

서답형

17 다음 문장에서 어법상 어색한 것을 바르게 고쳐 다시 쓰시오.

(1) He didn't let us know the way how he solved the problem.

➡ _____

_____

(2) Judy went to the restaurant which she had dinner with her friends.

➡ _____

_____

(3) Yuna remembers the day how she won the Olympic gold medal.

➡ _____

_____

(4) I can't believe that you're saying.

➡ _____

(5) I like the bag what I bought yesterday.

➡ _____

(6) I would like to do that I want when I want.

➡ _____

서답형

18 다음 〈보기〉와 같이 주어진 두 문장을 한 문장으로 바꾸어 쓰시오.

> ┤ 보기 ├
> • I know a small restaurant.
> • We can have very delicious cakes there.
> → I know a small restaurant where we can have very delicious cakes.

> • 1950 is the year.
> • The Korean War broke out in the year.

➡ _____

01 괄호 안의 지시대로 우리말을 영어로 옮기시오.

(1) 그가 왜 여기 왔는지 아니?

➡ _____

(관계부사를 써서)

➡ _____

_____

(관계대명사를 써서)

(2) 자연 재해(natural disasters)는 사람들이 살고 있는 곳에 피해를 입힌다.

➡ _____

(관계부사를 써서)

➡ _____

_____

(관계대명사를 써서)

02 다음 우리말에 맞게 주어진 어휘를 이용하여 영작하시오.

(1) 그녀는 인생에서 하고 싶은 것을 할 권리가 있다. (the right, in her life, have, do, what)

➡ _____

(2) 내가 하고 싶은 것은 개를 한 마리 입양하는 것이다. (to adopt, do, want)

➡ _____

(3) 왜 그런 결정을 하셨는지 물어봐도 될까요? (the reason, that decision, you, may, 11단어)

➡ _____

_____

03 그림을 보고, 주어진 어휘를 이용하여 빈칸을 알맞게 채우시오.

(1) This is the hotel _____ last summer. (stay, we) (3 words)

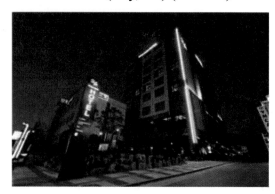

(2) Big Ben is _____ to see. (I, want) (3 words)

04 다음 문장의 빈칸에 알맞은 말을 쓰시오. (두 가지를 쓸 것.)

(1) I remember the café _____ he and I first met.

(2) We don't know _____ she solved the puzzle.

(3) I'm curious about the reason _____ she was late for the meeting.

05 주어진 두 문장을 what을 이용하여 하나의 문장으로 쓰시오.

(1) • He politely denied the thing.
  • I suggested it.

  ➡ _____

(2) • He did not listen to the thing.
  • I said the thing.

  ➡ _____

(3) • The thing was proposed by him.
  • It was not allowed.

  ➡ _____

(4) • Love is the thing.
  • It helps mend a broken heart.

  ➡ _____

06 주어진 두 문장을 관계부사를 이용하여 하나의 문장으로 쓰시오.

(1) • I don't know the reason.
  • He hides it for the reason.

  ➡ _____

(2) • Bill didn't know the time.
  • She would arrive at the time.

  ➡ _____

(3) • Avoid the area.
  • The accident took place in the area.

  ➡ _____

(4) • We studied the way.
  • Computers store information by the way.

  ➡ _____

(5) • Cambridge Park is a nice park.
  • You can sit on the grass in the park.

  ➡ _____

07 다음 두 문장에서 관계대명사의 사용을 비교하여 차이점을 서술하시오.

(1) He does something that really bothers me.

  ➡ _____

(2) He does what really bothers me.

  ➡ _____

08 다음 문장에서 어법상 어색한 것을 바르게 고치시오.

(1) That is the building where they built last year.

  ➡ _____

(2) Machines have changed the way how we work.

  ➡ _____

(3) Friday afternoon is the time which he is least busy.

  ➡ _____

(4) Do you remember the things what Megan brought at the mart?

  ➡ _____

(5) That I want to do is bring hope to my family.

  ➡ _____

(6) Did you understand that she said yesterday?

  ➡ _____

Reading

Speak Your Mind Effectively

Welcome to "All about Teens." I'm Dr. Carter. Today, we're going to talk about using good communication skills to express ourselves more effectively.

Let's start with our first clip about Brian. When he tries to talk to his brother, he always ends up arguing with his brother. Let's find out the reason why he has this problem.

Brian: *You lost my earphones again. Why are you so careless?*

Brian is starting a sentence with "you" to express his feelings. Instead, he should use the "I-message." Starting with "I" can help him focus on what he feels or thinks rather than point the finger at his brother.

Brian: ***I'm really upset because my favorite earphones are lost.***

Next is Calli. She is trying to talk to her mother, but she is busy preparing to go to work. Let's have a look.

effectively 효과적으로
welcome to: ~에 온 걸 환영하다
communication 의사소통
skill 기술
express 표현하다
clip 동영상
argue with ~와 말다툼을 벌이다
find out 알아내다
careless 부주의한
sentence 말, 문장
instead 대신에
focus on ~에 집중을 하다. ~에 초점을 맞추다
point the finger at ~을 비난하다

확인문제

● 다음 문장이 본문의 내용과 일치하면 T, 일치하지 <u>않으면</u> F를 쓰시오.

1 When Brian tries to talk to his brother, he always ends up arguing with his brother. ☐

2 Brian is starting a sentence with "I" to express his feelings. ☐

3 Starting with "I" can help Brian focus on what he feels or thinks. ☐

4 Starting with "I" can also help Brian point the finger at his brother. ☐

5 Calli is trying to talk to her mother. ☐

6 Calli is busy preparing to go on a trip. ☐

Calli: *Hey, Mom. Could I talk to you about something?*
Can보다 정중한 표현

Calli needs to find the right time to talk to her mom. Maybe Calli's
to부정사의 형용사적 용법

mom wanted to listen to what Calli was going to say. But she didn't
관계대명사(= the thing which)

have enough time to talk with her daughter. Calli should pick a time
to부정사의 형용사적 용법

when her mom is ready to listen.
be ready to: ~할 준비가 되어 있다

Calli: *Hey, Mom. Could I talk to you about something?*

Mom: *Sure.*

Now, let's take a look at our last clip. Anna and Julie are best
= have a look at = look at

friends, but Anna often hurts Julie's feelings.

Anna: *Don't put your bag on my desk!*

Julie probably felt uncomfortable because Anna made a demand
uncomfortably(×)

using the word "don't." People simply don't like taking orders.
현재분사   = to take

Anna should try to use words such as "can," "could," or "please."
= like

Then, what she says will sound like a request rather than a demand.
관계대명사(주어)   sound like+명사: ~처럼 들리다.   B rather than A: A라기보다는 B

Anna: *Could you put your bag on your desk?*
'요청'처럼 들리는 질문의 예

As we saw in the video clips, a small change in the way we express
~인 것처럼(접속사)   the way how (×)

ourselves can solve or even prevent communication problems. Let's
주어와 목적어가 같을 때 재귀대명사를 쓴다.

keep these tips in mind!
keep[bear] ~ in mind: ~을 명심하다

right 알맞은
enough 충분한
pick 고르다, 선택하다
hurt 마음을 아프게[감정을 상하게] 하다
feeling 감정
probably 아마도(=perhaps)
uncomfortable 불편한, 언짢은
(↔comfortable 편안한)
demand 요구, 강요
take orders 명령을 받다
request 요청
change 변화
solve 해결하다
prevent 예방하다
tip 조언

확인문제

● 다음 문장이 본문의 내용과 일치하면 T, 일치하지 않으면 F를 쓰시오.

1   Calli needs to find the right time to talk to her mom. ☐

2   Calli's mom didn't want to listen to what Calli was going to say. ☐

3   Calli's mom didn't have enough time to talk with her daughter. ☐

4   Anna and Julie aren't on good terms with each other. ☐

5   Anna should try to use words such as "can," "could," or "please." ☐

6   A small change in the way we express ourselves can't solve communication

    problems. ☐

● 우리말을 참고하여 빈칸에 알맞은 말을 쓰시오.

1 Speak Your Mind _____

2 _____ _____ "All about Teens."

3 _____ Dr. Carter.

4 Today, we're going to talk about _____ _____ _____ _____ to express ourselves more effectively.

5 Let's start with _____ _____ _____ about Brian.

6 When he tries to talk to his brother, he always _____ _____ with his brother.

7 Let's find out _____ _____ _____ he has this problem.

8 **Brian: *You lost my earphones again. Why are you so* _____ ?**

9 Brian is starting a sentence with "you" _____ _____ _____ _____.

10 _____, he should use the "_____."

11 Starting with "I" can help him _____ _____ what he feels or thinks _____ _____ point the finger at his brother.

12 **Brian: _____ *really* _____ *because my favorite earphones* _____ _____.**

13 _____ is Calli.

14 She is trying to talk to her mother, but she _____ _____ _____ to go to work.

15 Let's _____ _____ _____.

1 당신의 마음을 효과적으로 말하라!

2 '십 대들의 모든 것'에 오신 걸 환영합니다.

3 저는 Carter 박사입니다.

4 오늘 우리는 자신을 더 효과적으로 표현하기 위해 적절한 의사소통 기술을 사용하는 것에 대해 이야기해 보겠습니다.

5 Brian에 대한 첫 번째 동영상으로 시작해 보죠.

6 Brian이 남동생과 이야기하려고 할 때, 그는 결국 동생과 항상 말다툼을 하게 돼요.

7 그에게 이런 문제가 있는 이유를 알아봅시다.

8 Brian: "너 또 내 이어폰 잃어버렸지. 너는 왜 그렇게 조심성이 없니?"

9 Brian은 그의 감정을 표현하기 위해 '너'로 문장을 시작하고 있군요.

10 대신에 그는 '나 메시지'를 써야 해요.

11 '나'로 시작하는 것은 그가 남동생을 비난하기보다는 자신이 느끼거나 생각하는 것에 집중하도록 도울 수 있답니다.

12 Brian: "내가 가장 좋아하는 이어폰이 없어서서 난 정말 속상해."

13 다음은 Calli입니다.

14 그녀는 어머니와 이야기하려고 하지만, 어머니는 출근 준비로 바쁘시군요.

15 한번 보시죠.

16 **Calli:** *Hey, Mom. _____ _____ talk to you about something?*

17 Calli needs to find _____ _____ _____ to talk to her mom.

18 Maybe Calli's mom wanted to listen to _____ Calli was going to say.

19 But she didn't have _____ _____ to talk with her daughter.

20 Calli should _____ _____ _____ when her mom _____ _____ _____ _____.

21 **Calli:** *Hey, Mom. _____ _____ talk to you about something?*

22 **Mom:** _____.

23 Now, let's _____ _____ _____ _____ our last clip.

24 Anna and Julie are best friends, but Anna often _____ Julie's feelings.

25 **Anna:** _____ _____ *your bag on my desk!*

26 Julie probably _____ _____ because Anna made a demand using the word "don't."

27 People simply don't like _____ _____.

28 Anna should try to use words _____ _____ "can," "could," or "please."

29 Then, _____ she says will sound like a _____ rather than a _____.

30 **Anna:** _____ _____ *put your bag on your desk?*

31 As we saw in the video clips, _____ _____ _____ in the way we express ourselves can solve or even _____ _____ _____.

32 Let's _____ these tips _____ _____!

16 Calli: "저기, 엄마. 엄마랑 뭔가에 대해 이야기 좀 할 수 있을까요?"

16 Calli는 어머니와 이야기를 나눌 적절한 때를 찾아야 해요.

16 Calli의 어머니도 아마 Calli가 말하려고 했던 것을 듣고 싶어 하셨을 거예요.

16 그러나 어머니에게는 딸과 이야기할 시간이 충분하지 않았어요.

20 Calli는 어머니가 들으실 준비가 된 때를 골라야 해요.

21 Calli: "저기, 엄마. 엄마랑 뭔가에 대해 이야기 좀 할 수 있을까요?"

22 Mom: "물론이지."

23 이제 마지막 동영상을 봅시다.

24 Anna와 Julie는 가장 친한 친구 사이이지만, Anna가 종종 Julie의 마음을 상하게 합니다.

25 Anna: "네 가방을 내 책상에 놓지 마!"

26 Anna가 don't라는 단어를 써서 요구했기 때문에 Julie는 아마 불편하게 느꼈을 거예요.

27 사람들은 명령 받는 것을 전혀 좋아하지 않아요.

28 Anna는 can, could 또는 please와 같은 말을 사용하도록 노력해야 해요.

29 그러면 그녀가 하는 말이 요구보다는 요청처럼 들릴 거예요.

30 Anna: "네 가방은 네 책상에 놔두겠니?"

31 우리가 동영상에서 본 것처럼, 우리 자신을 표현하는 방식을 조금만 바꾸어도 의사소통의 문제를 해결하거나 심지어 막을 수도 있답니다.

32 이 조언들을 명심합시다!

● 우리말을 참고하여 본문을 영작하시오.

1 당신의 마음을 효과적으로 말하라!
➡ _____

2 '십 대들의 모든 것'에 오신 걸 환영합니다.
➡ _____

3 저는 Carter 박사입니다.
➡ _____

4 오늘 우리는 자신을 더 효과적으로 표현하기 위해 적절한 의사소통 기술을 사용하는 것에 대해 이야기해 보겠습니다.
➡ _____

5 Brian에 대한 첫 번째 동영상으로 시작해 보죠.
➡ _____

6 Brian이 남동생과 이야기하려고 할 때, 그는 결국 동생과 항상 말다툼을 하게 돼요.
➡ _____

7 그에게 이런 문제가 있는 이유를 알아봅시다.
➡ _____

8 Brian: "너 또 내 이어폰 잃어버렸지. 너는 왜 그렇게 조심성이 없니?"
➡ _____

9 Brian은 그의 감정을 표현하기 위해 '너'로 문장을 시작하고 있군요.
➡ _____

10 대신에 그는 '나 메시지'를 써야 해요.
➡ _____

11 '나'로 시작하는 것은 그가 남동생을 비난하기보다는 자신이 느끼거나 생각하는 것에 집중하도록 도울 수 있답니다.
➡ _____

12 Brian: "내가 가장 좋아하는 이어폰이 없어져서 난 정말 속상해."
➡ _____

13 다음은 Calli입니다.
➡ _____

14 그녀는 어머니와 이야기하려고 하지만, 어머니는 출근 준비로 바쁘시군요.
➡ _____

15 한번 보시죠.
➡ _____

16 Calli: "저기, 엄마. 엄마랑 뭔가에 대해 이야기 좀 할 수 있을까요?"
➡ _____

17 Calli는 어머니와 이야기를 나눌 적절한 때를 찾아야 해요.
➡ _____

18 Calli의 어머니도 아마 Calli가 말하려고 했던 것을 듣고 싶어 하셨을 거예요.
➡ _____

19 그러나 어머니에게는 딸과 이야기할 시간이 충분하지 않았어요.
➡ _____

20 Calli는 어머니가 들으실 준비가 된 때를 골라야 해요.
➡ _____

21 Calli: "저기, 엄마. 엄마랑 뭔가에 대해 이야기 좀 할 수 있을까요?"
➡ _____

22 Mom: "물론이지."
➡ _____

23 이제 마지막 동영상을 봅시다.
➡ _____

24 Anna와 Julie는 가장 친한 친구 사이이지만, Anna가 종종 Julie의 마음을 상하게 합니다.
➡ _____

25 Anna: "네 가방을 내 책상에 놓지 마!"
➡ _____

26 Anna가 don't라는 단어를 써서 요구했기 때문에 Julie는 아마 불편하게 느꼈을 거예요.
➡ _____

27 사람들은 명령 받는 것을 전혀 좋아하지 않아요.
➡ _____

28 Anna는 can, could 또는 please와 같은 말을 사용하도록 노력해야 해요.
➡ _____

29 그러면 그녀가 하는 말이 요구보다는 요청처럼 들릴 거예요.
➡ _____

30 Anna: "네 가방은 네 책상에 놔두겠니?"
➡ _____

31 우리가 동영상에서 본 것처럼, 우리 자신을 표현하는 방식을 조금만 바꾸어도 의사소통의 문제를 해결하거나 심지어 막을 수도 있답니다.
➡ _____
_____

32 이 조언들을 명심합시다!
➡ _____

[01~03] 다음 글을 읽고 물음에 답하시오.

Welcome to "All about Teens." I'm Dr. Carter. ⓐToday, we're going to talk about using good communication skills to express us more effectively.

Let's start with our first clip about Brian. When he tries ⓑto talk to his brother, he always ends up arguing with his brother. Let's find out the reason why he has this problem.

서답형

01 위 글의 밑줄 친 ⓐ에서 어법상 틀린 부분을 찾아 고치시오.

➡ _____

02 위 글의 밑줄 친 ⓑto talk와 to부정사의 용법이 같은 것을 모두 고르시오.

① He decided to talk to her.
② She hurried to talk about the news.
③ I have nothing to talk about.
④ It's necessary to talk to your doctor.
⑤ We were happy to talk over a cup of coffee.

03 위 글을 읽고 알 수 없는 것을 고르시오.

① the name of the program
② the name of the MC
③ the topic of the program
④ the subject of the first clip
⑤ the reason of the argument between Brian and his brother

[04~06] 다음 글을 읽고 물음에 답하시오.

Next is Calli. ①She is trying to talk to her mother, but (A)그녀는 출근 준비를 하느라고 바쁘십니다. Let's have a look.

Calli: *Hey, Mom. Could ②I talk to you about something?*

Calli needs to find the right time to talk to ③her mom.　ⓐ　Calli's mom wanted to listen to what Calli was going to say. But ④she didn't have enough time to talk with her daughter. Calli should pick a time when ⑤her mom is ready to listen.

Calli: *Hey, Mom. Could I talk to you about something?*

Mom: *Sure.*

04 위 글의 빈칸 ⓐ에 들어갈 가장 알맞은 말을 고르시오.

① Consequently　② Exactly
③ Particularly　④ Maybe
⑤ Especially

05 밑줄 친 ①~⑤ 중에서 가리키는 대상이 나머지 넷과 다른 것은?

①　　②　　③　　④　　⑤

06 위 글의 밑줄 친 (A)의 우리말에 맞게 주어진 어휘를 이용하여 8 단어로 영작하시오.

go to work

➡ _____

[07~09] 다음 글을 읽고 물음에 답하시오.

Let's start with our first clip about Brian. When he tries to talk to his brother, he always ends up arguing with his brother. Let's find out (A)the reason why he has this problem.

Brian: *You lost my earphones again. Why are you so careless?*

Brian is (B)<u>starting</u> a sentence with "you" to express his feelings. Instead, he should use the "l-message." (C)<u>Starting</u> with "I" can help him focus __ⓐ__ what he feels or thinks rather than point the finger __ⓑ__ his brother.

Brian: *I'm really upset because my favorite earphones are lost.*

07 위 글의 빈칸 ⓐ와 ⓑ에 들어갈 전치사가 바르게 짝지어진 것은?

ⓐ	ⓑ		ⓐ	ⓑ
① on	at		② for	to
③ in	to		④ for	at
⑤ on	from			

서답형

08 다음 빈칸 (a)와 (b)에 알맞은 단어를 넣어 위 글의 밑줄 친 (A)에 대한 설명을 완성하시오.

> Because Brian is starting a sentence with "you" to express (a)_____ _____ and points the finger at his brother, he always ends up arguing with (b)_____ _____.

서답형

09 아래 〈보기〉에서 위 글의 밑줄 친 (B)<u>starting</u>, (C)<u>Starting</u>과 문법적 쓰임이 같은 것을 각각 <u>모두</u> 고르시오.

> ┌─── 보기 ───
> ① Would you mind <u>opening</u> the door?
> ② I saw him <u>playing</u> the piano.
> ③ <u>Smiling</u> babies are the cutest in the world.
> ④ Her job is <u>designing</u> a building.
> ⑤ She sat <u>reading</u> a book.

➡ (B)와 같은 것: _____

(C)와 같은 것: _____

[10~12] 다음 글을 읽고 물음에 답하시오.

Now, let's take a look at our (A)[last / latest] clip. Anna and Julie are best friends, but Anna often hurts Julie's feelings.

Anna: *Don't put your bag on my desk!*

Julie probably felt (B)[uncomfortable / uncomfortably] because Anna made a demand using the word "don't." People simply don't like __ⓐ__. Anna should try to use words such as "can," "could," or "please." Then, what she says will sound like a request rather than a demand.

Anna: *Could you put your bag on your desk?*

As we saw in the video clips, a small change in the way we express ourselves can solve or even (C)[prevent / protect] communication problems. Let's keep these tips in mind!

10 위 글의 빈칸 ⓐ에 들어갈 알맞은 말을 고르시오.

① asking advice   ② taking orders
③ giving advice   ④ taking turns
⑤ giving orders

11 위 글의 괄호 (A)~(C)에서 문맥이나 어법상 알맞은 낱말을 골라 쓰시오.

➡ (A)_____ (B)_____ (C)_____

12 위 글에 어울리는 속담으로 가장 알맞은 것을 고르시오.

① Better late than never.
② A friend in need is a friend indeed.
③ One good turn deserves another.
④ Birds of a feather flock together.
⑤ A bird in the hand is worth two in the bush.

[13~15] 다음 글을 읽고 물음에 답하시오.

ⓐAs we saw in the video clips, ⓑa small change in the way how we express ourselves can solve or even prevent communication problems. ⓒLet's keep these tips in mind!

13 위 글의 밑줄 친 ⓐAs와 같은 의미로 쓰인 것을 고르시오.

① Her anger grew as she talked.
② As the poet says, a little learning is a dangerous thing.
③ He came up as I was speaking.
④ She works as a computer programmer.
⑤ As he is honest, he is trusted by everyone.

서답형
14 위 글의 밑줄 친 ⓑ에서 어법상 틀린 부분을 찾아 고치시오.

➡ _____

서답형
15 위 글의 밑줄 친 ⓒ를 다음과 같이 바꿔 쓸 때 빈칸에 들어갈 알맞은 단어를 쓰시오.

➡ Let's _____ these tips in mind!

[16~18] 다음 글을 읽고 물음에 답하시오.

Brian: *You lost my earphones again. Why are you so careless?*

Brian is starting a sentence with "___ⓐ___" to express his feelings. Instead, he should use the "I-message." Starting with "___ⓑ___" can help him focus on what ⓒhe feels or thinks rather than ⓓpoint the finger at his brother.

Brian: *I'm really upset because my favorite earphones are lost.*

서답형
16 Fill in the blanks ⓐ and ⓑ with suitable words.

➡ ⓐ _____ ⓑ _____

서답형
17 위 글의 밑줄 친 ⓒhe가 가리키는 것을 본문에서 찾아 쓰시오.

➡ _____

18 위 글의 밑줄 친 ⓓpoint the finger at과 바꿔 쓸 수 있는 단어를 모두 고르시오.

① insist   ② criticize
③ blame   ④ describe
⑤ suggest

[19~21] 다음 글을 읽고 물음에 답하시오.

Now, let's take a look at our last clip. Anna and Julie are best friends, but Anna often hurts Julie's feelings.

Anna: *Don't put your bag on my desk!*

Julie probably felt uncomfortable because Anna made a demand using the word "ⓐ___." People simply don't like taking ⓑorders. Anna should try to use words such as "can," "could," or "please." ⓒThen, what she says will sound like a demand rather than a request.

Anna: *Could you put your bag on your desk?*

서답형

19 Fill in the blank ⓐ with a suitable word.

➡ _____

20 위 글의 밑줄 친 ⓑorder와 같은 의미로 쓰인 것을 고르시오.

① The names are listed in alphabetical order.

② The house had been kept in good order.

③ The police are trying to restore public order.

④ Dogs can be trained to obey the order.

⑤ I would like to place an order for ten copies of this book.

서답형

21 위 글의 밑줄 친 ⓒ에서 흐름상 어색한 부분을 찾아 고치시오. (두 군데)

➡ _____

[22~24] 다음 글을 읽고 물음에 답하시오.

Next is Calli. She is trying to talk to her mother, but she is busy preparing to go to work. Let's have a look.

Calli needs to find the ⓐright time ⓑto talk to her mom. Maybe Calli's mom wanted to listen to what Calli was going to say. But she didn't have enough time to talk with her daughter. Calli should pick a time when her mom is ready to listen.

22 위 글의 밑줄 친 ⓐright와 같은 의미로 쓰인 것을 고르시오.

① Keep on the right side of the road.

② Was he right to leave her?

③ Lee was standing right behind her.

④ Everyone has a right to a fair trial.

⑤ I was waiting for the right moment to ask him.

중요

23 위 글의 밑줄 친 ⓑto talk와 to부정사의 용법이 같은 것을 모두 고르시오.

① I am happy to hear that.

② He worked hard only to fail.

③ There is no one to do it.

④ We expect her to pass the exam.

⑤ Do you have anything to eat?

서답형

24 위의 그림 A와 B에서 Calli는 그녀의 엄마에게 같은 말을 물어보고 있는데, 엄마의 반응이 다른 이유를 우리말로 쓰시오.

➡ 그림 A: _____

_____

➡ 그림 B: _____

_____

[01~03] 다음 글을 읽고 물음에 답하시오.

Welcome to "All about Teens." I'm Dr. Carter. Today, we're going to talk about using good communication skills (A)to express ourselves more effectively.

Let's start with our first clip about Brian. When he tries to talk to his brother, (B)그는 결국 남동생과 항상 말다툼을 하게 됩니다. Let's find out the reason ⓐ he has this problem.

01 Fill in the blank ⓐ with a suitable word.

➡ _____

02 위 글의 밑줄 친 (A)를 다음과 같이 바꿔 쓸 때 빈칸에 들어갈 알맞은 단어를 쓰시오.

➡ (1) _____ to express ourselves more effectively

(2) _____ to express ourselves more effectively

(3) _____ we can[may] express ourselves more effectively

(4) _____ we _____ express ourselves more effectively

03 위 글의 밑줄 친 (B)의 우리말에 맞게 주어진 어휘를 이용하여 8 단어로 영작하시오.

end up

➡ _____

[04~06] 다음 글을 읽고 물음에 답하시오.

Next is Calli. She is trying to talk to her mother, but she is busy ⓐ to go to work. Let's have a look.

Calli: *Hey, Mom. Could I talk to you about something?*

Calli needs to find the right time to talk to her mom. Maybe Calli's mom wanted to listen to ⓑwhat Calli was going to say. But she didn't have enough time to talk with her daughter. Calli should pick a time when her mom is ready to listen.

Calli: *Hey, Mom. Could I talk to you about something?*

Mom: *Sure.*

04 위 글의 빈칸 ⓐ에 prepare를 알맞은 형태로 쓰시오.

➡ _____

05 위 글의 밑줄 친 ⓑwhat을 선행사와 관계대명사로 바꿔 쓰시오.

➡ _____

06 위 글을 읽고 Calli가 엄마와 대화할 때의 문제점과 효과적인 의사소통 방법을 다음과 같이 정리하고자 한다. 빈칸 (A)와 (B)에 들어갈 알맞은 단어를 본문에서 찾아 쓰시오.

• 문제점: Calli didn't (A)_____ _____ _____ _____ to talk to her mom.

• 효과적인 의사소통 방법: Calli should pick a time when her mom (B)_____ _____ _____ _____.

[07~09] 다음 글을 읽고 물음에 답하시오.

Brian: *You lost my earphones again. Why are you so careless?*

Brian is starting a sentence with "you" to express his feelings. ⓐInstead, he should use ⓑthe "I-message." Starting with "I" can help him ⓒpoint the finger at his brother rather than focus on what he feels or thinks.

Brian: *I'm really upset because my favorite earphones are lost.*

07 위 글의 밑줄 친 ⓐInstead를 Instead of로 시작하여 고칠 때, 빈칸에 들어갈 알맞은 말을 쓰시오.

➡ Instead of _____ _____ _____
with "you" to express his feelings

08 위 글의 밑줄 친 ⓑthe "I-message"를 사용하는 방법을 30자 내외의 우리말로 설명하시오.

➡ _____
_____

09 위 글의 밑줄 친 ⓒ에서 흐름상 어색한 부분을 찾아 고치시오.

➡ _____
_____
_____

[10~14] 다음 글을 읽고 물음에 답하시오.

ⓐNow, let's take a look at our last clip. Anna and Julie are best friends, but Anna often hurts Julie's feelings.

Anna: ⓑ*Don't put your bag on my desk!*

Julie probably felt uncomfortable because Anna made a demand using the word "don't." People simply don't like taking orders. Anna should try to use words such as "can," "could," or "please." Then, what she says will sound like ⓒa request rather than a demand.

Anna: (A) _____

As we saw in the video clips, ⓓa small change in the way we express ourselves can solve or even prevent communication problems. Let's keep these tips in mind!

10 위 글의 밑줄 친 ⓐ를 다음과 같이 바꿔 쓸 때 빈칸에 들어갈 알맞은 단어를 쓰시오.

➡ Now, let's _____ a look at our last clip.
= Now, let's _____ _____ our last clip.

11 위 글의 빈칸 (A)에, 밑줄 친 ⓑ의 어감이 '요청하는 말'처럼 들리도록 바꿔 쓰시오.

➡ _____

12 위 글의 밑줄 친 ⓒ를 다음과 같이 바꿔 쓸 때 빈칸에 들어갈 알맞은 단어를 쓰시오.

➡ rather[more] a _____ than a _____
= not so much a _____ as a _____
= less a _____ than a _____

13 위 글의 밑줄 친 ⓓ에 해당하는 것을 본문에서 찾아 쓰시오.

➡ _____

14 위 글에서 Anna가 사용하지 말아야 할 단어와 사용하려고 노력해야 하는 단어들을 각각 쓰시오.

➡ 사용하지 말아야 할 단어: _____
사용하려고 노력해야 하는 단어들: _____,
_____ or _____

구석구석

Wrap Up 1-2

1. **M:** You look upset, Anna. What's wrong?
~하게 보이다 = What's the problem? = Is there anything wrong? = What happened?

W: Well, I'm upset about my sister, Elsa.
~에 대해서 화가 난다

M: Why are you upset about her?

W: She keeps ordering me around.
keep 동사ing: ~을 계속하다, 반복하다 order+사람+around: ~에게 자꾸 이래라저래라 하다

M: Oh, maybe you should tell her how you feel.
'you should+동사원형 ~. ~해야 한다'는 상대방에게 충고할 때 쓰는 표현. tell은 4형식 동사로
간접목적어(her)와 직접목적어(how you feel)를 취하고 있다.

2. **W:** Hey, Mike! How come you didn't come to my birthday party yesterday?
How come을 이용해 이유를 물어볼 수 있다.

M: Sorry. I really had to hit the books yesterday.
hit the books: 공부하다

W: Why did you hit your books? Were you angry about something?

M: Oh no, that's not what I meant. I had to study yesterday because I had an
That's not what I meant (to say).: 그런 뜻이 아니야. 상대방이 자신의 말의 의도를 오해할 때 정정하기 위해 쓰는 표현.
exam this morning.

> **구문해설** · upset: 화가 난, 기분 나쁜 · be angry about: ~에 대해서 화가 나다

Read and Think B

Which tip was the most helpful to you, and why?
의문형용사   뒤에 was it the most helpful 생략
Using the "I-message" was the most helpful. I often have an argument with
동명사로 주어   동명사가 주어일 경우 단수 취급
my sister, and now I understand the reason.
뒤에 why I often have an argument with my sister 생략

> **구문해설** · argument: 논쟁, 말다툼

After You Read A. Read and Write

By using good communication skills,
동명사
we can express ourselves more effectively.
us(×)

ⓐ Use the "I-message."
You can focus on what you feel or think rather than point the finger at others.
B rather than A: A라기보다는 B
ⓑ Pick the right time.
Others will listen to you when they have enough time to talk with you.
to부정사의 형용사적 용법
ⓒ Make a request.
Use words such as "can," "could," or "please."
= like

> **구문해설** · focus on: ~에 집중하다, 초점을 맞추다 · point the finger at: …을 비난[책망]하다
> · pick: 고르다, 선택하다 · request: 요청 · such as: ~와 같은

해석

1. **M:** 너 화나 보여, Anna. 무슨 일 있니?
W: 음, 난 내 여동생 Elsa에 대해 화가 나.
M: 왜 Elsa 때문에 화가 났니?
W: 그녀는 계속 나한테 이래라저래라 해.
M: 오, 어쩌면 네가 어떻게 느끼는지 그녀에게 말해야 할지도 몰라.
2. **W:** 안녕, Mike! 너는 왜 어제 내 생일 파티에 안 왔니?
M: 미안해. 나는 어제 정말 'hit the books(열심히 공부하다)' 해야 했어.
W: 왜 책을 쳤니? 너 뭔가에 화가 났니?
M: 아 아니, 그런 뜻이 아니야. 나는 오늘 아침에 시험이 있어서 어제 공부를 해야 했어.

어떤 조언이 너에게 가장 도움이 되었니, 그리고 이유는? "나 메세지"를 사용하는 것이 가장 도움이 되었어. 나는 자주 내 여동생과 논쟁을 벌이곤 했는데, 이제 그 이유를 이해해.

좋은 대화 기술을 사용함으로써, 우리는 스스로를 더 효과적으로 표현할 수 있다.
ⓐ "나 메세지"를 사용하라.
남을 비난하기보다 당신이 느끼거나 생각하는 것에 초점을 맞출 수 있다.
ⓑ 올바른 시간을 선택하라.
다른 사람들은 그들이 당신과 이야기할 충분한 시간이 있을 때 당신의 말을 들을 것이다.
ⓒ 요청을 하라.
"can," "could," 또는 "please"와 같은 말을 사용하라.

Words & Expressions

01 주어진 단어 중 접두사 'pre-'를 이용해 만들어지지 <u>않은</u> 단어를 고르시오.

① precaution ② preview
③ prepare ④ premium
⑤ prevent

02 다음 빈칸에 공통으로 들어갈 말을 쓰시오.

> • _____ this lesson in mind.
> • She told him to do the dishes, so he couldn't _____ watching TV.

03 다음 빈칸에 들어갈 말을 〈보기〉에서 찾아 쓰시오.

> ┤ 보기 ├
> about at in off on up

(1) Don't cut me _____ when I'm talking.
(2) He focused _____ taking pictures.
(3) I'm _____ the middle of doing something quite important.

04 다음 영영풀이가 나타내는 말을 고르시오.

> cruel or not kind

① clever ② mean
③ different ④ hard
⑤ wild

Conversation

[05~07] 다음 대화를 읽고 물음에 답하시오.

M: Sally, (A)_____ come you don't talk much with Anna these days?
W: Well, I'm upset about an argument we had.
M: Why are you upset?
W: She kept cutting me off in the middle of my sentences, so I got mad. We argued and I stopped talking to her.
M: Oh, I'm sorry to hear that.

05 빈칸 (A)에 알맞은 말을 고르시오.

① what ② why ③ which
④ how ⑤ how long

06 위 대화에서 다음 영영풀이에 해당하는 단어를 찾아 쓰시오.

> an angry disagreement between people

➡ _____

07 위 대화의 내용과 일치하는 것을 <u>모두</u> 고르시오.

① Sally는 Anna의 말을 중간에 끊었다.
② Sally는 Anna와 요즘 말을 하고 있지 않다.
③ 남자는 Sally와 Anna가 싸운 것에 대해 안타까워하고 있다.
④ 남자는 Sally가 왜 Anna와 사이가 안 좋은지 알고 있었다.
⑤ Sally는 Anna가 한 행동에 대해 즐거워했다.

[08~10] 다음 대화를 읽고 물음에 답하시오.

W: Mr. Brown, I want to get a good grade in English. (①)

M: (②) Well, Sujin, you should concentrate in class, (A)_____ . I see you often have your head in the clouds. (③)

W: Clouds? (④) I can't see the sky from inside the classroom. (⑤)

M: (B)_____ I meant you don't focus in class.

08 ①~⑤ 중 주어진 문장이 들어갈 곳은?

What should I do?

①   ②   ③   ④   ⑤

09 빈칸 (A)에 알맞은 말을 고르시오.

① instead   ② in advance
③ exactly   ④ however
⑤ first of all

10 빈칸 (B)에 들어갈 내용으로 적절하지 <u>않은</u> 것을 고르시오.

① You got me wrong.
② I didn't mean to say that.
③ You misunderstood me.
④ That's exactly what I meant.
⑤ That's not what I meant.

[11~12] 다음 대화를 읽고 물음에 답하시오.

M: You look upset, Anna. What's wrong?

W: Well, I'm upset (A)_____ my sister, Elsa.

M: Why are you upset (B)_____ her?

W: She keeps ordering me around.

M: Oh, maybe (C)_____ .

11 빈칸 (A)와 (B)에 공통으로 들어갈 수 있는 말을 <u>모두</u> 고르시오.

① about   ② in   ③ for
④ of   ⑤ with

12 빈칸 (C)에 알맞은 말을 고르시오.

① I advise you to keep your promise
② you had better follow the order
③ you should have written the letter
④ you should tell her how you feel
⑤ you can see her ordering

[13~14] 다음 대화를 읽고 물음에 답하시오.

W: 나는 시험에 대해 너무 스트레스를 받는다, Jinsu.

M: Yeah, me, too. We have two more to go.

W: After finishing my exams, I want to go on a trip and just (A)_____ .

M: You want to change your hair style?

W: No, that's not what I meant. I want to go somewhere and feel free from all my troubles.

13 밑줄 친 우리말과 일치하도록 주어진 단어를 이용해 문장을 만드시오. (7 words)

➡ _____

(stress, so, exams)

14 빈칸 (A)에 들어갈 말을 고르시오.

① let my hair down
② keep my hair on
③ pull my hair out
④ make my hair grow
⑤ keep my hair long

15 다음 두 문장의 뜻이 같도록 빈칸에 들어갈 알맞은 말은?

> I went to the hospital where my boyfriend works.
> = I went to the hospital _____ my boyfriend works.

① which
② in which
③ which in
④ for which
⑤ on which

16 다음 중 밑줄 친 부분이 어법상 어색한 것을 고르시오.

① I didn't read the book that you gave to me the other day.
② What is the reason for which she was absent from school?
③ I like that she bought for me.
④ You'd better change the way that you study English.
⑤ You may bring what you want to sell on Sale Day.

17 다음 밑줄 친 부분의 쓰임이 〈보기〉와 같은 것은?

> ─ 보기 ─
> Sandwich is also the name of the town where he lived.

① I wonder where they will take us to.
② Where do you stand on this question?
③ Where there is a will, there is a way.
④ The where and the when of the accident is important.
⑤ Do you know the hotel where they stayed for the night?

18 다음 두 문장의 의미가 같도록 빈칸에 알맞은 말을 3단어로 쓰시오.

(1) The thing that she said on the phone made her mom angry.
= _____ on the phone made her mom angry.

(2) The teacher always finds out something that I've missed.
= The teacher always finds out _____.

(3) Gimbap is the food that I ate for breakfast.
= Gimbap is _____ for breakfast.

19 두 문장을 관계부사를 사용하여 한 문장으로 썼을 때, 빈칸의 문장을 쓰시오.

(1) This is the day.
+ _____
→ This is the day when my parents got married.

(2) Let me show you the way.
+ _____
→ Let me show you how I make gimchi.

20 다음 두 문장과 같은 의미의 한 문장으로 바꿔 쓰시오.

> • The house has a small garden.
> • Anne lives in the house.

(1) _____
(2) _____
(3) _____

다음 ⓐ~ⓖ 중 어법상 옳은 것을 <u>모두</u> 고르시오.

> ⓐ What I didn't know was how hard it was going to be.
> ⓑ Living in a small and quiet town is that I wanted.
> ⓒ I need your advice about something that I want to do for him.
> ⓓ I'm searching for a nice restaurant which I can have dinner with her.
> ⓔ He remembers the spring when hills and valleys were full of wildflowers.
> ⓕ I don't know the reason for which she changed her mind.
> ⓖ If you don't like the way how I drive, then you can drive.

➡ _____

Reading

[22~24] 다음 글을 읽고 물음에 답하시오.

Welcome to "All about Teens." I'm Dr. Carter. Today, we're going to talk about ⓐ<u>using</u> good communication skills to express ourselves more effectively.

Let's start with our first clip about Brian. ⓑ<u>When he tries to talk to his brother, he always ends up arguing with his brother.</u> Let's find out the reason ⓒ<u>why</u> he has this problem.

22 위 글의 밑줄 친 ⓐ<u>using</u>과 문법적 쓰임이 같은 것을 <u>모두</u> 고르시오.

① Do you know that boy <u>playing</u> the piano?
② <u>Barking</u> dogs seldom bite.
③ Her dream is <u>being</u> a scientist.
④ <u>Traveling</u> by car is exciting.
⑤ His father was <u>reading</u> a newspaper.

23 위 글의 밑줄 친 ⓑ를 다음과 같이 바꿔 쓸 때 빈칸에 들어갈 알맞은 말을 쓰시오.

➡ _____ he tries to talk to his brother, he ends up arguing with his brother.

24 위 글의 밑줄 친 ⓒwhy를 전치사를 사용하여 두 단어로 고치시오.

➡ _____

[25~26] 다음 글을 읽고 물음에 답하시오.

Next is Calli. She is trying to talk to her mother, but she is busy preparing to go to work. (①) Let's have a look.
(②) Calli needs to find the right time to talk to her mom. (③) But she didn't have enough time to talk with her daughter. (④) Calli should pick a time when her mom is ready to listen. (⑤)

25 위 글의 흐름으로 보아, 주어진 문장이 들어가기에 가장 적절한 곳은?

> Maybe Calli's mom wanted to listen to what Calli was going to say.

①　　②　　③　　④　　⑤

26 According to the passage, which is NOT true?

① Calli is trying to talk to her mother.
② Calli needs to find the right time to talk to her mom.
③ Maybe Calli's mom wanted to listen to what Calli was going to say.
④ Calli didn't have enough time to talk with her mom.
⑤ Calli should pick a time when her mom is ready to listen.

[27~29] 다음 글을 읽고 물음에 답하시오.

Now, let's take a look at our last clip. Anna and Julie are best friends, but Anna often hurts Julie's feelings.

Anna: *Don't put your bag on my desk!*

Julie ⓐ<u>probably</u> felt uncomfortable because Anna made a demand using the word "don't." People simply don't like taking orders. Anna should try to use words such as "can," "could," or "please." Then, ⓑ<u>그녀가 말하는 것이 요구라기 보다는 요청처럼 들릴 것입니다.</u>

Anna: *Could you put your bag on your desk?*

27 위 글의 밑줄 친 ⓐprobably와 바꿔 쓸 수 있는 말을 쓰시오.

➡ _____

28 위 글의 밑줄 친 ⓑ의 우리말에 맞게 한 단어를 보충하여, 주어진 어휘를 알맞게 배열하시오.

sound / a demand / will / rather than / says / a request / she / like

➡ _____

_____

29 위 글을 읽고 Anna가 Julie와 대화할 때의 문제점과 효과적인 의사소통 방법을 다음과 같이 정리하고자 한다. 빈칸 (A)와 (B)에 들어갈 알맞은 단어를 본문에서 찾아 쓰시오.

• 문제점: A n n a (A)_____ _____
_____ using the word "don't."

• 효과적인 의사소통 방법: Anna should make what she says sound like less a demand than a request by using words such as (B)"_____" "_____" or "_____".

[30~32] 다음 글을 읽고 물음에 답하시오.

Next is Calli. She is trying to talk to her mother, but (A)<u>she</u> is busy preparing to go to work. Let's have a look.

Calli: *Hey, Mom. Could I talk to you about something?*

Calli needs to find the right time to talk to her mom. Maybe Calli's mom wanted to listen to what Calli was going to say. But she didn't have enough time to talk with her daughter. Calli should pick a time _____ⓐ_____ her mom is ready to listen.

Calli: *Hey, Mom. Could I talk to you about something?*

Mom: *Sure.*

30 위 글의 빈칸 ⓐ에 들어갈 알맞은 말을 고르시오.

① where   ② when
③ why   ④ how
⑤ which

31 위 글의 밑줄 친 (A)she가 가리키는 것을 본문에서 찾아 쓰시오.

➡ _____

32 Which question CANNOT be answered after reading the passage?

① Does Calli's mom always have enough time to talk with her daughter?
② When is it difficult for Calli to talk to her mom?
③ What does Calli need to find in order to talk to her mom?
④ Is it likely that Calli's mom wants to listen to what Calli is going to say?
⑤ How often can Calli talk with her mom?

01 다음 괄호 안의 단어를 문맥에 맞게 고쳐 쓰시오. 출제율 90%

> A: I feel _____ (comfortable) about the food.
> B: What's the problem?

02 밑줄 친 단어들의 영영풀이에 해당하지 않은 것을 고르시오. 출제율 95%

> • People express their sorrow by crying.
> • You are clever enough to solve the problem.
> • Are you disappointed at losing the race?
> • The book was really helpful for the exam.

① to find a solution to something that is causing difficulties

② a fact, situation, or intention that explains why something happened, why someone did something, or why something is true

③ useful, or providing help

④ to tell someone about a feeling, opinion, or goal by speaking or writing about it

⑤ unhappy because something that you hoped for or expected did not happen or because someone or something was not as good as you expected

03 다음 빈칸에 공통으로 들어갈 말을 쓰시오. 출제율 90%

> • Sally _____ cold feet at the last moment and called off the wedding.
> • I _____ a good grade in the piano festival last Saturday.

04 다음 빈칸에 들어갈 말을 고르시오. 출제율 90%

> You are not in a position to _____ demands right now.

① have   ② let   ③ find
④ come   ⑤ make

[05~07] 다음 대화를 읽고 물음에 답하시오.

> W: (A)_____
> M: Not good. 나는 과학 그룹에 화가 나.
> W: What's wrong?
> M: The group members only speak and never listen. I (B)_____ we can finish the homework on time.
> W: That's too bad.

05 빈칸 (A)에 알맞은 말을 고르시오. 출제율 100%

① How is your science homework going?

② How was your grade of science test?

③ When are you going to do your science homework?

④ Why are you mad at your science group?

⑤ How come you finished your science homework?

06 빈칸 (B)에 알맞은 말을 고르시오.

① think that
② think what
③ don't think that
④ don't think how
⑤ don't think whether

밑줄 친 우리말과 일치하도록 주어진 단어를 이용해 문장을 만드시오.

➡ _____

(upset)

[08~10] 다음 대화를 읽고 물음에 답하시오.

M: Why the long face, Julie?
W: I got angry at my sister yesterday and said some (A)mean things to her. (①)
M: Oh, why were you angry?
W: I was really tired and I wanted to sleep. (②) But she was talking loudly on the phone. I was really upset about that.
M: I see. (③)
W: No, not yet. (④) I want to say I'm sorry that I was mean to her, but I don't know how.
M: (⑤) Why don't you write her a note or send her a text message?
W: Hmm, that's a good idea. Thanks.

08 ①~⑤ 중 주어진 문장이 들어갈 곳은?

And you two haven't worked it out yet?

①   ②   ③   ④   ⑤

09 밑줄 친 (A)와 같은 의미로 쓰인 것은?

① Are there any means of contacting her?
② What does this mean?
③ Don't be so mean to your sister.
④ You mean we start all again?
⑤ This word means something different in French.

10 위 대화의 내용과 일치하지 않는 것은?

① Julie was tired yesterday, so she wanted to sleep.
② Julie was upset, so she talked to her sister loudly.
③ Julie is depressed because of what she did to her sister.
④ Julie will be likely to send her sister a text message.
⑤ Julie wants to tell her sister that she's sorry.

11 다음 빈칸에 알맞은 말을 쓰시오.

_____ you will watch on Movie Day is a famous animation.

12 다음 빈칸에 알맞은 말이 순서대로 짝지어진 것은?

• _____ you're saying is hard to believe.
• Do you know the reason _____ Clare didn't come to the party?

① What – how
② That – how
③ What – why
④ That – why
⑤ Which – how

출제율95%

13 다음 중 어법상 적절한 문장은?

① Calli's mom wanted to listen to that Calli was going to say.
② That I want for breakfast is just a glass of juice.
③ The painting is which you saw in the house.
④ The ideas are not what I thought.
⑤ I'd rather talk about the things what are happening.

출제율100%

14 다음 중 어법상 바르지 않은 것은?

① A small change in the way we express ourselves can solve or even prevent communication problems.
② He took her to the TV station which their new drama was in production.
③ What my dad planted in the garden is an apple tree.
④ I can't imagine what happened last night.
⑤ I remember the time when she was very disappointed with me because I told a lie to her.

출제율90%

15 다음 우리말을 주어진 어휘를 이용하여 주어진 단어 수대로 영작하시오.

(1) 그 보고서는 내가 알고 싶어하는 것을 보여 주었다. (the report, show, want, 8 단어)
➡ _____

(2) 그는 자기가 한 것에 대하여 자랑스러워했다. (proud, do, of, 7 단어)
➡ _____

(3) 이 망원경은 다른 것들이 할 수 없는 일들을 할 수 있습니다. (this telescope, others, 7 단어)
➡ _____

(4) 7월은 여름의 열기가 본격적으로 시작되는 달이다. (the summer heat, actually, the month, begin, 10 단어)
➡ _____
_____

(5) 우리는 시간이 정지해 버린 것 같은 어느 마을에서 머물렀다. (a village, stay, has stood, still, in, 10 단어)
➡ _____

(6) 인터넷은 사람들이 쇼핑하는 방법을 바꾸고 있다. (the Internet, is changing, people, 8 단어)
➡ _____

[16~18] 다음 글을 읽고 물음에 답하시오.

Among my relationships, I have the worst ⓐ one with my mom. I remember the time when she got angry because I didn't keep a promise with her. I also remember the time when she was very disappointed with me because I told a lie to her. I want to make my relationship better with her. So, I will keep my promises. Also I will try to be honest with her. I hope ⓑ my effort will help me work things out with my mom.

출제율95%

16 위 글의 밑줄 친 ⓐ와 ⓑ가 가리키는 것을 각각 본문에서 찾아 쓰시오.

➡ _____
_____

✍ 출제율 90%

17 글쓴이가 자신의 엄마를 (1) 화나게 만든 경우와 (2) 실망시킨 경우를 우리말로 쓰시오.

➡ (1) 화나게 만든 경우: _____
(2) 실망시킨 경우: _____

✍ 출제율 95%

18 본문의 내용과 일치하도록 다음 빈칸에 알맞은 단어를 쓰시오.

> The writer wants to make the relationship with Mom _____.

[19~20] 다음 글을 읽고 물음에 답하시오.

> By using (A)good communication skills, we can express ourselves more effectively.
> ⓐ Use the "I-message."
> You can focus on what you feel or think rather than point the finger at others.
> ⓑ Pick the right time.
> Others will listen to you when they have enough time to talk with you.
> ⓒ Make a request.
> Use words such as "can," "could," or "please."

✍ 출제율 90%

19 When will others listen to you? Answer in English in a full sentence.

➡ _____
_____

✍ 출제율 95%

20 위 글의 밑줄 친 (A)good communication skills에 해당하는 것 3가지를 본문에서 찾아 쓰시오.

➡ (1) _____
(2) _____
(3) _____

[21~23] 다음 글을 읽고 물음에 답하시오.

> **Brian:** *You lost my earphones again. Why are you so careless?*
> Brian is starting a sentence with "you" ⓐto express his feelings. Instead, he should use the "I-message." Starting with "I" can help him ⓑ <u>그의 남동생을 비난하기보다는 자신이 느끼거나 생각하는 것에 집중하도록.</u>
> **Brian:** *I'm really upset because my favorite earphones are lost.*

✍ 출제율 90%

21 to부정사의 세 가지 용법 중, 위 글의 밑줄 친 ⓐto express 와 용법이 <u>다른</u> 것의 개수를 아래 〈보기〉에서 고르시오.

┌─ 보기 ─┐
① She went to the store to buy some fruit.
② I don't know how to make it.
③ I'm pleased to meet you.
④ He grew up to be a doctor.
⑤ He must be rich to buy such an expensive car.
└─────┘

① 1개 ② 2개 ③ 3개 ④ 4개 ⑤ 5개

✍ 출제율 95%

22 위 글의 밑줄 친 ⓑ의 우리말에 맞게 주어진 어구를 알맞게 배열하시오.

> at his brother / what / on / rather than / he feels or thinks / focus / point the finger

➡ _____
_____

✍ 출제율 100%

23 According to the passage, which is NOT true?

① Brian is starting a sentence with "you."
② Brian wants to express his feelings.
③ Brian should use the "I-message."
④ Starting with "I" can help him focus on what he feels or thinks.
⑤ Starting with "I" can also help him point the finger at his brother.

01 대화의 흐름상 빈칸에 들어갈 말을 주어진 단어를 이용해 문장을 완성하시오.

> **A:** Guess what I'm trying to say.
> **B:** Are you saying "It's hot"?
> **A:** No. _____ This means "It's delicious" in Italy.

➡ _____ (what, that, 5 단어)
_____ (that, mean, 6 단어)
_____ (misunderstand, 3 단어)

[02~03] 다음 대화를 읽고 물음에 답하시오.

> **M:** ⓐSally, how come you don't talk much with Anna these days?
> **W:** ⓑWell, I'm upset about an argument we had.
> **M:** ⓒWhy are you upset?
> **W:** 그녀가 계속해서 내가 말을 하고 있는 도중에 끊어서, 내가 화가 났어. ⓓWe argued and I stopped to talk to her.
> **M:** ⓔOh, I'm sorry to hear that.

02 밑줄 친 우리말을 주어진 단어를 이용해 영작하시오.

➡ _____
_____
(mad, cut, in, off, so, get, keep)

03 ⓐ~ⓔ 중 흐름이나 어법상 어색한 것을 고르고 바르게 고치시오.

➡ _____

04 다음 〈보기〉에 주어진 어휘와 what을 이용하여 빈칸을 채워 문맥에 맞게 문장을 완성하시오.

┌─ 보기 ─┐
want to wear, want to explain, remember

(1) _____ is that he got a lot of trouble in the dark.
(2) You can put on _____ on No Uniform Day.
(3) I couldn't understand _____ to the people.

05 다음 우리말을 괄호 안의 지시대로 영작하시오.

(1) 나는 Jane이 우는 이유를 모르겠다.
➡ _____
(관계부사를 써서)
➡ _____
(관계대명사를 써서)
(2) 스마트폰이 사람들이 사는 방식을 바꾸어 왔다.
➡ _____
(선행사를 써서)
➡ _____
(관계부사를 써서)
➡ _____
(that을 써서)

06 다음 두 문장을 관계부사를 이용하여 한 문장으로 쓰시오.

(1) • Do you remember the library?
   • We studied together there.

   ➡ _____

(2) • Do you know the date?
   • Jake will get married on the date.

   ➡ _____

07 다음 중 생략할 수 있는 두 단어를 쓰시오.

(1) This is the place where we spent so many years.

   ➡ _____

(2) I know the reason why she didn't stay there.

   ➡ _____

[08~10] 다음 글을 읽고 물음에 답하시오.

> Brian: *You lost my earphones again. Why are you so careless?*
>
> Brian is starting a sentence with "you" to express his feelings. Instead, he should use the "I-message." Starting with "I" can help him focus on ___ⓐ___ he feels or thinks ⓑrather than point the finger at his brother.
>
> Brian: *I'm really upset because my favorite earphones are lost.*

08 Fill in the blank ⓐ with a suitable word.

   ➡ _____

09 위 글의 밑줄 친 ⓑ를 instead of로 바꿀 때, 빈칸에 들어갈 알맞은 말을 쓰시오.

   ➡ instead of _____ the finger at his brother

10 위 글을 읽고 Brian이 동생과 대화할 때의 문제점과 Brian에게 효과적인 의사소통 방법을 다음과 같이 정리하고자 한다. 빈칸 (A)와 (B)에 들어갈 알맞은 단어를 본문에서 찾아 쓰시오.

> • 문제점: Brian is starting a sentence with "(A)_____" to express his feelings.
> • 효과적인 의사소통 방법: He should use the "I-message." Then, he can focus on (B)_____ _____ _____ _____ _____ rather than point the finger at his brother.

[11~13] 다음 글을 읽고 물음에 답하시오.

> Welcome to "All about Teens." I'm Dr. Carter. Today, we're going to talk about using good communication skills to express ourselves more effectively.
> Let's start with (A)our first clip about Brian. When he tries to talk to his brother, he always ends up ___ⓐ___ with his brother. Let's find out the reason why he has (B)this problem.

11 위 글의 빈칸 ⓐ에 argue를 알맞은 형태로 쓰시오.

   ➡ _____

12 다음 빈칸 (a)와 (b)에 알맞은 단어를 넣어 밑줄 친 (A)에 대한 소개를 완성하시오.

> This clip shows (a)_____ _____ why Brian's attempt to talk to (b)_____ _____ always ends up with argument between his brother and him.

13 위 글의 밑줄 친 (B)의 내용을 우리말로 쓰시오.

   ➡ _____

   _____

01 다음 주어진 표현과 이에 대한 뜻을 보고 아래 대화의 빈칸을 완성하시오.

> put something on ice – be postponed

> A: Our project is put on ice.
> B: I didn't put anything on ice.
> A: _____ .

02 (A)와 (B)에 주어진 것 중 각각 하나씩과 관계부사를 이용하여 어법에 맞게 3 문장 이상 쓰시오.

> (A) know the reason / my grandparents' house / show me / Saturday
> (B) she left early / go to school / this copy machine / my first birthday party

(1) _____
(2) _____
(3) _____
(4) _____

03 다음 내용을 바탕으로 소중한 사람과의 관계를 회복하기 위한 행동 계획서를 쓰시오.

> **Q1** With whom do you have the worst relationship?
> **A1** I have the worst relationship with my mom.
>
> **Q1** Write two things that made her angry or disappointed.
> **A2** (1) There was a time when my mom got angry because I didn't keep a promise with her. (2) There was also a time when my mom was very disappointed with me because I told a lie to her.
>
> **Q3** What are you going to do to make the relationship better?
> **A3** (1) I will keep my promises. (2) I will try to be honest with her.

> Among my relationships, I have the (A)_____ one with my mom. I remember the time when she (B)_____ because I didn't keep a promise with her. I also remember the time when she was very (C)_____ with me because I told a lie to her. I want to make my relationship better with her. So, I will (D)_____.
> Also I will try (E)_____. I hope my effort will help me work things out with my mom.

단원별 모의고사

01 두 문장이 같은 의미가 되도록 빈칸을 채우시오. (철자가 주어진 경우 주어진 철자로 시작할 것)

> If he is late, don't blame me.
> = If he is late, don't p_____ _____ _____ at me.

02 다음 밑줄 친 부분의 쓰임이 자연스럽지 않은 것을 찾아 고치시오. (1개)

> ⓐ The doctor advised him to stop smoking.
> ⓑ If you keep to work, you'll pass the test.
> ⓒ The gym tends to get very busy at around six o'clock.
> ⓓ I try to avoid unnecessary arguments.

➡ _____

03 빈칸 (A)~(C)에 들어갈 말로 알맞은 것끼리 짝지어진 것을 고르시오.

> • Don't let her (A)_____ you around.
> • They didn't (B)_____ on studying.
> • We've (C)_____ out our difficulties.

　　　(A)　　　(B)　　　　　(C)
① have – interest – got
② have – concentrate – worked
③ order – interest – worked
④ order – encourage – got
⑤ order – concentrate – worked

04 다음 짝지어진 단어의 관계가 같도록 빈칸에 알맞은 말을 쓰시오.

> honest : dishonest = certain : _____

[05~06] 다음 대화를 읽고 물음에 답하시오.

> W: Did you finally go diving yesterday, Nick?
> M: Actually, I (A)_____ cold feet, Mina.
> W: That's too bad. How did you get a cold?
> M: No, Mina. That's not what I meant. I meant that I (B)_____ scared, so I didn't dive.

다음 빈칸 (A)와 (B)에 공통으로 들어갈 말을 쓰시오.

➡ _____

06 위 대화를 읽고 답할 수 없는 질문을 모두 고르시오.

① Did Nick dive yesterday?
② What does "get cold feet" mean?
③ How come Nick was scared of diving?
④ Why didn't Nick dive?
⑤ Where did Nick go diving?

[07~08] 다음 대화를 읽고 물음에 답하시오.

> W: How is your science homework (A)going?
> M: Not good. I'm upset about my science group.
> W: What's wrong?
> M: The group members only speak and never listen. I don't think that we can finish the homework on time.
> W: That's too bad.

07 밑줄 친 (A)와 같은 의미로 쓰인 것은?

① Where did Sue go?
② When the program is going on, the director sits in the control room.
③ We're planning to go to Arizona this winter.
④ Are you ready to go for lunch yet?
⑤ They'll be going from London to Paris by train.

08 위 대화의 내용과 일치하지 <u>않는</u> 것은?

① The man is worried that the science homework will not be finished on time.

② The members of his science group don't listen but speak.

③ The man is annoyed by the science group members.

④ The woman feels sorry for the man.

⑤ The science homework is individual work.

[09~11] 다음 대화를 읽고 물음에 답하시오.

W: Hey, Mike! (①) How come you didn't come to my birthday party yesterday? (②)

M: Sorry. I really had to hit the books yesterday. (③)

W: (④) Were you angry about something?

M: Oh no, that's not what I meant. (⑤) I had to study yesterday (A)_____ I had an exam this morning.

09 ①~⑤ 중 주어진 문장이 들어갈 곳은?

Why did you hit your books?

①　　②　　③　　④　　⑤

10 빈칸 (A)에 알맞은 말을 고르시오.

① when　　② although　　③ but
④ however　　⑤ because

11 According to the dialogue, what does "to hit the books" means?

➡ _____

[12~14] 다음 대화를 읽고 물음에 답하시오.

A: People keep telling me that I talk too much. (①)

B: Well, sometimes you tend (A)[talking / to talk] about too (B)[much / many] details. (②)

A: (③) Should I just keep (C)[quiet / loud], then?

B: That's not what I meant. (④) You can try (D)[talking / to talk] about only the important details. (⑤)

12 ①~⑤ 중 주어진 문장이 들어갈 곳은?

I'm upset about that.

①　　②　　③　　④　　⑤

13 위 대화의 괄호 (A)~(D)에서 적절한 것을 골라 쓰시오.

➡ (A)_____　(B)_____
(C)_____　(D)_____

14 위 대화에서 다음 영영풀이에 해당하는 단어를 찾아 쓰시오.

one of many small facts or pieces of information relating to a situation

➡ _____

15 다음 중 어법상 <u>어색한</u> 것을 고르시오.

① I remember the time when my mom got angry because I didn't keep a promise with her.

② Tell me the reason which you were upset.

③ What I like most is listen to the music.

④ I can't remember where I put my smart phone.

⑤ Let me see what you brought.

16 다음 빈칸에 공통으로 알맞은 말을 쓰시오.

> • He finally told me the reason _____ he was so excited.
> • This is _____ I refuse to go.

17 다음 문장에서 어법상 어색한 것을 바르게 고치시오.

(1) We have the freedom to wear that we want.

➡ _____

(2) This smart phone is not the thing what I want to have.

➡ _____

(3) Tell me the way how I can make a delicious pizza.

➡ _____

(4) 1939 is the year which World War Ⅱ broke out.

➡ _____

18 다음 문장의 빈칸에 들어갈 말이 <u>다른</u> 하나를 고르시오.

① I don't understand _____ they're talking about.

② I lost _____ you had bought me.

③ That's exactly _____ I am doing again.

④ I want you to buy _____ you really want.

⑤ I believe _____ you need to listen carefully to your inner voice.

19 <보기>와 같이 두 문장을 한 문장으로 바꿔 쓰시오.

> ┤ 보기 ├
> • I can't forget the moment.
> • I rode my bike for the first time then.
> → I can't forget the moment when I rode my bike for the first time.

(1) • I know a restaurant.
   • We can have delicious *samgyupsal* there.

➡ _____
_____

(2) • Winter is the season.
   • Leaves fall in the season.

➡ _____

[20~21] 다음 글을 읽고 물음에 답하시오.

Welcome to "All about Teens." I'm Dr. Carter. Today, we're going to talk about using good communication skills ⓐto express ourselves more effectively.

Let's start with our first clip about Brian. When he tries to talk to his brother, he always ends up arguing with his brother. Let's find out the reason why he has this problem.

20 위 글의 밑줄 친 ⓐto express와 to부정사의 용법이 같은 것을 <u>모두</u> 고르시오.

① She stood up to go out.

② I think it important to use your time well.

③ I need a pencil to write with.

④ I used a computer to draw it.

⑤ I asked Jane to drive slowly.

21 주어진 영영풀이에 해당하는 단어를 본문에서 찾아 쓰시오.

> a short video recording that you can see on a website

➡ _____

[22~23] 다음 글을 읽고 물음에 답하시오.

> Now, let's take a look at our last clip. Anna and Julie are best friends, but Anna often hurts Julie's feelings.
>
> **Anna:** *Don't put your bag on my desk!*
>
> Julie probably felt uncomfortable because Anna made a demand ⓐusing the word "don't." People simply don't like taking orders. Anna should try to use words such as "can," "could," or "please." Then, what she says will sound like a request rather than a demand.
>
> **Anna:** *Could you put your bag on your desk?*

22 아래 〈보기〉에서 위 글의 밑줄 친 ⓐusing과 문법적 쓰임이 다른 것의 개수를 고르시오.

> ┤ 보기 ├
> ① I won't give up underline playing baseball.
> ② He is watching TV now.
> ③ Skiing there is exciting.
> ④ The man working in the garden is my father.
> ⑤ His hobby is fishing in the river.

① 1개   ② 2개   ③ 3개   ④ 4개   ⑤ 5개

23 According to the passage, which is NOT true?

① Anna and Julie are best friends.
② Julie often hurts Anna's feelings.
③ People don't like taking orders.

④ Anna should try to use words such as "can," "could," or "please."
⑤ There is a way that Anna can make what she says sound like a request rather than a demand.

[24~25] 다음 글을 읽고 물음에 답하시오.

> Next is Calli. She is trying to talk to her mother, but she is busy preparing to go to work. Let's have a look.
>
> **Calli:** *Hey, Mom. Could I talk to you about something?*
>
> Calli needs to find the right time to talk to her mom. Maybe Calli's mom wanted to listen to what Calli was going to say. But she didn't have enough time to talk with her daughter. ⓐ Calli는 어머니가 들으실 준비가 된 때를 골라야 합니다.
>
> **Calli:** *Hey, Mom. Could I talk to you about something?*
>
> **Mom:** *Sure.*

24 위 글의 밑줄 친 ⓐ의 우리말에 맞게 주어진 어휘를 이용하여 12 단어로 영작하시오.

> pick, when, ready, to

➡ _____
_____

25 다음 문장에서 위 글의 내용과 다른 부분을 찾아서 고치시오. (3 군데)

> Calli had no time to talk to her mom, because she was busy preparing to go to school.

➡ _____

Lesson 2

Wonderful Nature

 의사소통 기능

- 기대하는 일 표현하기
  A: What's your summer plan?
  B: My family is going to China. I can't wait to visit the Rainbow Mountains.
- 알고 있는 정보 말하기
  A: What are the white things in the picture?
  B: They are snow rollers. I've heard that they are made by strong wind and sticky snow.

 언어 형식

- to부정사의 의미상의 주어
  Iceland is the best place **for many location scouts** to visit.
- 현재완료진행형
  I've been visiting the forest to study animals for 20 years.

교과서

Words & Expressions

Key Words

- **actually** [ǽktʃuəli] 분 실제로
- **adventure** [ədvéntʃər] 명 모험
- **alive** [əláiv] 형 생기 넘치는, 살아 있는
- **amazing** [əméiziŋ] 형 놀라운, 멋진
- **anywhere else** 다른 곳
- **aurora** [ɔ́:rərə] 명 오로라
- **award** [əwɔ́:rd] 명 상
- **canvas** [kǽnvəs] 명 도화지, 캔버스
- **cave** [keiv] 명 동굴
- **chance** [tʃæns] 명 기회
- **cliff** [klif] 명 절벽
- **clothing** [klóuðiŋ] 명 의류, 옷
- **colorist** [kʌ́lərist] 명 색채화가
- **combination** [kàmbənéiʃən] 명 조합
- **community center** 지역 문화 회관
- **competition** [kàmpətíʃən] 명 대회
- **countless** [káuntlis] 형 많은, 셀 수 없는
- **develop** [divéləp] 동 만들다, 발전하다
- **ecologist** [ikɑ́lədʒist] 명 생태학자
- **environment** [inváiəiərənmənt] 명 환경
- **field** [fi:ld] 명 분야, 영역
- **glacier** [gléiʃər] 명 빙하
- **glow** [glou] 동 빛나다
- **harsh** [hɑ:rʃ] 형 (날씨·생활 환경이) 혹독한, 가혹한
- **honor** [ɑ́nər] 동 영광으로 생각하다
- **improve** [imprú:v] 동 개선하다, 향상시키다
- **insight** [ínsàit] 명 통찰력
- **inspire** [inspáiər] 동 영감을 주다, 고무하다, 격려하다
- **investigate** [invéstəgèit] 동 조사하다
- **jack-in-the-box** 열면 인형 등이 튀어나오는 상자, (각종) 기계 장치
- **lemur** [lí:mər] 명 (마다가스카르산) 여우원숭이
- **level** [lévəl] 명 (건물·땅의) 층
- **location** [loukéiʃən] 명 위치, 장소
- **Maldives** [mǽldaivz] 명 몰디브 공화국
- **miracle** [mírəkl] 명 놀라운 일, 기적
- **mixed** [mikst] 형 섞인, 혼합한
- **Mongolia** [maŋgóuliə] 명 몽골
- **mountain range** 산맥
- **palm tree** 야자나무
- **peak** [pi:k] 동 절정[최대한도]에 이르다
- **period** [pí:əriəd] 명 기간
- **personal** [pə́rsənl] 형 개인적인
- **pyramid** [pírəmìd] 명 피라미드
- **rainfall** [réinfɔl] 명 강우
- **recent** [rí:snt] 형 최근의
- **reef** [ri:f] 명 암초
- **research** [risə́:rtʃ] 동 조사하다, 연구하다
- **scout** [skaut] 명 정찰
- **set** [set] (해·달 등이) 지다
- **shape** [ʃeip] 명 모양, 형태
- **shoot** [ʃu:t] 동 촬영하다
- **shooting star** 유성, 별똥별
- **snow roller** (기상학) 두루마리 눈
- **spiky** [spáiki] 형 끝이 뾰족한
- **sticky** [stíki] 형 끈적거리는, 달라붙는
- **survive** [sərváiv] 동 살아남다, 생존하다
- **travel** [trǽvəl] 동 이동하다
- **unique** [ju:ní:k] 형 독특한, 특별한
- **unusual** [ənjúʒuəl] 형 특이한, 흔치 않은
- **view** [vju:] 명 풍경, 전망
- **weather report** 일기 예보
- **yellow dust** 황사

Key Expressions

- **be caused by** ~ ~에 기인하다
- **be filled with** ~로 가득차다
- **be made by** ~ ~에 의해 만들어지다
- **be[get] inspired by** ~에 의해 영감을 받다
- **come back from** ~ ~에서 돌아오다
- **come true** 실현되다, 사실이 되다
- **cut down** 자르다
- **due to** 명사 ~ 때문에
- **find out** 발견하다, 알아보다
- **get in shape** 좋은 몸 상태를 유지하다
- **hundreds of** ~ 수백의 ~, 수많은 ~
- **in the middle of the night** 한밤중에
- **keep ~ on one's toes** ~에게 정신을 바짝 차리게 하다
- **make plans (for)** (~의) 계획을 세우다
- **millions of** 수백만의
- **run up (to** 장소) (~에) 달려가다
- **seem+형용사** ~처럼 보이다
- **stand in for** ~을 대신하다
- **turn out** (일·진행·결과가 특정 방식으로) 되다
- **walk along** 산책하다

Word Power

※ 접두어 in-

in-은 '안에(**in**)'의 의미가 있는 접두어이다.

- □ **in**(= in) + **sight**(시야) → 안을 들여다보는 시야 → **insight**(통찰력)
- □ **in**(= in) + **come**(오다) → 안으로 들어오는 것 → **income**(소득)
- □ **in**(= in) + **side**(면, 지역) → **inside**(내부, 안쪽)
- □ **in**(= in) + **door**(문) → **indoor**(실내의)

※ a-로 시작하는 형용사는 주로 서술적 용법으로 쓰인다.

- □ **a** + **live**(살아 있는, 생방송의) → **alive**(생기 넘치는, 살아 있는)
- □ **a** + **lone**(단 하나의, 혼자의) → **alone**(혼자, 홀로)
- □ **a** + **like**(같은, 동등한) → **alike**(비슷한, 동등한)
- □ **a** + **sleep**(자다) → **asleep**(잠이 든, 자는)
- □ **a** + **wake**(깨다, 일어나다) → **awake**(깨어 있는, 잠자지 않는)

English Dictionary

- □ **adventure** 모험
  → an exciting experience in which dangerous or unusual things happen
  위험하고 흔치 않은 일이 발생하는 신나는 경험

- □ **cave** 동굴
  → a large hole in the side of a hill or under the ground
  언덕의 한쪽 면이나 땅 밑에 있는 큰 구멍

- □ **cliff** 절벽
  → the steep side of an area of high land
  높은 땅이 있는 지역의 가파른 면

- □ **combination** 조합
  → something that combines several things
  몇몇 개의 것들을 결합시킨 것

- □ **countless** 많은, 셀 수 없는
  → very many, especially more than you think is reasonable
  매우 많은, 특히 당신이 생각하기에 합당한 것보다 더 많은

- □ **ecologist** 생태학자
  → a scientist who studies the environment and the way that plants, animals, and humans live together and affect each other
  환경과 식물, 동물, 인간이 함께 살면서 서로에게 영향을 미치는 방법에 대해 연구하는 과학자

- □ **glacier** 빙하
  → a very large mass of ice that moves very slowly
  매우 느리게 움직이는 아주 큰 얼음 덩어리

- □ **glow** 빛나다
  → to shine with a soft light
  부드러운 빛으로 빛나다

- □ **harsh** (날씨·생활 환경이) 혹독한
  → difficult to live in and very uncomfortable
  살기에 힘들고 매우 불편한

- □ **inspire** 영감을 주다, 고무하다, 격려하다
  → to encourage someone by making them feel confident and eager to do something
  어떤 사람을 자신감 있게 그리고 어떤 것을 하고 싶게 만듦으로써 북돋우다

- □ **mixed** 섞인, 혼합한
  → consisting of several different types of things or people 몇 개의 다른 종류의 사물이나 사람으로 구성된

- □ **peak** 절정[최대한도]에 이르다
  → to reach the highest point or level
  가장 높은 지점이나 수준에 이르다

- □ **period** 기간
  → a particular length of time with a beginning and an end 처음과 끝을 가진 특정한 시간의 길이

- □ **rainbow** 무지개
  → a large curve of different colors that can appear in the sky when there is both sun and rain
  태양과 비 둘 다 있을 때 하늘에 나타날 수 있는 여러 가지의 색깔을 가진 큰 곡선

- □ **research** 조사하다, 연구하다
  → to study a subject in detail, especially in order to discover new facts or test new ideas
  특히 새로운 사실을 발견하거나 새로운 생각을 검사하기 위해 자세히 어떤 대상을 연구하다

- □ **shooting star** 유성, 별똥별
  → a piece of rock or metal from space that burns brightly as it falls towards the Earth
  지구로 떨어질 때 밝은 빛을 내며 타는 우주로부터 온 돌이나 금속 조각

- □ **unique** 독특한, 특별한
  → very special, unusual, or good
  매우 특별한, 흔하지 않은, 혹은 좋은

- □ **unusual** 특이한, 흔치 않은
  → different from what is usual or normal
  보통의 평범한 것과는 다른

[01~02] 다음 빈칸에 알맞은 단어를 고르시오.

01

> Because of the _____ weather conditions, the marathon was postponed for two weeks.

① harsh
② soft
③ sticky
④ moderate
⑤ mild

02

> Oil production _____ in the early 1980s.

① peaked
② acquired
③ became
④ determined
⑤ fought

03 다음 빈칸에 들어갈 말이 나머지와 다른 하나를 고르시오. (대·소문자 무시)

① I know the mayor really well. _____ fact, I had dinner with her last week.
② The phone rang _____ the middle of the night.
③ The movie was inspired _____ real events.
④ During the dangerous scenes, a stunt woman stood _____ for Goldie Hawn.
⑤ I really want to get _____ shape before summer.

04 다음 밑줄 친 부분의 의미로 알맞지 않은 것은?

① I haven't had a <u>chance</u> to look at it yet. (기회)
② Keith has a degree in engineering, but couldn't find a job in his <u>field</u>. (분야)
③ Our problems were due to a <u>combination</u> of bad management and lack of experience. (조합, 결합)
④ If I'm going out for a meal, I prefer to <u>try</u> something different. (노력하다)
⑤ They forgot that Picasso was a brilliant <u>colorist</u>. (색채화가)

05 다음 빈칸에 공통으로 들어갈 말을 고르시오.

> • We need someone who can _____ the team.
> • They think his music _____s and moves people.

① investigate
② bring
③ set
④ increase
⑤ inspire

06 다음 빈칸 (A)와 (B)에 알맞은 말로 짝지어진 것을 고르시오.

> • However, the parents and teachers (A)_____ out a problem with the race.
> • Did you (B)_____ plans for your summer vacation?

	(A)	(B)
①	found	call
②	found	make
③	made	call
④	made	make
⑤	made	have

01 두 문장이 같은 의미가 되도록 빈칸을 채우시오.

> Every time I wash my car, it rains the next day.
> = _____ I wash my car, it rains the next day.

02 빈칸에 적절한 말을 주어진 단어를 이용하여 채우시오.

> The research provides new _____ into the way we process language. (sight)

03 다음 밑줄 친 부분의 쓰임이 자연스럽지 않은 것을 찾아 고치시오.

> ⓐ Sorry, but I need to be <u>lone</u> right now.
> ⓑ Are all your grandparents still <u>alive</u>?
> ⓒ I think my mother and I are very much <u>alike</u> in some ways.

➡ _____

[04~05] 다음 빈칸에 공통으로 들어갈 말을 쓰시오.

04

> • When did you _____ back from the States?
> • This is the land where dreams _____ true.

05

> • I just need a car to get me from my house _____ the station.
> • This project will not continue next year due _____ a lack of funds.

06 다음 우리말에 맞도록 빈칸에 알맞은 말을 쓰시오.

(1) 오로라의 색깔들은 공기의 조건에 따라 달라집니다.
➡ An _____ colors depend on the conditions of the air.

(2) 기후 변화는 다양한 인간 활동에 의해서 야기된다.
➡ Climate change _____ _____ _____ various human activities.

(3) 몇몇 생태학자들은 많은 다양한 방식으로 생명을 연구한다.
➡ Some _____ study life in many different ways.

(4) 누가 그녀를 대신해 줄 수 있는가?
➡ Who could possibly _____ _____ _____ her?

07 다음 빈칸을 〈보기〉에 있는 어휘를 이용하여 채우시오.

> ┌─ 보기 ─────────────────┐
> cut   fill   keep   turn
> └───────────────────────┘

(1) They do random checks to _____ workers on their toes.

(2) It was a difficult time, but eventually things _____ out all right.

(3) People _____ down too many trees, destroying the habitats of wildlife.

(4) The air was _____ with the scent of roses.

Conversation

① 기대하는 일 표현하기

A: What's your summer plan? 여름 계획은 무엇이니?

B: My family is going to China. I can't wait to visit the Rainbow Mountains.
나의 가족은 중국에 갈 거야. 나는 레인보우 산맥을 빨리 방문하고 싶어.

- 'can't wait to+동사원형'은 '~하기를 몹시 바라다' 또는 '어서 ~하고 싶다'라는 의미로 기대를 나타낼 때 사용하는 표현이다.
- 'can't wait to+동사원형' 대신에 'can't wait for+(동)명사'나 'look forward to+(동)명사', 'expect to+동사원형'을 사용할 수 있다.
- 'I can't wait to' 다음에는 동사원형이 오고, 'I'm looking forward to' 다음에는 명사나 동명사가 오는 것에 유의한다.

    I can't wait to take the trip. (나는 어서 여행을 하고 싶다.)
    = I can't wait for taking the trip.
    = I'm looking forward to taking the trip.
    = I'm looking forward to the trip.

기대하는 일을 나타내는 표현

- I can't wait to 동사원형. (나는 어서 ~하고 싶어.)
- I'm looking forward to (동)명사.
- I can't wait for (동)명사.
- I expect to 동사원형. (나는 ~을 기대한다.)

핵심 Check

1. 다음 우리말과 일치하도록 주어진 단어를 배열하여 문장을 만드시오.

    A: I am going to have a pizza party this Friday. Can you come?
    B: Of course. _____ (can't, the, I, wait, party, to, to, go) (나는 어서 파티에 가고 싶어.)

2. 다음 문장과 같은 의미가 되도록 주어진 단어를 이용하여 쓰시오.

    I can't wait to try them out on my friends. (나는 어서 내 친구들한테 그것들을 사용해 보고 싶어.)

    ➡ _____ (look)

② 알고 있는 정보 말하기

A: What are the white things in the picture? 사진의 그 흰 것들은 무엇이니?

B: They are snow rollers. I've heard that they are made by strong wind and sticky snow. 그것들은 두루마리 눈이야. 나는 그것들이 강한 바람과 끈적거리는 눈에 의해 만들어진다는 말을 들었어.

■ 'I've heard that ~.'은 '~에 대해 들었다'의 의미로 알고 있거나 들은 것에 대해 말할 때 쓰는 표현이다.

■ 일반적으로 현재완료의 형태인 'I've heard that ~.'을 쓰지만 'I heard that ~.'이라고 할 수도 있다. that절이 아닌 전치사 about을 써서 표현할 수도 있다.

알고 있는 정보 말하기

- I've heard that 주어+동사 ~.
- I heard that 주어+동사 ~.
- I know that 주어+동사 ~.
- I've heard about (동)명사 ~.
- I heard about[of] (동)명사 ~. (나는 ~에 대해 들었다.)
- I know about (동)명사 ~. (나는 ~을 알고 있다.)
- I'm aware of (동)명사 ~.

핵심 Check

3. 다음 우리말과 일치하도록 빈칸에 알맞은 말을 쓰시오.

> B: I am having trouble with my eyes.
>
> A: I've heard _____.
>   (토마토를 먹는 것이 눈에 좋다고 들었어.)

4. 주어진 문장 이후에 올 대화의 순서를 바르게 배열하시오.

> What's wrong?

> (A) I've heard that having seaweed is good for your hair.
> (B) I'll try to have it more often.
> (C) I am having trouble with my hair.

➡ _____

Listen & Talk 1 A-1

W: David, what's your summer plan?

M: My family is going to China. I ❶can't wait to visit the Rainbow Mountains.

W: The Rainbow Mountains?

M: They are some mountains ❷that ❸look like ❹canvases ❺in rainbow colors.

W: ❻That sounds amazing! ❼Take lots of pictures!

W: David, 여름 계획은 뭐야?

M: 우리 가족은 중국에 갈 거야. 나는 레인보우 산맥을 빨리 방문하고 싶어.

W: 레인보우 산맥?

M: 그것은 무지개 색깔의 화폭처럼 보이는 산들이야.

W: 정말 멋지구나! 사진 많이 찍어!

❶ can't wait to+동사원형: 빨리 ~하고 싶다, ~하기를 몹시 바라다 visit: 방문하다
❷ that은 선행사 some mountains를 수식하고 있는 주격 관계대명사이다.
❸ look like 명사: ~처럼 보이다 / 선행사가 some mountains이므로 복수 동사인 look의 형태를 사용한다.
❹ canvas: 도화지, 캔버스
❺ in rainbow colors: 무지개 색깔로
❻ sound+형용사: ~하게 들리다 amazing: 멋진
❼ take a picture: 사진을 찍다 lots of: 많은

Check(√) True or False

(1) David has no plans for summer. T ☐ F ☐

(2) You can visit the Rainbow Mountains in China. T ☐ F ☐

 Listen & Talk 2 A-1

M: Mom, did you watch ❶the weather report today? We ❷will be able to see ❸hundreds of ❹shooting stars tonight!

W: Wow, fantastic! When is the best time ❺to see them?

M: ❻I've heard that the shooting stars will peak between 12 a.m. and 2 a.m.

W: Wow, it will be a special night!

M: 엄마, 오늘 일기예보 보셨어요? 우리는 오늘 밤 수많은 유성을 볼 수 있을 거예요!

W: 와, 환상적이야! 그것들을 보기에 가장 좋은 시간은 언제니?

M: 저는 유성이 오전 12시에서 2시 사이에 절정에 이를 거라고 들었어요.

W: 와, 특별한 밤이 되겠구나!

❶ weather report: 일기 예보
❷ will: ~할 것이다 be able to 동사원형: ~할 수 있다 / 조동사는 2개를 연달아(will can) 사용할 수 없기 때문에 can을 be able to로 바꿔서 사용한다.
❸ hundreds of ~: 수백의 ~, 수많은 ~
❹ shooting star: 유성, 별똥별
❺ to see them에서 them은 shooting stars를 받는 인칭대명사이다. to see them은 the best time을 꾸며주는 형용사적 용법으로 사용되고 있다.
❻ I've heard that ~: ~에 대해 들었다, ~에 대해 알고 있다 peak: 절정[최대한도]에 이르다 between A and B: A와 B 사이에서

Check(√) True or False

(3) There will be many shooting stars tomorrow. T ☐ F ☐

(4) The man knows when the shooting stars will peak. T ☐ F ☐

Listen & Talk 1 A-2

M: Do you ❶want to watch the new 3D movie?

W: Which ❷one?

M: The one about ❸adventures under the sea. ❹It was shot near Australia's Great Barrier Reef.

W: Oh, ❺I've heard of it. It has the most beautiful sea life.

M: Right. I ❻can't wait to watch the movie. ❼Let's go and get the ticket.

M: 너 새로 나온 3D 영화 보고 싶니?

W: 어느 영화?

M: 바다 밑의 모험에 관한 거야. 그것은 오스트레일리아의 Great Barrier Reef 근처에서 촬영되었어.

W: 오, 난 그것에 대해 들어본 적이 있어. 거기에는 가장 아름다운 해양 생물이 있어.

M: 맞아. 난 그 영화를 빨리 보고 싶어. 가서 표를 사자.

❶ want는 'to+동사원형'을 목적어로 취할 수 있다.

❷ one은 a 3D movie를 받는 부정대명사이다.

❸ adventure: 모험 under ~: ~ 아래에

❹ shoot: 촬영하다 (shoot-shot-shot) near: ~ 가까이에서 reef: 암초
주어진 It은 새로 나온 3D 영화 중 하나를 의미한다. 영화가 촬영되었으므로 동사는 수동태인 'be shot'으로 사용되었다.

❺ 'I've heard of it.'은 '그것에 대해 들어 본 적이 있다'의 의미로 알고 있거나 들은 것에 대해 말할 때 쓰는 표현이다. 전치사 of 대신에 about을 사용할 수 있다.

❻ can't wait to+동사원형: 빨리 ~하고 싶다, ~하기를 몹시 바라다(= can't wait for (동)명사 ~ = be looking forward to (동)명사 ~ = expect to 동사원형 ~)

❼ go와 get은 접속사 and로 연결되어 있다. Let's 다음에 동사원형이 나와야 하므로 get도 동사원형으로 사용되었다.

Check(√) True or False

(5) The woman has never heard of the movie about adventures under the sea.　T ☐ F ☐

(6) The woman and the man will watch the movie together.　T ☐ F ☐

Listen & Talk 2 B

M: Jisu, ❶did you know that the sun never sets in Norway during summer?

W: No, I didn't know ❷that. How interesting!

M: Yeah, and ❸I've heard that people go hiking and even cycling at night ❹because it isn't dark.

W: I'd love to go hiking and cycling ❺in the middle of the night!

M: Me, too. I hope we ❻get the chance ❼to try it someday.

M: 지수야, 여름 동안 노르웨이에서는 해가 지지 않는다는 걸 알고 있니?

W: 아니, 그건 몰랐어. 정말 흥미롭구나!

M: 그래, 그리고 난 사람들이 밤에 어둡지 않아서 하이킹 가고 심지어 자전거를 타러 간다고 들었어.

W: 나는 한밤중에 하이킹 가고 자전거를 타러 가고 싶어!

M: 나도. 언젠가 그것을 해볼 기회가 있으면 좋겠어.

❶ 'Did you know that ~?'은 '~에 대해 알고 있었니?'의 의미로, 알고 있는지 여부를 묻는 표현이다. 같은 의미로 'Are you aware that ~?'나 'Have you heard that ~?'을 사용할 수 있다. set: (해·달 등이) 지다 during+명사: ~ 동안에

❷ 대명사 that은 앞 문장의 'the sun never sets in Norway during summer(노르웨이에서는 여름 동안에는 해가 지지 않는다)'의 내용을 받고 있다.

❸ I've heard that ~: ~에 대해 들었다, ~에 대해 알고 있다 go+동사ing: ~하러 가다 at night: 밤에

❹ because(~ 때문에)는 이유를 나타내는 접속사이므로 뒤에 주어와 동사가 와야 한다.

❺ in the middle of the night: 한밤중에

❻ get the chance: 기회를 얻다(= have the chance)

❼ to try it은 앞의 명사 the chance를 수식하는 형용사적 용법으로 사용하였다. try: 시도하다, 해보다

Check(√) True or False

(7) Jisu knew that the sun never sets in Norway during summer.　T ☐ F ☐

(8) The man wishes to go hiking and cycling in the middle of the night.　T ☐ F ☐

Listen & Talk 1 Get Ready

A: The ❶view of the top of the mountain ❷is going to be amazing.

B: Yeah, ❸I can't wait to see the view. ❹Let's run up there!

❶ view: 경치, 풍경, 전망

❷ 주어가 The view로 단수 명사이므로 단수 동사인 is가 어울린다. be going to 동사원형: ～할 것이다

❸ 'can't wait to+동사원형'은 '～하기를 몹시 바라다' 또는 '어서 ～하고 싶다'의 의미로 기대를 나타낼 때 사용하는 표현이다.

❹ 어떤 활동을 함께하자고 제안할 경우에는 'Let's+동사원형'을 사용할 수 있다. run up (to 장소): (～에) 달려가다

Listen & Talk 1 B

W: Dad, my science club ❶is going to go to Dokdo in July.

M: Oh, really? What do you plan to do there?

W: We are going to ❷study the caves on the island and go bird watching.

M: ❸Sounds like it will be an interesting trip.

W: Yeah. I've ❹only read about Dokdo in books. I can't wait to actually visit there.

M: I ❺hope you enjoy your trip!

❶ be going to 동사원형: ～할 예정이다 go to 장소: ～에 가다. 월(month)을 나타내는 명사 앞에는 전치사 in을 사용한다.

❷ study: 연구하다 cave: 동굴 / 접속사 and로 study와 go가 병렬 구조를 이루고 있다.

❸ Sounds like 명사/명사절: ～처럼 들리다, ～일 것 같다

❹ only는 in books를 수식하는 부사이다.

❺ 'I hope (that)+주어+동사 ～.'는 '～를 바란다.'의 의미로 희망이나 바람을 나타내는 표현이다.

Listen & Talk 2 Get Ready

A: ❶The level of yellow dust is really high today.

B: Yeah. ❷I've heard that the yellow dust travels from the deserts of Mongolia to Korea.

❶ level: 정도, 수준 yellow dust: 황사 high: 격심한

❷ I've heard that ～: ～에 대해 들었다, ～에 대해 알고 있다 from A to B: A에서 B로 travel: 이동하다

Listen & Talk 2 A-2

M: Erica, what are the white things in the picture?

W: They are snow rollers. I've heard that ❶ they ❷are made by strong wind and ❸ sticky snow.

M: ❹Interesting! They look like snow rings.

W: Yeah, I'd like to actually see them someday.

❶ they는 snow rollers(두루마리 눈)를 받는 대명사이다.

❷ be made by ～: ～에 의해 만들어지다

❸ sticky: 끈적거리는, 달라붙는

❹ 'Interesting!'은 상대방이 한 말에 대하여 '재미있겠다!'라는 표현으로 'How interesting!'이나 'Sounds interesting!' 등의 표현을 사용할 수 있다.

Communication

M: Let's welcome ❶Ms. Scarlett Lee, the winner of this year's photo competition.

W: Hello, thank you for inviting me. ❷I've honored ❸to receive the award.

M: ❹Let's talk about your photo. I've heard that this photo ❺was taken in the Maldives. Is that true?

W: Yes, ❻this glowing beach is caused by plankton.

M: Wow, it truly is amazing!

W: Yes, it is. I can't wait to take more pictures of amazing beaches.

M: ❼I wish you the best of luck!

❶ Ms. Scarlett Lee와 the winner of this year's photo competition은 동격 관계이다. winner: 우승자 competition: 대회

❷ honor: 영광으로 생각하다

❸ to receive the award는 honored(영광으로 생각하다)의 이유를 설명하고 있으므로, to부정사의 부사적 용법 중 감정의 원인(～해서)으로 사용하고 있다. award: 상

❹ 'Let's talk about ～'는 '～에 대해 이야기해 보자'의 의미로 주제를 소개할 때 사용한다.

❺ that절의 주어인 this photo가 찍히는 것이므로 수동태(be+p.p.)인 'be taken'이 적절하다.

❻ glowing: 빛나는 be caused by ～: ～에 기인하다

❼ wish가 4형식으로 간접목적어(you)와 직접목적어(the best of luck)를 취하고 있다.

● 다음 우리말과 일치하도록 빈칸에 알맞은 말을 쓰시오.

Listen & Talk 1 Get Ready

A: The _____ of the top of the mountain is going to be _____.

B: Yeah, I can't _____ _____ see the view. Let's _____ _____ there!

Listen & Talk 1 A-1

W: David, _____ your summer _____?

M: My family is _____ to China. I can't _____ _____ _____ the Rainbow Mountains.

W: The Rainbow Mountains?

M: They _____ some mountains _____ look _____ canvases in rainbow colors.

W: That _____ amazing! _____ lots of pictures!

Listen & Talk 1 A-2

M: Do you _____ _____ _____ _____ the new 3D movie?

W: Which one?

M: The one _____ _____ under the sea. It _____ _____ near Australia's Great Barrier Reef.

W: Oh, I've _____ of it. It _____ the most beautiful sea life.

M: Right. I _____ _____ _____ _____ the movie. Let's _____ _____ _____ the ticket.

Listen & Talk 1 B

W: Dad, my science club _____ _____ to go to Dokdo _____ July.

M: Oh, really? _____ do you _____ _____ do there?

W: We are going to _____ the _____ on the island and _____ bird _____.

M: Sounds _____ it will be an _____ trip.

W: Yeah. _____ _____ _____ _____ Dokdo in books. I can't _____ _____ _____ _____ there.

M: I _____ you _____ your trip!

Listen & Talk 2 Get Ready

A: The level of yellow dust _____ really _____ today.

B: Yeah. _____ _____ _____ the yellow dust _____ _____ the deserts of Mongolia _____ Korea.

Listen & Talk 2 A-1

M: Mom, did you watch the _____ _____ today? We will be _____ to see hundreds of _____ _____ tonight!

W: Wow, fantastic! _____ is the best time _____ _____ _____?

M: I've _____ _____ the _____ _____ will peak _____ 12 a.m. _____ 2 a.m.

W: Wow, it will be a _____ _____!

Listen & Talk 2 A-2

M: Erica, what _____ the white things in the picture?

W: _____ _____ snow rollers. _____ _____ _____ they are _____ _____ strong wind and _____ snow.

M: Interesting! They look _____ snow rings.

W: Yeah, I'd _____ to _____ see them someday.

Listen & Talk 2 B

M: Jisu, did you know _____ the sun never _____ in Norway during summer?

W: No, I didn't know _____. _____ interesting!

M: Yeah, and I've _____ _____ people go hiking and even _____ at night _____ it isn't dark.

W: I'd _____ to go hiking and cycling _____ the middle _____ the night!

M: Me, _____. I hope we get the _____ _____ _____ it someday.

M: 지수야, 여름 동안 노르웨이에서는 해가 지지 않는다는 걸 알고 있니?

W: 아니, 그건 몰랐어. 정말 흥미롭구나!

M: 그래, 그리고 난 사람들이 밤에 어둡지 않아서 하이킹 가고 심지어 자전거를 타러 간다고 들었어.

W: 나는 한밤중에 하이킹과 자전거를 타러 가고 싶어!

M: 나도. 언젠가 그것을 해볼 기회가 있으면 좋겠어.

Communication

M: Let's welcome Ms. Scarlett Lee, the _____ of this year's photo competition.

W: Hello, thank you _____ _____ me. I've _____ to receive the award.

M: Let's _____ about your photo. I've _____ _____ this photo _____ _____ in the Maldives. Is that _____?

W: Yes, this glowing beach is _____ _____ plankton.

M: Wow, it truly is _____!

W: Yes, it is. I _____ _____ _____ _____ more pictures of amazing beaches.

M: I _____ you the _____ of luck!

M: 올해 사진 대회 우승자인 Scarlett Lee 양을 환영합시다.

W: 안녕하세요, 초대해 주셔서 감사합니다. 상을 받게 되어 영광으로 생각합니다.

M: 사진에 대해 얘기해 봅시다. 저는 이 사진이 몰디브에서 찍힌 거라고 들었어요. 그게 사실인가요?

W: 네, 이 빛나는 해변은 플랑크톤 때문에 생긴 거예요.

M: 와, 정말 놀랍네요!

W: 네, 그래요. 저는 빨리 멋진 해변의 사진을 더 많이 찍고 싶어요.

M: 행운을 빌어요!

01 다음 대화의 빈칸에 알맞은 것을 <u>모두</u> 고르시오.

> W: David, what's your summer plan?
> M: My family is going to China. _____
> W: The Rainbow Mountains?
> M: They are some mountains that look like canvases in rainbow colors.
> W: That sounds amazing! Take lots of pictures!

① I hope you will enjoy the Rainbow Mountains.

② I can't wait to visit the Rainbow Mountains.

③ I'm sure you will visit the Rainbow Mountains.

④ I can wait to visit the Rainbow Mountains.

⑤ I'm looking forward to visiting the Rainbow Mountains.

02 주어진 문장 다음에 올 대화의 순서를 바르게 배열한 것을 고르시오.

> M: Mom, did you watch the weather report today? We will be able to see hundreds of shooting stars tonight!

> (A) I've heard that the shooting stars will peak between 12 a.m. and 2 a.m.
> (B) Wow, fantastic! When is the best time to see them?
> (C) Wow, it will be a special night!

① (A) – (C) – (B)　　② (B) – (A) – (C)　　③ (B) – (C) – (A)

④ (C) – (A) – (B)　　⑤ (C) – (B) – (A)

03 다음 대화의 빈칸에 알맞은 것을 고르시오.

> M: Do you want to watch the new 3D movie?
> W: Which one?
> M: The one about adventures under the sea. It was shot near Australia's Great Barrier Reef.
> W: Oh, _____ It has the most beautiful sea life.
> M: Right. I can't wait to watch the movie. Let's go and get the ticket.

① I've heard of it.　　② I didn't hear of it.

③ You have no idea of that.　　④ I've never heard of it.

⑤ Did you hear about it?

[01~02] 다음 대화를 읽고 물음에 답하시오.

W: Dad, my science club is going to go to Dokdo in July. (①)

M: Oh, really? (②)

W: (③) We are going to study the caves on the island and go bird watching.

M: Sounds like it will be an interesting trip. (④)

W: Yeah. I've only read about Dokdo in books. (⑤) I can't wait to actually visit there.

M: I hope you enjoy your trip!

 01 위 대화의 ①~⑤ 중 주어진 문장이 들어갈 알맞은 곳은?

> What do you plan to do there?

①   ②   ③   ④   ⑤

02 위 대화를 읽고 답할 수 없는 질문을 고르시오.

① Has the girl's dad been to Dokdo?

② When will the girl's science club go to Dokdo?

③ What is the girl going to do in Dokdo?

④ Where will the girl's science club go in July?

⑤ Is the girl looking forward to going to Dokdo?

[03~05] 다음 대화를 읽고 물음에 답하시오.

M: Let's welcome Ms. Scarlett Lee, the winner of this year's photo competition. (①)

W: Hello, thank you (A)_____ inviting me. I've honored to receive the award. (②)

M: Let's talk about your photo. (③) Is that true?

W: Yes, this glowing beach is caused by plankton. (④)

M: Wow, it truly is amazing! (⑤)

W: Yes, it is. I can't wait to take more pictures of amazing beaches.

M: I wish you the best of luck!

03 위 대화의 ①~⑤ 중 주어진 문장이 들어갈 알맞은 곳은?

> I've heard that this photo was taken in the Maldives.

①   ②   ③   ④   ⑤

서답형

04 빈칸 (A)에 들어갈 전치사를 쓰시오.

➡ _____

05 위 대화를 읽고 답할 수 없는 질문을 고르시오.

① Why is the beach in the Maldives glowing?

② What are they talking about?

③ Who is the winner of this year's photo competition?

④ What country is Ms. Scarlett Lee going to visit to take more pictures?

⑤ Where did Ms. Scarlett Lee take the award-winning photo?

06 다음 대화의 ⓐ~ⓔ 중 가리키는 것이 다른 하나를 고르시오.

> M: Erica, what are ⓐthe white things in the picture?
>
> W: ⓑThey are snow rollers. I've heard that ⓒthey are made by strong wind and sticky snow.
>
> M: Interesting! They look like ⓓsnow rings.
>
> W: Yeah, I'd like to actually see ⓔthem someday.

① ⓐ   ② ⓑ   ③ ⓒ   ④ ⓓ   ⑤ ⓔ

07 다음 중 짝지어진 대화가 어색한 것은?

① A: I gained 2 kilograms recently.
　 B: Don't worry. I've heard that gaining some weight is natural for teens.

② A: Do you have any plans for this weekend?
　 B: I'm going to climb Halla Mountain. I can't wait to do it.

③ A: I can't wait for next Sunday.
　 B: What are you going to do then?

④ A: Do you want to go to a rock concert?
　 B: No, I don't. I can't wait for it.

⑤ A: I can't wait to travel to Hawaii.
　 B: Have you decided what you will do there?

08 주어진 문장 다음에 올 대화의 순서를 바르게 배열한 것을 고르시오.

> Jisu, did you know that the sun never sets in Norway during summer?

> (A) Me, too. I hope we get the chance to try it someday.

> (B) I'd love to go hiking and cycling in the middle of the night!
>
> (C) No, I didn't know that. How interesting!
>
> (D) Yeah, and I've heard that people go hiking and even cycling at night because it isn't dark.

① (B)–(A)–(C)–(D)   ② (B)–(C)–(A)–(D)
③ (C)–(A)–(B)–(D)   ④ (C)–(B)–(A)–(D)
⑤ (C)–(D)–(B)–(A)

[09~10] 다음 대화를 읽고 물음에 답하시오.

> W: Have you made plans for this vacation?
>
> M: Yeah, I'm going to go to Uyuni Salt Flats in Bolivia. I can't (A)_____ to go bike riding there.

09 빈칸 (A)에 알맞은 말을 고르시오.

① need   ② look forward   ③ see
④ wait   ⑤ keep

서답형
10 위 대화의 내용에 맞게 빈칸을 완성하시오.

> The man is _____ to go to _____
> _____ _____ in Bolivia this vacation.
> He wishes to _____ _____ there.

11 다음 빈칸에 알맞은 말을 고르시오.

> A: I've _____ you can walk on the seabed once a year in Jindo, Korea.
>
> B: Sounds interesting! I'd like to go there someday.

① hear that   ② heard what
③ heard that   ④ know what
⑤ know that

[01~02] 다음 대화를 읽고 물음에 답하시오.

> M: Mom, ⓐdid you watch the weather report today? ⓑWe will be able to see hundreds of shooting stars tonight!
>
> W: ⓒWow, fantastic! ⓓWhere is the best place to see them?
>
> M: I've heard that the shooting stars will peak between 12 a.m. (A)_____ 2 a.m.
>
> W: ⓔWow, it will be a special night!

01 빈칸 (A)에 알맞은 말을 쓰시오.

➡ _____

02 ⓐ~ⓔ 중 흐름상 어색한 것을 바르게 고치시오.

➡ _____

[03~04] 다음 대화를 읽고 물음에 답하시오.

> W: David, what's your summer plan?
>
> M: My family is going to China. (A)나는 빨리 the Rainbow Mountains를 방문하고 싶어.
>
> W: The Rainbow Mountains?
>
> M: They are some mountains that look (B)_____ canvases in rainbow colors.
>
> W: That sounds amazing! Take lots of pictures!

03 밑줄 친 (A)의 우리말을 영작하시오.

➡ _____

04 빈칸 (B)에 들어갈 말을 쓰시오.

➡ _____

[05~06] 다음 대화를 읽고 물음에 답하시오.

> M: Do you want to watch the new 3D movie?
>
> W: Which one?
>
> M: The one about adventures under the sea. It (A)_____ (shoot) near Australia's Great Barrier Reef.
>
> W: Oh, (B)나는 그것에 대해 들었어. It has the most beautiful sea life.
>
> M: Right. I can't wait to watch the movie. Let's go and get the ticket.

05 빈칸 (A)를 괄호 안의 주어진 단어를 이용하여 쓰시오.

➡ _____

06 밑줄 친 (B)의 우리말을 주어진 단어를 이용하여 쓰시오.

➡ _____ (of, have)

07 빈칸 (A)를 괄호 안에 주어진 단어를 알맞게 배열하여 채우시오.

> M: Erica, what are the white things in the picture?
>
> W: They are snow rollers. (A) _____ _____ (made, and, snow, heard, are, sticky, I've, strong, by, wind, they, that)
>
> M: Interesting! They look like snow rings.
>
> W: Yeah, I'd like to actually see them someday.

➡ _____
_____

Grammar

① to부정사의 의미상의 주어

> • Iceland is the best place **for many location scouts** to visit.
> 아이슬랜드는 사진 촬영 장소를 찾으러 다니는 사람들이 방문할 가장 좋은 장소이다.
>
> • It's very considerate **of her** to have said so. 그녀가 그렇게 말했다니 참 이해심도 많네요.

■ to부정사의 의미상의 주어
to부정사의 동작을 실제로 하는 주체를 to부정사의 의미상의 주어라고 한다. to부정사의 의미상의 주어는 to부정사 바로 앞에 'for+명사 또는 대명사의 목적격'으로 나타낸다. 이때 문장에 쓰인 형용사가 nice, kind, smart, wise 등과 같이 사람의 성향, 성격을 나타내는 말일 때는 for 대신 of를 쓴다.

- Is three weeks enough time **for you** to finish? 3주면 당신이 충분히 끝낼 수 있는 시간이죠?
- It is impossible **for him** to do that. 그가 그것을 하기는 불가능하다.
- It is quite silly **of you** to try to force him to consent. 네가 강제로 그의 승낙을 받으려는 것은 아주 어리석은 일이다.

■ 비교적 긴 to부정사 부분이 문장의 주어로 쓰일 때 보통 그 to부정사 부분을 문장 제일 뒤에 두고 주어 자리에 가주어 it을 넣어준다.

- **It** is hard **to criticize** the people one loves. 자기가 사랑하는 사람들을 비난하는 것은 어려운 일이다.
  = **To criticize** the people one loves is hard.

■ to부정사의 의미상의 주어가 일반적인 사람일 경우는 보통 생략한다. 또한 to부정사의 부정은 to부정사 앞에 not이나 never를 써서 'not[never]+to부정사'로 나타낸다.

- It is interesting **to compare** their situation and ours. 그들의 상황과 우리의 상황을 비교해 보면 재미있다.
- Try **not to let** him bother you. 그가 당신을 괴롭히게 내버려 두지 말아요.

핵심 Check

1. 빈칸에 알맞은 말을 어법에 맞게 쓰시오.
   (1) It is exciting _____ go to the amusement park.
   (2) It is interesting _____ me to speak to a foreign friend.
   (3) Was it wise _____ you to come to the hotel?

2 현재완료진행형

- I**'ve been visiting** the forest to study animals for 20 years.
  나는 20년간 동물들을 연구하기 위해 그 숲을 방문하고 있다.

- Scientists **have been suggesting** their possible presence since 1992.
  과학자들은 1992년 이래 그들의 존재 가능성을 제기해 왔다.

■ 현재완료진행형은 'have[has] been+동사원형-ing'의 형태로 보통 for(~ 동안)나 since(~ 이래로)와 함께 쓰여 '~이래로[~ 동안] …해 오고 있다'라고 해석한다.
  • The problem **has been bothering** me until now. 그 문제는 지금까지 나를 괴롭혀 왔다.

■ 현재완료진행형은 어떤 상태나 행위가 과거 어느 때부터 시작되어 현재까지 계속 진행되고 있음을 나타내거나 현재까지 계속적으로 반복되고 있는 것을 나타낸다.
  • My back **has been bothering** me lately. 요즘은 허리가 영 시원찮다.

■ 현재완료진행형에서 진행형이 가능한 동사는 현재완료진행형으로 동작의 계속을 표현하고, 진행형으로 쓸 수 없는 동사(have(소유), belong, know, like, hate 등)는 현재완료형으로 상태의 계속을 표현한다. 즉, 현재완료진행은 '상태'가 아닌, '동작'만을 나타낸다.
  • It **has been snowing** for around 5 days. 약 5일 동안 내내 눈이 내리고 있다. (동작의 계속)
  • She **has known** Mary for two years. 그녀는 2년 동안 Mary와 알고 지냈다. (상태의 계속)

■ 현재완료 / 현재완료진행형
  현재완료는 동작의 결과에 초점을 맞춘다고 생각할 수 있지만, 현재완료진행형은 계속되고 있는 동작 그 자체에 초점을 맞춘다고 생각할 수 있다.
  • What **has** he **done**? (그는 무엇을 했는가?) → 결과에 초점
  • What **has** he **been doing**? (그는 무엇을 하고 있는가?) → 동작에 초점

핵심 Check

2. 주어진 어휘를 빈칸에 어법에 맞게 쓰시오.
  (1) He has been _____ the guitar for two hours. (play)
  (2) Wendy has been _____ the flute since she was six. (play)
  (3) Mike has been _____ it in secret. (do)

Grammar 시험대비 기본평가

01 다음 빈칸에 알맞은 것을 고르시오.

> **A:** Is it important _____?
> **B:** Yes, it is.

① practice playing the flute
② practices playing the flute
③ to practicing playing the flute
④ for you to practice playing the flute
⑤ of you to practice playing the flute

02 다음 두 문장을 한 문장으로 바꾸어 쓸 때 알맞게 표현한 것을 고르시오.

> • The problem started bothering me a long time ago.
> • It is still bothering me.

① The problem is bothering me now.
② The problem bothered me a long time ago.
③ The problem has been bothering me for a long time
④ The problem was bothering me for a long time.
⑤ The problem will be bothering me for a long time.

03 다음 괄호 안에서 알맞은 말을 고르시오.

(1) The research has been (suggesting / suggested) that drinking coffee may actually be good for your health.
(2) I (am living / have been living) in New York for 6 years.
(3) It is foolish (for / of) you to think so.
(4) Global warming and water pollution make it harder (for / of) the animals to live.

04 다음 우리말에 맞게 주어진 어휘를 바르게 배열하시오.

> 학생들이 그들의 숙제를 하는 것은 중요하다.
> (students, their homework, important, it, do, is, to, for)

➡ _____

01 다음 중 어법상 올바른 것은?

① It has been rain all day long.
② The argument has been going on since years.
③ Rana has been planted trees in the valleys for the last 31 years.
④ China has been cutting down many trees.
⑤ I've been visiting the forest to study animals since 20 years.

02 다음 중 어법상 올바르지 <u>않은</u> 것은?

① The shopping center is close enough for us to drop by.
② It's necessary for you to talk to her again.
③ This is no time of us to remain idle.
④ It isn't easy for me to teach history to students.
⑤ It was unwise of him not to have booked the travel insurance.

03 다음 빈칸에 알맞은 말이 올바르게 짝지어진 것은?

> • Mildred _____ Korean for two years.
> • Is the book easy enough _____ you to read?

① studies – of
② studied – of
③ is studying – of
④ has been studied – for
⑤ has been studying – for

서답형

04 다음 괄호 안에서 알맞은 말을 고르시오.

(1) How long have you (collect / been collecting) stamps?
(2) She has been living in London (since / for) three years.
(3) They have been shouting at us (since / for) this morning
(4) It is easy (for / of) us to take photos of many kinds of animals.
(5) It's so kind (for / of) you to invite me tonight.

05 다음 대화의 빈칸에 들어갈 말로 알맞은 것은?

> M: Is it safe _____ you to play outside at night in Seoul?
> W: Of course.

① of   ② for
③ by   ④ at
⑤ to

06 다음 문장의 빈칸에 들어갈 알맞은 것은?

> It has been raining cats and dogs _____ this morning.

① since   ② for
③ at   ④ during
⑤ with

07 밑줄 친 부분의 쓰임이 올바른 것은?

① We <u>have been knowing</u> Emily since she was a child.

② James <u>has been making</u> the film for one year.

③ Fans <u>has been waiting</u> for their favorite stars for two hours.

④ I <u>have been playing</u> computer games 3 hours ago.

⑤ Brian <u>has been studying</u> Korean last night.

서답형
08 우리말과 일치하도록 빈칸에 알맞은 말을 쓰시오.

이 컴퓨터는 내가 휴대할 수 있을 정도로 작다.
= This computer is small enough
_____ _____ _____ carry.

서답형
09 주어진 어휘를 이용하여 다음 우리말을 영작하시오.

그는 2001년 이래로 NASA의 다양한 분야에서 근무해 오고 있다. (11 단어)
(fields, NASA, work, various, at, in)

➡ _____

10 다음 문장의 빈칸에 알맞은 말은?

How stupid _____ to believe such a man!

① for him ② for us
③ for your ④ of him
⑤ of his

11 주어진 우리말을 영어로 바르게 옮긴 것은?

우리 가족은 10년이 넘는 동안 그 집에서 살아오고 있다.

① My family lived in the house during over 10 years.

② My family has living in the house since over 10 years.

③ My family has been lived in the house for over 10 years.

④ My family had lived in the house for over 10 years.

⑤ My family has been living in the house for over 10 years.

12 다음 빈칸에 들어갈 말이 나머지와 다른 하나는?

① It is important _____ Rachel to prepare special food.

② The restaurant had delicious foods _____ us to enjoy.

③ It's nice _____ you to come all the way to the airport.

④ It's so difficult _____ him to bring up his children.

⑤ It was hard _____ him to live on his low salary.

서답형
13 괄호 속의 단어들을 자연스럽게 배열하시오.

(1) I (interviewing / have / for / actors / been) one hour.

➡ _____

(2) Julie (knitting / a / been / has / sweater / since) this morning.

➡ _____

14 다음 문장에서 어법상 <u>어색한</u> 것을 바르게 고쳐 다시 쓰시오.

(1) Mr. Lee has been teach math for more than 30 years.

  ➡ _____

  _____

(2) Mariel has been learning Korean at the school 5 years ago.

  ➡ _____

  _____

(3) I have been climbing the mountain for Monday.

  ➡ _____

(4) We have been waiting for her since 2 hours.

  ➡ _____

(5) What time would be best of me to talk to you?

  ➡ _____

(6) I think it is very polite for her to ask permission.

  ➡ _____

(7) It will be difficult for the children swimming across this river.

  ➡ _____

  _____

15 다음 문장을 바꾸어 쓸 때 빈칸에 알맞은 말을 쓰시오.

> It is natural that she should cry.
> = _____ is natural _____ _____
> _____ _____ .

16 다음 두 문장을 한 문장으로 바르게 연결한 것은?

> • Actors and actresses started arriving here at 5 o'clock.
> • They are still arriving here.

① Actors and actresses arrived here since 5 o'clock.

② Actors and actresses had arrived here for 5 o'clock.

③ Actors and actresses have arriving here since 5 o'clock.

④ Actors and actresses have been arriving here for 5 o'clock.

⑤ Actors and actresses have been arriving here since 5 o'clock.

17 다음 중 어법상 <u>어색한</u> 것을 고르시오. (3개)

① I have been loving Lily since I met her for the first time.

② The Ice Cube is the best place for David to investigate the climate of the earth.

③ The little girl has been crying an hour ago.

④ It was so rude for you to say so.

⑤ I've been visiting the forest to study animals for 20 years.

18 다음 주어진 어휘를 이용하여 우리말을 영작하시오.

> 겨울이 오고 있기 때문에 우리는 겨울을 준비해야 한다. (as, winter, it, come, prepare, necessary, the, 14 단어)

  ➡ _____

  _____

01 괄호 안의 단어 수대로 주어진 두 문장을 하나의 문장으로 쓰시오.

(1) • Naomi reached the station at two o'clock to take the train.
  • She is still waiting for her train. (10 단어)

  ➡ _____
  _____

(2) • It started raining three hours ago.
  • It is still raining. (7 단어)

  ➡ _____

(3) • Women have made important contributions to sports for centuries.
  • They are still making contributions. (10 단어)

  ➡ _____
  _____

02 다음 우리말에 맞게 주어진 어구를 바르게 배열하시오.

(1) 이 책은 네가 읽기엔 너무 어렵다. (you, this book, difficult, read, is, too, for, to)

  ➡ _____

(2) 그는 영리하게도 그 기회를 놓치지 않았다. (it, him, the chance, was, miss, very smart, not, to, of)

  ➡ _____

(3) 나는 부모님의 사랑을 당연한 것으로 받아들여 왔다. (I, love, my parents', been, granted, taking, have, for)

  ➡ _____

03 그림을 보고, 주어진 어휘를 이용하여 빈칸을 알맞게 채우시오.

(1)

They _____ her birthday party
_____. (enjoying, two hours)

(2)

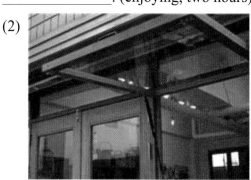

It was _____ the window open. (leave, careless, her)

04 다음 〈보기〉에 주어진 단어를 이용하여 문맥에 맞게 문장을 완성하시오.

┌─ 보기 ─────────────────────┐
│   since   for   │
└────────────────────────────┘

(1) My mom has been watching TV _____ two hours.

(2) Nancy has been studying Korean _____ 2010.

05 괄호 안에 주어진 말을 이용하여 어법에 맞게 문장을 완성하시오.

(1) This book is _____ read. (you, difficult, too)

(2) Is the room _____ get together? (big, us, enough)

(3) It was _____ give food to the children. (nice, her, to)

06 〈보기〉와 같이 문장을 바꿔 쓸 때 빈칸에 알맞은 말을 쓰시오.

> ┌─ 보기 ─
> You should choose good friends.
> → It is important for you to choose good friends.

(1) You should listen carefully to the advice.

→ It is important _____

_____.

(2) Abigail helped me to stand on my own feet.

→ It was nice _____

_____.

07 다음 문장에서 어법상 어색한 것을 바르게 고치시오.

(1) How long have you been thought about joining us?

➡ _____

(2) I have been waiting for him since 30 minutes.

➡ _____

(3) He has been collecting insects in a remote desert for 2009.

➡ _____

(4) The country has been possessing a strong military power.

➡ _____

(5) I have been living here 5 years ago.

➡ _____

(6) It is necessary of her to finish the report.

➡ _____

(7) It was difficult for me finding out what he wanted.

➡ _____

08 다음 우리말을 괄호 안에 주어진 어휘를 이용하여 영작하시오.

(1) 지난 몇 달 동안 모두가 열심히 공부해 왔다. (everyone, the last few months, hard, studying, 10 단어)

➡ _____

_____

(2) 그는 오랜 시간 동안 그 책을 써 오고 있다. (the book, write, long, 8 단어)

➡ _____

(3) 그녀는 5월부터 거기서 일해 왔어요. (work, there, May, 7 단어)

➡ _____

(4) 고맙게도 그녀가 내게 차편을 제공해 주었다. (it, nice, offer me a ride, to, 10 단어)

➡ _____

(5) 아직 내가 처리해야 할 일이 두 가지 더 있어. (there, still, chores, to do, more, 10 단어)

➡ _____

Reading

교과서

The World Through My Eyes

"The beauty of nature inspires us all. Let's find out how people from different fields of work get inspired by nature."

Lin Wang, Ecologist
Tsingy, the Stone Forest of Madagascar

I've been visiting the stone forest of Madagascar to study plants and animals for over 20 years. The spiky stones of this place are true miracles of nature. This amazing shape has been created by rainfall. Rain has cut down the stones and made them sharp and spiky over a long period of time. The environment is harsh for animals to live in, but they have found ways to survive. For example, lemurs, which only live in Madagascar, have frog-like legs that help them jump from one stone tower to another. For me, the stone forest is like a jack-in-the-box. It always surprises me and keeps me on my toes!

inspire 영감을 주다, 고무[격려]하다
field 분야
forest 숲
spiky 뾰족뾰족한
miracle 기적
shape 모양
rainfall 강우
sharp 날카로운
environment 환경
harsh 가혹한
survive 살아남다, 생존하다
lemur 여우원숭이
from A to B A에서 B로
jack-in-the-box 열면 인형이 튀어나오는 상자

 확인문제

● 다음 문장이 본문의 내용과 일치하면 T, 일치하지 않으면 F를 쓰시오.

1 We are all inspired by the beauty of nature. ☐

2 Lin Wang has visited the stone forest of Madagascar more than 20 times. ☐

3 The amazing shape of Tsingy has been created by rainfall. ☐

4 It is comfortable for animals to live in the environment. ☐

5 Lemurs only live in Madagascar. ☐

6 Lemurs have frog-like arms that help them jump from one stone tower to another. ☐

Amber Smith, Fashion Colorist
Caño Cristales, the River of Five Colors of Colombia

The world is filled with millions of different colors. It is my job to
[= is full of] [수백만의] [가주어]
mix, develop, and create colors for clothing. Over the years, I've been
[진주어(to부정사의 명사적 용법)]
gaining insights from the beautiful colors of Caño Cristales.
[현재완료진행형]
You cannot see the wonderful mixed colors of this river anywhere
[다른 어떤 곳에서도]
else in the world. The combination of colorful plants under the water
and sunlight makes the colors more alive and bright.
[make(×): The combination이 주어임.] [서술 용법(보어로만 쓰임)의 형용사]
Whenever I visit the Caño Cristales, it makes me think that maybe
[= Every time] [사역동사+목적어+원형부정사]
there are still countless colors that are waiting to be created.
[주격 관계대명사+be동사] [to부정사의 수동태]

Danny Mehta, Location Scout
Vatnajökull National Park, Frozen Beauty of Iceland

I'm a location scout and my job is finding perfect places to shoot
[동명사 (보어)] [to부정사의 형용사적 용법]
movies. Iceland is the best place for many location scouts to visit
[to부정사의 의미상의 주어(for+목적격)] [to부정사의 형용사적 용법]
due to its unusual beauty. My personal favorite is the Vatnajökull
[~ 때문에]
National Park. The sharp cliffs, blue glacier caves, and long mountain
ranges can stand in for any place in the world or the universe. In fact,
[~을 대신하다(replace)] [= As a matter of fact. Actually]
the recent sci-fi movie we shot here was produced without using
[(that) we shot] [전치사의 목적어로 쓰인 동명사]
computer graphics! Iceland can help make our wildest dreams come
[= to make] [=realize]
true on the movie screen.

Vocabulary
different 각양각색의, 각기 다른
mix 섞다
clothing 의류, 옷
insight 통찰력
combination 결합
colorful 다채로운
alive (생기·감정·활기 등이) 넘치는
bright 밝은
countless 무수한, 셀 수 없이 많은
perfect 완벽한
shoot (영화를) 촬영하다
unusual 특이한, 흔치 않은
beauty 아름다움
personal 개인의, 개인적인
cliff 절벽
glacier 빙하

📎 **확인문제**

● 다음 문장이 본문의 내용과 일치하면 T, 일치하지 <u>않으면</u> F를 쓰시오.

1 Amber Smith is a fashion colorist. ☐

2 Amber Smith cannot see the wonderful mixed colors of Caño Cristales. ☐

3 The combination of colorful plants under the water and sunlight makes the colors of

Caño Cristales more alive and bright. ☐

4 Danny Mehta is a location scout who makes perfect places to shoot movies. ☐

5 Danny Mehta's personal favorite is the Vatnajökull National Park. ☐

● 우리말을 참고하여 빈칸에 알맞은 말을 쓰시오.

1 The World _____ My Eyes

2 "The _____ of nature _____ us all.

3 Let's _____ _____ how people from different _____ _____ _____ _____ _____ by nature."

4 **Lin Wang, _____**

5 **Tsingy, the _____ _____ of Madagascar**

6 _____ _____ _____ the stone forest of Madagascar to study plants and animals _____ _____ 20 years.

7 The _____ stones of this place are _____ _____ of nature.

8 This _____ shape _____ _____ _____ by rainfall.

9 Rain has cut down the stones and made them _____ and _____ _____ a long period of time.

10 The environment is harsh _____ _____ _____ _____, but they have found ways _____ _____.

11 For example, lemurs, _____ only live in Madagascar, have _____ legs _____ help them jump _____ one stone tower _____ another.

12 For me, the stone forest _____ _____ a _____.

13 It always surprises me and _____ _____ _____ _____!

14 **Amber Smith, _____ _____**

15 **Caño Cristales, the _____ _____ _____ _____ of Colombia**

16 The world _____ _____ _____ millions of different colors.

---

1 내 눈에 비친 세계

2 "자연의 아름다움은 우리 모두에게 영감을 준다.

3 서로 다른 직업 분야의 사람들이 자연에 의해 어떻게 영감을 받는지 알아보자."

4 Lin Wang, 생태학자

5 Tsingy, 마다가스카르의 석림

6 나는 20년 이상 동안 식물과 동물을 연구하기 위해서 마다가스카르의 석림을 방문하고 있다.

7 이 지역의 뾰족한 돌들은 진정한 자연의 놀라움이다.

8 이 놀라운 모양은 비에 의해서 만들어졌다.

9 비가 오랜 기간 동안 돌을 침식해서 날카롭고 뾰족하게 만들었다.

10 이런 환경은 동물들이 살기에 험난하지만, 동물들은 생존할 방법들을 찾아냈다.

11 예를 들어, 마다가스카르에서만 사는 여우원숭이는 한 개의 돌탑에서 다른 돌탑으로 뛸 수 있도록 도와주는 개구리와 같은 다리를 가지고 있다.

12 나에게 석림은 '잭인더박스(열면 인형이 튀어나오는 상자)'와 같다.

13 그것은 늘 나를 놀라게 하고 정신을 바짝 차리게 한다!

14 Amber Smith, 패션 색채 전문가

15 Caño Cristales, 콜롬비아의 다섯 색깔의 강

16 세계는 수백만의 다양한 색깔로 가득 차 있다.

17 It is my job to mix, develop, and _____ _____ for clothing.

18 Over the years, _____ _____ _____ insights from the beautiful colors of Caño Cristales.

19 You cannot see the wonderful _____ _____ of this river _____ _____ in the world.

20 The _____ of colorful plants under the water and sunlight _____ the colors _____ _____ and _____.

21 _____ I visit the Caño Cristales, it makes me think that maybe there are still _____ colors that are _____ _____ _____ _____.

22 Danny Mehta, _____ _____

23 Vatnajökull National Park, _____ _____ of Iceland

24 I'm a location scout and my job is finding perfect places _____ _____ _____.

25 Iceland is the best place _____ _____ _____ _____ to visit _____ _____ its _____ _____.

26 _____ _____ _____ is the Vatnajökull National Park.

27 The sharp cliffs, blue glacier caves, and long mountain ranges can _____ _____ _____ _____ _____ in the world or the universe.

28 _____ _____, the recent sci-fi movie _____ _____ _____ was produced _____ _____ computer graphics!

29 Iceland can _____ _____ our wildest dreams _____ _____ on the movie screen.

17 의류를 위해서 색을 섞고, 발전시키고, 만들어 내는 것이 나의 일이다.

18 수년 동안, 나는 카뇨 크리스탈레스의 아름다운 색으로부터 영감을 얻어 오고 있다.

19 이 강의 아름답게 혼합된 색깔은 세상 어느 다른 곳에서도 볼 수 없다.

20 물속의 화려한 식물들과 햇빛의 결합은 그 색깔을 더 생생하고 밝게 만든다.

21 내가 카뇨 크리스탈레스를 방문할 때마다 그 강은 나로 하여금 아마도 여전히 만들어지기를 기다리고 있는 셀 수 없이 많은 색깔이 있음을 생각하게 한다.

22 Danny Mehta, 장소 섭외가

23 Vatnajökull 국립 공원, 아이슬란드의 얼음으로 덮인 아름다움

24 나는 장소 섭외가이고 나의 일은 영화를 찍기에 완벽한 장소를 찾는 것이다.

25 아이슬란드는 비범한 아름다움 때문에 많은 장소 섭외가들이 방문하기에 최고의 장소이다.

26 내가 개인적으로 가장 선호하는 곳은 바트나이외쿠틀 국립 공원이다.

27 가파른 절벽, 푸른 빙하 동굴, 그리고 긴 산맥들은 세계나 혹은 우주의 어느 장소도 대신할 수 있다.

28 사실상, 우리가 여기서 찍은 최근의 공상 과학 영화는 컴퓨터 그래픽 없이 만들어졌다!

29 아이슬란드는 우리의 가장 무모한 꿈을 영화 스크린에서 실현할 수 있게 해 준다.

● 우리말을 참고하여 본문을 영작하시오.

1 내 눈에 비친 세계
➡ _____

2 "자연의 아름다움은 우리 모두에게 영감을 준다.
➡ _____

3 서로 다른 직업 분야의 사람들이 자연에 의해 어떻게 영감을 받는지 알아보자."
➡ _____

4 Lin Wang, 생태학자
➡ _____

5 Tsingy, 마다가스카르의 석림
➡ _____

6 나는 20년 이상 동안 식물과 동물을 연구하기 위해서 마다가스카르의 석림을 방문하고 있다.
➡ _____

7 이 지역의 뾰족한 돌들은 진정한 자연의 놀라움이다.
➡ _____

8 이 놀라운 모양은 비에 의해서 만들어졌다.
➡ _____

9 비가 오랜 기간 동안 돌을 침식해서 날카롭고 뾰족하게 만들었다.
➡ _____

10 이런 환경은 동물들이 살기에 험난하지만, 동물들은 생존할 방법들을 찾아냈다.
➡ _____

11 예를 들어, 마다가스카르에서만 사는 여우원숭이는 한 개의 돌탑에서 다른 돌탑으로 뛸 수 있도록 도와주는 개구리와 같은 다리를 가지고 있다.
➡ _____
   _____

12 나에게 석림은 '잭인더박스(열면 인형이 튀어나오는 상자)'와 같다.
➡ _____

13 그것은 늘 나를 놀라게 하고 정신을 바짝 차리게 한다!
➡ _____

14 Amber Smith, 패션 색채 전문가
➡ _____

15 Caño Cristales, 콜롬비아의 다섯 색깔의 강
➡ _____

16 세계는 수백만의 다양한 색깔로 가득 차 있다.
➡ _____

17 의류를 위해서 색을 섞고, 발전시키고, 만들어 내는 것이 나의 일이다.

➡ _____

18 수년 동안, 나는 카뇨 크리스탈레스의 아름다운 색으로부터 영감을 얻어 오고 있다.

➡ _____

19 이 강의 아름답게 혼합된 색깔은 세상 어느 다른 곳에서도 볼 수 없다.

➡ _____

20 물속의 화려한 식물들과 햇빛의 결합은 그 색깔을 더 생생하고 밝게 만든다.

➡ _____

21 내가 카뇨 크리스탈레스를 방문할 때마다 그 강은 나로 하여금 아마도 여전히 만들어지기를 기다리고 있는 셀 수 없이 많은 색깔이 있음을 생각하게 한다.

➡ _____

_____

22 Danny Mehta, 장소 섭외가

➡ _____

23 Vatnajökull 국립 공원, 아이슬란드의 얼음으로 덮인 아름다움

➡ _____

24 나는 장소 섭외가이고 나의 일은 영화를 찍기에 완벽한 장소를 찾는 것이다.

➡ _____

25 아이슬란드는 비범한 아름다움 때문에 많은 장소 섭외가들이 방문하기에 최고의 장소이다.

➡ _____

26 내가 개인적으로 가장 선호하는 곳은 바트나이외쿠틀 국립 공원이다.

➡ _____

27 가파른 절벽, 푸른 빙하 동굴, 그리고 긴 산맥들은 세계나 혹은 우주의 어느 장소도 대신할 수 있다.

➡ _____

_____

28 사실상, 우리가 여기서 찍은 최근의 공상 과학 영화는 컴퓨터 그래픽 없이 만들어졌다!

➡ _____

29 아이슬란드는 우리의 가장 무모한 꿈을 영화 스크린에서 실현할 수 있게 해 준다.

➡ _____

[01~03] 다음 글을 읽고 물음에 답하시오.

Danny Mehta, Location Scout
Vatnajökull National Park, Frozen Beauty of Iceland

I'm a location scout and my job is finding perfect places ⓐto shoot movies. Iceland is the best place for many location scouts to visit due to its unusual beauty. My personal favorite is the Vatnajökull National Park. The sharp cliffs, blue glacier caves, and long mountain ranges can ⓑstand in for any place in the world or the universe. ⓒ In fact, the recent sci-fi movie we shot here was produced by using computer graphics! Iceland can help make our wildest dreams come true on the movie screen.

01 아래 〈보기〉에서 위 글의 밑줄 친 ⓐto shoot과 to부정사의 용법이 같은 것의 개수를 고르시오.

┌─ 보기 ─────────────────┐
① She has a few books to read.
② Give me something to eat.
③ I don't like to read books.
④ They came here to see you.
⑤ To speak English is not easy.
└────────────────────────┘

① 1개　② 2개　③ 3개　④ 4개　⑤ 5개

 중요
02 위 글의 밑줄 친 ⓑstand in for와 바꿔 쓸 수 있는 말을 <u>모두</u> 고르시오.

① change
② replace
③ remove
④ exchange
⑤ take the place of

서답형
03 위 글의 밑줄 친 ⓒ에서 흐름상 <u>어색한</u> 부분을 찾아 고치시오.

➡ _____

[04~06] 다음 글을 읽고 물음에 답하시오.

"The beauty of nature inspires us all. Let's find out how people from different fields of work get ⓐ by nature."

Lin Wang, Ecologist
Tsingy, the Stone Forest of Madagascar

I've been ⓑ the stone forest of Madagascar to study plants and animals for over 20 years. (①) The spiky stones of this place are true miracles of nature. (②) This amazing shape has been ⓒ by rainfall. (③) Rain has cut down the stones and made them sharp and spiky over a long period of time. (④) For example, lemurs, which only live in Madagascar, have frog-like legs that help them jump from one stone tower to another. (⑤) For me, the stone forest is like a jack-in-the-box. ⓓIt always surprises me and keeps me on my toes!

서답형
04 위 글의 빈칸 ⓐ, ⓑ, ⓒ에 각각 inspire, visit, create를 알맞은 형태로 쓰시오.

➡ ⓐ_____ ⓑ_____ ⓒ_____

05 위 글의 흐름으로 보아, 주어진 문장이 들어가기에 가장 적절한 곳은?

┌────────────────────────┐
The environment is harsh for animals to live in, but they have found ways to survive.
└────────────────────────┘

①　　②　　③　　④　　⑤

서답형
06 위 글의 밑줄 친 ⓓIt이 가리키는 것을 본문에서 찾아 쓰시오.

➡ _____

[07~09] 다음 글을 읽고 물음에 답하시오.

Amber Smith, Fashion Colorist
Caño Cristales, the River of Five Colors of Colombia

ⓐThe world is filled with millions of different colors. It is my job to mix, develop, and create colors for clothing. Over the years, I've been gaining insights from the beautiful colors of Caño Cristales. You cannot see the wonderful (A)[mixing / mixed] colors of this river anywhere else in the world. The combination of colorful plants under the water and sunlight makes the colors more (B)[alive / live] and bright. Whenever I visit the Caño Cristales, it makes me (C)[think / to think] that maybe there are still ⓑcountless colors that are waiting to be created.

07 위 글의 밑줄 친 ⓐ를 다음과 같이 바꿔 쓸 때 빈칸에 들어갈 알맞은 말을 두 단어로 쓰시오.

➡ The world is _____ _____ millions of different colors.

서답형
08 위 글의 괄호 (A)~(C)에서 어법상 알맞은 낱말을 골라 쓰시오.

➡ (A)_____ (B)_____ (C)_____

09 위 글의 밑줄 친 ⓑcountless와 바꿔 쓸 수 <u>없는</u> 말을 고르시오.

① a great many
② numerous
③ a great deal of
④ innumerable
⑤ a good number of

[10~13] 다음 글을 읽고 물음에 답하시오.

"The beauty of nature inspires us all. Let's find out how people from different (A)fields of work get inspired by nature."
Lin Wang, Ecologist
Tsingy, the Stone Forest of Madagascar

I've been visiting the stone forest of Madagascar to study plants and animals ⓐ_____ over 20 years. The spiky stones of this place are true miracles of nature. This amazing shape has been created by rainfall. Rain has cut down the stones and made them sharp and spiky over a long period of time. The environment is harsh for animals to live in, but they have found ways to survive. For example, lemurs, which only live in Madagascar, have frog-like legs that help them jump from one stone tower to another. For me, the stone forest is like a jack-in-the-box. It always surprises me and keeps me ⓑ_____ my toes!

10 위 글의 빈칸 ⓐ와 ⓑ에 들어갈 전치사가 바르게 짝지어진 것은?

	ⓐ	ⓑ		ⓐ	ⓑ
①	for – on		②	during – by	
③	in – to		④	during – on	
⑤	for – to				

11 위 글의 밑줄 친 (A)fields와 같은 의미로 쓰인 것을 고르시오.

① People were working in the <u>fields</u>.
② Many soldiers died in the <u>fields</u> of battle.
③ His homeland is famous for many beautiful ice <u>fields</u>.
④ How many flying <u>fields</u> are there in this region?
⑤ All of them are experts in their chosen <u>fields</u>.

12 위 글의 제목으로 가장 알맞은 것을 고르시오.

① Visit the Stone Forest to Study Nature!

② How Does Rainfall Create an Amazing Shape?

③ How Did Lin Wang Get Inspired by Nature?

④ The Harsh Environment for Animals to Live in

⑤ Lemurs with Frog-like Legs Can Survive in Tsingy!

13 According to the passage, which is NOT true?

① All of us are inspired by the beauty of nature.

② Lin Wang is an ecologist.

③ Lin has been visiting Tsingy to study plants and animals for over 20 years.

④ The round stones of this place are true miracles of nature.

⑤ For Lin, the stone forest is like a jack-in-the-box.

[14~16] 다음 글을 읽고 물음에 답하시오.

I've been visiting the stone forest of Madagascar to study plants and animals for over 20 years. The spiky stones of this place are true miracles of nature. This amazing shape has been created by rainfall. Rain has cut down the stones and made (A)them sharp and spiky over a long period of time. (B)이런 환경은 동물들이 살기에 험난하다, but (C)they have found ways to survive. __ⓐ__, lemurs, which only live in Madagascar, have frog-like legs that help them jump from one stone tower to another. For me, the stone forest is like a jack-in-the-box. It always surprises me and keeps me on my toes!

14 위 글의 빈칸 ⓐ에 들어갈 알맞은 말을 고르시오.

① As a result   ② For example

③ However   ④ In other words

⑤ Therefore

15 위 글의 밑줄 친 (A)them과 (C)they가 가리키는 것을 본문에서 찾아 쓰시오.

➡ (A) _____ (C) _____

16 위 글의 밑줄 친 (B)의 우리말에 맞게 주어진 어휘를 이용하여 9 단어로 영작하시오.

harsh

➡ _____

[17~20] 다음 글을 읽고 물음에 답하시오.

Amber Smith, Fashion Colorist
Caño Cristales, the River of Five Colors of Colombia

The world is filled with millions of different colors. (A)It is my job to mix, develop, and create colors for clothing. Over the years, I've been __ⓐ__ insights from the beautiful colors of Caño Cristales. You cannot see the wonderful mixed colors of this river anywhere else in the world. The combination of colorful plants under the water and sunlight makes the colors more alive and bright. Whenever I visit the Caño Cristales, it makes me think that maybe there are (B)still countless colors that are waiting to be created.

17 위 글의 빈칸 ⓐ에 gain을 알맞은 형태로 쓰시오.

➡ _____

18 위 글의 밑줄 친 (A)It과 문법적 쓰임이 같은 것을 모두 고르시오.

① It was raining this morning.

② I find it strange that she doesn't want to go.

③ It is important for you to choose good friends.

④ It is time for you to go to bed.

⑤ It is strange that she says so.

19 위 글의 밑줄 친 (B)still과 같은 의미로 쓰인 것을 모두 고르시오.

① I had a still better idea.

② I'm still hungry!

③ Keep still while I brush your hair.

④ He is still there.

⑤ The weather was cold and wet. Still, we had a great time.

20 Which question CANNOT be answered after reading the passage?

① What is Caño Cristales?

② Where is Caño Cristales?

③ What is Amber Smith's job?

④ What color has Amber Smith created for clothing?

⑤ What makes the colors of Caño Cristales more alive and bright?

[21~24] 다음 글을 읽고 물음에 답하시오.

Danny Mehta, Location Scout

Vatnajökull National Park, Frozen Beauty of Iceland

I'm a location scout and my job is ⓐfinding perfect places to shoot movies. Iceland is the best place for many location scouts to visit due to its unusual beauty. My personal favorite is the Vatnajökull National Park. The sharp cliffs, blue glacier caves, and long mountain ranges can stand in for any place in the world or the universe. ⓑIn fact, ⓒ the recent sci-fi movie we shot here was produced without using computer graphics! Iceland can help make our wildest dreams come true on the movie screen.

21 위 글의 밑줄 친 ⓐfinding과 문법적 쓰임이 같은 것을 모두 고르시오.

① Look at the sleeping baby.

② I forget posting the letter.

③ She was cooking in the kitchen.

④ He is good at speaking English.

⑤ I saw him dancing.

22 위 글의 밑줄 친 ⓑIn fact와 바꿔 쓸 수 있는 말을 모두 고르시오.

① Therefore　　② As a matter of fact

③ Actually　　④ However

⑤ As a result

서답형
23 위 글의 밑줄 친 문장 ⓒ에 생략된 단어를 넣어 문장을 다시 쓰시오.

➡ _____

_____

서답형
24 다음 문장에서 위 글의 내용과 다른 부분을 찾아서 고치시오.

The common beauty of Iceland makes it the best place for many location scouts to visit.

➡ _____

[01~04] 다음 글을 읽고 물음에 답하시오.

"The beauty of nature inspires us all. Let's find out ⓐ서로 다른 직업 분야의 사람들이 자연에 의해 어떻게 영감을 받는지."

Lin Wang, Ecologist

Tsingy, the Stone Forest of Madagascar

ⓑI've been visiting the stone forest of Madagascar to study plants and animals for over 20 years. The spiky stones of this place are true miracles of nature. This amazing shape has been created by rainfall. Rain has cut down the stones and made them sharp and spiky over a long period of time. ⓒThe environment is mild for animals to live in, but they have found ways to survive. For example, lemurs, which only live in Madagascar, have frog-like legs that help them jump from one stone tower to another. ⓓFor me, the stone forest is like a jack-in-the-box. It always surprises me and keeps me on my toes!

01 위 글의 밑줄 친 ⓐ의 우리말에 맞게 한 단어를 보충하여, 주어진 어휘를 알맞게 배열하시오.

> by / fields / get / people / different / from / inspired / of / nature / work

➡ _____

_____

02 위 글의 밑줄 친 ⓑ를 다음과 같이 바꿔 쓸 때 빈칸에 들어갈 알맞은 단어를 쓰시오.

➡ I started _____ _____ the stone forest of Madagascar to study plants and animals over 20 years _____, and I am still _____ it.

03 위 글의 밑줄 친 ⓒ에서 흐름상 어색한 부분을 찾아 고치시오.

➡ _____

04 다음 빈칸에 공통으로 들어갈 알맞은 단어를 넣어, Lin Wang이 위 글의 밑줄 친 ⓓ처럼 말한 이유를 완성하시오.

➡ It's because the stone forest always _____ Lin Wang as a jack-in-the-box _____ people when they open the box.

[05~07] 다음 글을 읽고 물음에 답하시오.

Danny Mehta, Location Scout

Vatnajökull National Park, Frozen Beauty of Iceland

I'm a location scout and my job is finding perfect places to shoot movies. Iceland is the best place __ⓐ__ many location scouts to visit due to its unusual beauty. My personal favorite is the Vatnajökull National Park. The sharp cliffs, blue glacier caves, and long mountain ranges can stand in for any place in the world or the universe. __ⓑ__ fact, the recent sci-fi movie we shot here was produced without using computer graphics! Iceland can help (A) 우리의 가장 무모한 꿈을 실현되도록 만들다 on the movie screen.

05 위 글의 빈칸 ⓐ와 ⓑ에 들어갈 전치사가 바르게 짝지어진 것은?

ⓐ ⓑ | ⓐ ⓑ
① for – To | ② of – In
③ to – In | ④ for – In
⑤ of – To

06 위 글의 밑줄 친 (A)의 우리말에 맞게 6 단어로 영작하시오.

➡ _____

07 다음 빈칸 (A)와 (B)에 알맞은 단어를 넣어 Vatnajökull National Park에 대한 소개를 완성하시오.

> Vatnajökull National Park is in Iceland and its (A)_____ _____, blue glacier caves, and long mountain ranges can (B)_____ _____ _____ any place in the world or the universe.

[08~10] 다음 글을 읽고 물음에 답하시오.

Amber Smith, Fashion Colorist
Caño Cristales, the River of Five Colors of Colombia

 The world is filled with millions of different colors. It is my job to mix, develop, and create colors for clothing. Over the years, I've been gaining insights from the beautiful colors of Caño Cristales. ⓐYou can see the wonderful mixed colors of this river anywhere else in the world. The combination of colorful plants under the water and sunlight makes the colors more alive and bright. ⓑWhenever I visit the Caño Cristales, it makes me think that maybe ⓒthere are still countless colors that are waiting to be created.

08 위 글의 밑줄 친 ⓐ에서 흐름상 어색한 부분을 찾아 고치시오.

➡ _____

09 위 글의 밑줄 친 ⓑ를 다음과 같이 바꿔 쓸 때 빈칸에 들어갈 알맞은 단어를 쓰시오.

➡ When I visit the Caño Cristales, it _____ makes me think

10 위 글의 밑줄 친 ⓒ에서 생략할 수 있는 부분을 찾아 쓰시오.

➡ _____

[11~13] 다음 글을 읽고 물음에 답하시오.

Lin Wang, Ecologist
Tsingy, the Stone Forest of Madagascar

 I've been visiting the stone forest of Madagascar to study plants and animals for over 20 years. The spiky stones of this place (A)[is / are] true miracles of nature. ⓐThis amazing shape has been created by rainfall. Rain has cut down the stones and made them sharp and spiky over a long period of time. The environment is harsh for animals to (B)[live / live in], but they have found ways to survive. For example, lemurs, which only live in Madagascar, have frog-like legs that help them (C)[jump / jumping] from one stone tower to another. For me, the stone forest is like a jack-in-the-box. It always surprises me and keeps me on my toes!

11 위 글의 괄호 (A)~(C)에서 어법상 알맞은 낱말을 골라 쓰시오.

➡ (A) _____ (B) _____ (C) _____

12 위 글의 밑줄 친 ⓐ를 능동태로 고치시오.

➡ _____

13 다음 빈칸 (A)와 (B)에 알맞은 단어를 넣어 Lin Wang에 대한 소개를 완성하시오.

> Lin Wang is an (A)_____ and has been visiting Tsingy, (B)_____ _____ _____ of Madagascar, to study plants and animals for over 20 years.

교과서
구석구석

Communication Step B

A: Congratulations on receiving the award. I've heard that this photo was
　　　　　　　　동명사 (전치사 on의 목적어)　　　　　　　　　현재완료
taken in India. Is that true?
　　　　　　　　= this photo was taken in India

B: Yes, this rainbow cloud is caused by thin clouds and water drops.
　　　　　　　　　　　　　　　수동태

A: Wow, it truly is amazing!

B: Yes, it is. I can't wait to take more photos of amazing clouds.
　　　　　　　　어서 ~하고 싶다

A: I wish you the best of luck!

해석

A: 상 받은 것을 축하해. 이 사진이 인도에서 찍힌 것이라고 들었어. 맞니?
B: 응, 이 무지개 구름은 얇은 구름과 물방울에 의해 생긴 거야.
A: 와, 정말 멋지다!
B: 응, 그래. 어서 더 많은 멋진 구름 사진을 찍고 싶어.
A: 행운을 빌어!

Wrap Up 1

W: Your uncle, John, is coming back from South America this weekend.
　　　　　　　　come back from ~: ~에서 돌아오다

M: That's great. He has been away for almost 2 years, right?
　　　　　　　　be away: 떨어져 있다

W: Yeah, he's been in the jungle most of the time to research.
　　　　　　　　대체로, 대부분의 시간에　　to부정사의 부사적 용법(~하기 위해서)

M: Wow, that's amazing. I can't wait to see him and listen to his stories.
　　　　　　　　can't wait to+동사원형: 빨리 ~하고 싶다　　see와 병렬 구조

W: Me, too. We're having dinner with him this Saturday, so don't make other plans.

M: Okay, I won't, Mom.
　　　　　　　　뒤에 make other plans가 생략되어 있다.

구문해설 • almost: 거의 • research: (연구) 조사, 연구

W: 네 삼촌, John이 이번 주말에 남아메리카에서 돌아올 거야.
M: 잘됐네요. 그는 거의 2년 동안 떨어져 있었죠, 그렇죠?
W: 그래. 그는 연구를 위해 대부분의 시간을 정글에 있었어.
M: 와, 정말 놀랍네요. 빨리 그를 보고 그의 이야기를 듣고 싶어요.
W: 나도. 이번 토요일에 그와 저녁 식사를 할 거니까 다른 계획은 세우지 마.
M: 알았어요, 안 그럴게요. 엄마.

Think & Write Step A

Mt. Jiri and Mt. Seorak
Trip for Hiking Fans
• walk along beautiful hiking routes
　~을 따라 걷다
• learn how to get in shape and keep fit
　의문사+to부정사(명사적 용법) = how you should get

Trip for Soccer Fans
Madrid and Manchester
• meet famous players
• learn how to improve your soccer skills
　의문사 to부정사(명사적 용법) = how you should improve

Paris and London
Trip for Art Fans
• visit famous art museums
• learn how to draw pictures creatively
　의문사+to부정사(명사적 용법) = how you should draw

구문해설 • route: 길[경로/루트] • get in shape: 좋은 몸 상태(몸매)를 유지하다
• keep fit: 건강을 유지하다 • improve: 개선되다, 향상시키다 • art museum: 미술관

지리산과 설악산
하이킹 팬들을 위한 여행
• 아름다운 하이킹 길을 따라 걷는다
• 좋은 몸매를 유지하고 건강을 유지하는 법을 배운다

축구 팬들을 위한 여행
마드리드와 맨체스터
• 유명한 선수들을 만난다
• 여러분의 축구 기술을 향상시키는 법을 배운다

파리와 런던
예술 팬들을 위한 여행
• 유명한 미술관을 방문한다
• 창조적으로 그림을 그리는 법을 배운다

Words & Expressions

01 접두어 in-의 성격이 <u>다른</u> 하나를 고르시오.

① insight   ② indoor
③ income   ④ independent
⑤ inside

02 다음 괄호 안의 단어를 문맥에 맞게 고쳐 쓰시오.

(1) We were beginning to worry. It was _____ for David to be so late. (usual)
(2) The new device is a _____ of copier, fax, image scanner, and document printer. (combine)

03 다음 우리말에 맞도록 빈칸에 알맞은 말을 쓰시오. (철자가 주어진 경우 주어진 철자로 시작할 것.)

(1) 황사가 있을 때마다 내 눈과 목이 아파.
  ➡ My eyes and throat hurt w_____ there is _____ _____.
(2) 새로운 상품을 판매하기 위해 시장에 제공하기 전에 시장을 충분히 조사하는 것이 중요하다.
  ➡ It is important to _____ the market fully before offering a new product for sale.
(3) 호수 가까이에 많은 하이킹 등산로가 있다.
  ➡ There are c_____ hiking trails _____ the lake.

04 다음 빈칸에 들어갈 말을 〈보기〉에서 찾아 쓰시오.

┌─── 보기 ───┐
of at by out to with
└──────────┘

(1) To everybody's surprise, temple stays turned _____ to be a popular travel program.
(2) His death was due _____ heart disease.
(3) The songs were made _____ the world's best musicians.
(4) Most _____ the lung cancer is caused by smoking.

Conversation

[05~06] 다음 대화를 읽고 물음에 답하시오.

M: Do you want to watch the new 3D movie? (①)
W: Which one? (②)
M: (③) It was shot near Australia's Great Barrier Reef.
W: Oh, I've heard of it. (④) It has the most beautiful sea life.
M: Right. (⑤) I can't wait to watch the movie. Let's go and get the ticket.

05 위 대화의 빈칸에 들어갈 말로 적절한 것은?

The one about adventures under the sea.

①   ②   ③   ④   ⑤

06 위 대화의 내용과 일치하지 <u>않는</u> 것을 고르시오.

① The man is going to get the ticket after the conversation.
② The man wants to watch the new 3D movie.
③ Australia's Great Barrier Reef has the most beautiful sea life.
④ The movie is about the sea life at Australia's Great Barrier Reef.
⑤ The woman heard of Great Barrier Reef.

[07~08] 다음 대화를 읽고 물음에 답하시오.

W: Dad, my science club is going to go to Dokdo in July.
M: Oh, really? What do you plan to do there?
W: We are going to study the caves on the island and go bird watching.
M: Sounds (A)_____ it will be an interesting trip.
W: Yeah. I've only read about Dokdo in books. (B)_____(to, there, can't, actually, I, wait, visit)
M: I hope you enjoy your trip!

07 빈칸 (A)에 알맞은 말을 쓰시오.

➡ _____

08 빈칸 (B)를 괄호 안에 주어진 단어를 알맞게 배열하여 채우시오.

➡ _____

[09~10] 다음 대화를 읽고 물음에 답하시오.

W: Your uncle, John, is coming back from South America this weekend.
M: That's great. He has been away for almost 2 years, right?

W: Yeah, he's been in the jungle most of the time to research.
M: Wow, that's amazing. I can't wait to see him and listen to his stories.
W: Me, too. We're having dinner with him this Saturday, so don't make other plans.
M: Okay, I won't, Mom.

09 위 대화에서 다음 영영풀이에 해당하는 단어를 찾아 쓰시오.

to study a subject in detail, especially in order to discover new facts or test new ideas

➡ _____

10 위 대화를 읽고 답할 수 <u>없는</u> 질문을 고르시오.

① When the man is going to have dinner with his uncle?
② Where is John coming from?
③ How long has John been away?
④ What does John research in the jungle?
⑤ Is the man looking forward to see his uncle, John?

[11~12] 다음 대화를 읽고 물음에 답하시오.

M: Jisu, did you know that the sun never (A)_____ in Norway during summer?
W: No, I didn't know that. How interesting!
M: Yeah, and I've heard that people go hiking and even cycling at night (B)_____ it isn't dark.
W: I'd love to go hiking and cycling in the middle of the night!
M: Me, too. (C)_____(we, someday, chance, it, get, hope, the, I, to, try)

11 빈칸 (A)와 (B)에 들어갈 말이 알맞게 짝지어진 것은?

① rises – although ② rises – because

③ sets – unless ④ sets – although

⑤ sets – because

12 빈칸 (C)를 괄호 안에 주어진 단어를 알맞게 배열하여 채우시오.

➡ _____

Grammar

13 다음 문장의 빈칸에 알맞은 말이 바르게 짝지어진 것은?

> • Grace has been watching TV _____ 30 minutes.
> • He has been doing it _____ 10 years ago.

① for – for ② for – since

③ since – for ④ since – since

⑤ during – since

14 다음 중 어색한 문장을 모두 고르시오.

① The children are too noisy for me to concentrate.

② He expects me to visit Korea.

③ How silly for her to tell him such a thing!

④ Emma has been teaching English three years ago.

⑤ Miriam has been growing vegetables since last year.

⑥ It has been snowing heavily for over three hours.

15 그림을 보고, 주어진 어휘를 이용하여 빈칸을 알맞게 채우시오.

It was _____ the window.
(break, careless, Mike)

16 다음 빈칸에 들어갈 말이 나머지와 다른 하나는?

① Mr. Jones has been writing a letter _____ 30 minutes.

② My brother has been repairing his computer _____ an hour.

③ He has been using the pen _____ long.

④ He has been learning Spanish _____ five years.

⑤ Eva has been living in this house _____ last year.

17 다음 중 어법상 옳은 것을 모두 고르시오.

① Amanda has been traveling around the world for the past two months.

② Molly has been trying to solve the problem since an hour.

③ It has been raining two days ago.

④ It was not easy for me to choose the best movie.

⑤ This jungle is a wonderful place of animals to live in.

18 다음 두 문장의 의미가 같도록 빈칸에 알맞은 말을 쓰시오.

(1) He was generous to give her that money.

= It was generous _____.

(2) The book was difficult for her to read.

= It was difficult _____.

Reading

[19~21] 다음 글을 읽고 물음에 답하시오.

"The beauty of nature inspires us all. Let's find out how people from different fields of work get inspired by nature."

Lin Wang, Ecologist

Tsingy, the Stone Forest of Madagascar

ⓐI've been visiting the stone forest of Madagascar to study plants and animals for over 20 years. The spiky stones of this place are true miracles of nature. This amazing shape has been created by rainfall. Rain has cut down the stones and made them sharp and spiky over a long period of time. The environment is harsh for animals to live in, but they have found ways to survive. For example, lemurs, ___ⓑ___ only live in Madagascar, have frog-like legs that help them jump from one stone tower to another. For me, the stone forest is like a jack-in-the-box. It always surprises me and ⓒ나를 정신을 바짝 차리게 한다!

19 위 글의 밑줄 친 ⓐ와 현재완료의 용법이 같은 것을 모두 고르시오.

① She has gone to Japan.

② She has been sick since last Friday.

③ I've watched the movie twice.

④ She has just come.

⑤ He has lived in Seoul for ten years.

20 위 글의 빈칸 ⓑ에 알맞은 것은?

① that   ② who   ③ what

④ which   ⑤ whose

21 위 글의 밑줄 친 ⓒ의 우리말에 맞게 주어진 어휘를 이용하여 5 단어로 영작하시오.

toes

➡ _____

[22~23] 다음 글을 읽고 물음에 답하시오.

Amber Smith, Fashion Colorist

Caño Cristales, the River of Five Colors of Colombia

The world is filled with millions of different colors. It is my job to mix, develop, and create colors for (A)[clothing / clothings]. Over the years, I've been gaining insights from the beautiful colors of Caño Cristales. You cannot see the wonderful mixed colors of this river (B)[anywhere / somewhere] else in the world. The combination of colorful plants under the water and sunlight (C)[make / makes] the colors more alive and bright. Whenever I visit the Caño Cristales, it makes me think that maybe there are still countless colors that are waiting to be created.

22 위 글의 괄호 (A)~(C)에서 어법상 알맞은 낱말을 골라 쓰시오.

➡ (A)_____ (B)_____ (C)_____

23 According to the passage, which is NOT true?

① Amber Smith is a fashion colorist.

② Caño Cristales is the River of Five Colors of Colombia.

③ Amber Smith has been gaining insights from the beautiful colors of Caño Cristales over the years.

④ The colors of Caño Cristales become more alive and bright thanks to the combination of colorful plants under the water and sunlight.

⑤ Amber Smith thinks that maybe there are no more colors that are waiting to be created.

[24~26] 다음 글을 읽고 물음에 답하시오.

THE PLACE THAT INSPIRES ME
01 Tsingy, Madagascar
• Recommended by an ecologist
• The sharp and spiky stones have been created by rainfall(rain). Animals (A)like lemurs have found ways to survive in the harsh environment.
02 Caño Cristales, Colombia
• Recommended by a fashion colorist
• The river has wonderful mixed colors. The colorful plants and the sunlight make the colors more alive and bright.
03 Vatnajökull National Park, Iceland
• Recommended by a location scout
• There are sharp cliffs, blue glacier caves, and long mountain ranges. Sci-fi movies can be ___(B)___ without computer graphics.

24 위 글의 밑줄 친 (A)like와 바꿔 쓸 수 있는 단어를 쓰시오. (두 단어)

➡ _____

25 위 글의 빈칸 (B)에 shoot을 알맞은 형태로 쓰시오.

➡ _____

26 Which question CANNOT be answered after reading the passage?

① Who recommends Tsingy, Madagascar?

② By what have the sharp and spiky stones of Tsingy been created?

③ What does an ecologist do?

④ Why does a fashion colorist recommend Caño Cristales?

⑤ Where can sci-fi movies be shot without computer graphics?

[27~28] 다음 글을 읽고 물음에 답하시오.

Danny Mehta, Location Scout
Vatnajökull National Park, Frozen Beauty of Iceland

I'm a location scout and my job is finding perfect places to shoot movies. (①) Iceland is the best place for many location scouts to visit ⓐdue to its unusual beauty. (②) My personal favorite is the Vatnajökull National Park. (③) The sharp cliffs, blue glacier caves, and long mountain ranges can stand in for any place in the world or the universe. (④) Iceland can help make our wildest dreams come true on the movie screen. (⑤)

27 위 글의 흐름으로 보아, 주어진 문장이 들어가기에 가장 적절한 곳은?

> In fact, the recent sci-fi movie we shot here was produced without using computer graphics!

①   ②   ③   ④   ⑤

28 위 글의 밑줄 친 ⓐdue to와 바꿔 쓸 수 있는 말을 고르시오.

① as for   ② instead of

③ in place of   ④ because of

⑤ in spite of

출제율 100%

01 〈보기〉에 주어진 단어로 빈칸을 채울 수 <u>없는</u> 문장을 고르시오.

┌─ 보기 ┤
countless   personal   recent   unique

① Employees said their job is good for _____ growth.
② Everyone is _____ and people should be encouraged to express their individual identities.
③ The light in here is not _____ enough to read by.
④ They spent _____ hours talking to one another.
⑤ What's been happening in _____ weeks?

출제율 95%

02 다음 빈칸에 공통으로 들어갈 말을 쓰시오.

• Can you stand in _____ me at the meeting next week?
• Thank you so much _____ your call last week.

출제율 90%

03 두 문장이 같은 의미가 되도록 빈칸을 채우시오. (철자가 주어진 경우 주어진 철자로 시작할 것.)

He had to retire because of ill health.
= He had to retire d_____ _____ ill health.

출제율 95%

04 〈보기 1〉의 영영풀이에 해당하는 단어를 〈보기 2〉의 문장의 빈칸에 알맞게 연결한 것은?

┌─ 보기 1 ┤
(A) a very large mass of ice that moves very slowly
(B) a particular length of time with a beginning and an end
(C) the steep side of an area of high land
(D) something that combines several things

┌─ 보기 2 ┤
ⓐ Banana, orange juice, and cream may seem an odd _____, but together they make a delicious drink.
ⓑ Such a rise in temperatures could melt ice sheets and _____s.
ⓒ His playing improved in a very short _____ of time.
ⓓ He dives off the edge of the _____ into the sea.

(A) – (B) – (C) – (D)
① ⓐ – ⓑ – ⓒ – ⓓ
② ⓐ – ⓒ – ⓑ – ⓓ
③ ⓑ – ⓒ – ⓐ – ⓓ
④ ⓑ – ⓒ – ⓓ – ⓐ
⑤ ⓑ – ⓓ – ⓐ – ⓒ

[05~07] 다음 대화를 읽고 물음에 답하시오.

M: Mom, did you watch the weather report today? (①)
W: Wow, fantastic! (②) When is the best time to see them? (③)
M: (④) I've heard what the shooting stars will peak between 12 a.m. or 2 a.m. (⑤)
W: Wow, it will be a special night!

5 ①~⑤ 중 주어진 문장이 들어갈 곳은?

> We will be able to see hundreds of shooting stars tonight!

①   ②   ③   ④   ⑤

6 위 대화에서 다음 영영풀이에 해당하는 단어를 찾아 쓰시오.

> a piece of rock or metal from space, which burns brightly as it falls towards the Earth

➡ _____

7 밑줄 친 문장에서 어색한 부분을 모두 고쳐 완전한 문장으로 쓰시오.

➡ _____

_____

[08~09] 다음 대화를 읽고 물음에 답하시오.

> M: Jisu, did you know (A)[that / what / how] the sun never sets in Norway (B)[from / during / while] summer?
> W: No, I didn't know that. (①) (C)[What / How / Which] interesting! (②)
> M: Yeah! (③)
> W: I'd love to go hiking and cycling in the middle of the night! (④)
> M: Me, too. (⑤) I hope we get the chance to try it someday.

8 ①~⑤ 중 주어진 문장이 들어갈 곳은?

> I've heard that people go hiking and even cycling at night because it isn't dark.

①   ②   ③   ④   ⑤

9 위 대화의 괄호 (A)~(C)에서 적절한 것을 골라 쓰시오.

➡ (A)_____ (B)_____ (C)_____

[10~12] 다음 대화를 읽고 물음에 답하시오.

> W: Look at this picture on Jake's blog. He went indoor rock climbing!
> M: Oh, it looks interesting (A)_____ seems too hard.
> W: Actually, I've heard that there are different levels of courses at the community center.
> M: Really? Then, maybe I should visit the center and find (B)_____ more about the courses.
> W: Let me know how it turns (C)_____.

10 빈칸 (A)에 알맞은 말을 고르시오.

① but   ② so   ③ because
④ if   ⑤ or

11 빈칸 (B)와 (C)에 공통으로 들어갈 말을 쓰시오.

➡ _____

12 위 대화의 내용과 일치하지 <u>않는</u> 것은?

① There are few indoor rock climbing courses at the community center.
② The man is interested in indoor rock climbing.
③ The man is going to go to the community center to search into the rock climbing courses.
④ There is a picture in which Jake went indoor rock climbing on his blog.
⑤ The woman knows that there are rock climbing courses at the community center.

13 다음 빈칸에 알맞은 말이 순서대로 짝지어진 것은?

> • It was foolish _____ to waste his money on such a thing.
> • Kim has been talking on the phone with her friend _____ noon.

① of him – since ② for him – for

③ of him – for ④ for him – since

⑤ for him – ago

14 다음 빈칸에 알맞지 않은 것은?

> It was _____ for her to solve the problems.

① impossible ② difficult

③ easy ④ wise

⑤ necessary

15 다음 중 어법상 적절한 문장은?

① My dad has been work in New York for a year.

② Brian has been painting his house since two hours.

③ She has been cleaning her house then.

④ Anne has been listening to the music since an hour ago.

⑤ What's been happened in recent weeks?

16 다음 빈칸에 들어갈 말이 나머지와 다른 하나는?

① It is necessary _____ Jamie to counsel people because they are far from their family and friends.

② It was very thoughtful _____ you to send her the flowers.

③ It would be dangerous _____ you to stay here.

④ It's an exciting opportunity _____ me to do some traveling.

⑤ It was difficult _____ me to remember things.

17 다음 괄호 안에 주어진 어휘를 이용하여 빈칸에 알맞게 쓰시오.

> The woman _____ _____ _____ for her husband _____ an hour. (wait)

[18~20] 다음 글을 읽고 물음에 답하시오.

Lin Wang, Ecologist

Tsingy, the Stone Forest of Madagascar

I've been visiting the stone forest of Madagascar to study plants and animals for over 20 years. The spiky stones of this place are true miracles of nature. This amazing shape has been created by rainfall. Rain has cut down the stones and made them sharp ! and spiky over a long period of time. The environment is harsh for animals ⓐto live in but they have found ways ⓑto survive. ⓒFor example, lemurs, that only live in Madagascar, have frog-like legs that help them jump from one stone tower to another. For me, the stone forest is like a jack-in-the-box. It always surprises me and keeps me on my toes.

출제율 95%

18 위 글의 밑줄 친 ⓐto live, ⓑto survive와 to부정사의 용법이 같은 것을 각각 **모두** 고르시오.

┌─── 보기 ───┐

① They were happy to survive the crisis.

② I have no house to live in.

③ There are many ways to live in the jungle.

④ Many birds migrate south to survive the cold winter.

⑤ He must be clever to survive on $10 a week.

└──────┘

➡ ⓐ _____, ⓑ _____

출제율 90%

19 위 글의 밑줄 친 ⓒ에서 어법상 틀린 부분을 찾아 고치시오.

➡ _____

출제율 100%

20 위 글을 읽고 알 수 없는 것을 고르시오.

① Where is Tsingy?

② How many times has Lin Wang visited Tsingy?

③ By what have the spiky stones of Tsingy been created?

④ Is the environment of Tsingy proper for animals to live in?

⑤ Are there any animals that live in the stone forest of Tsingy?

[21~22] 다음 글을 읽고 물음에 답하시오.

Amber Smith, Fashion Colorist

Caño Cristales, the River of Five Colors of Colombia

The world is filled with millions of different colors. It is my job to mix, develop, and create colors for clothing. Over the years, I've been gaining insights from the beautiful colors of Caño Cristales. You cannot see the wonderful mixed colors of this river anywhere else in the world. ⓐThe combination of colorful plants under the water and sunlight makes the colors more alive and bright. Whenever I visit the Caño Cristales, it makes me think that maybe there are still countless colors ⓑ만들어지기를 기다리고 있는.

출제율 90%

21 다음 빈칸 (A)와 (B)에 알맞은 단어를 넣어 위 글의 밑줄 친 ⓐ가 의미하는 것을 완성하시오.

┌──────────────┐

When the sun shines on the (A)_____ _____ under Caño Cristales, the (B)_____ of Caño Cristales can be made more alive and bright.

└──────────────┘

출제율 95%

22 위 글의 밑줄 친 ⓑ의 우리말에 맞게 주어진 어휘를 이용하여 6 단어로 영작하시오.

┌──────────────┐

created

└──────────────┘

➡ _____

01 대화의 흐름상이나 어법상 어색한 것을 골라 바르게 고치시오. (3개)

> M: Let's welcome Ms. Scarlett Lee, the winner of this year's photo competition.
> W: Hello, thank you for invite me. I've honored to receive the award.
> M: Let's talk about your photo. I've heard that this photo took in the Maldives. Is that true?
> W: Yes, this glowing beach is caused by plankton.
> M: Wow, it truly is amazing!
> W: Yes, it is. I can't wait taking more pictures of amazing beaches.
> M: I wish you the best of luck!

➡ (1) _____

(2) _____

_____

(3) _____

_____

[02~03] 다음 대화를 읽고 물음에 답하시오.

> W: Your uncle, ⓐJohn is coming back from South America this weekend.
> M: That's great. ⓑHe has been away for almost 2 years, right?
> W: Yeah, ⓒhe's been in the jungle most of the time to research.
> M: Wow, that's amazing. 나는 빨리 그를 보고 그의 이야기 듣고 싶어.
> W: Me, too. ⓓWe're having dinner with him this Saturday, so don't make other plans.
> M: Okay, ⓔI will, Mom.

02 밑줄 친 우리말을 주어진 단어를 이용하여 영작하시오.

➡ _____

(can't, listen, see)

03 ⓐ~ⓔ 중 문맥상이나 어법상 어색한 것을 골라 바르게 고치시오.

➡ _____

04 주어진 두 문장을 한 문장으로 바꾸시오.

(1) • I started visiting the Wimbledon tennis tournament when I was in high school.
• I am still visiting it.

➡ _____

_____

(2) • Phil began repairing mobile phones ten years ago.
• He is still repairing mobile phones.

➡ _____

(3) • I am still staying at the hotel.
• I started to stay there a few days ago.

➡ _____

05 다음 문장을 it을 사용하여 같은 뜻의 문장으로 바꾸어 쓰시오.

(1) The comic book is fun for me to read.

➡ _____

(2) People here need to eat well to stay warm and healthy. (necessary를 이용할 것.)

➡ _____

_____

(3) This book is too difficult for me to understand.

➡ _____

06 다음 문장에서 어법상 <u>어색한</u> 것을 바르게 고쳐 다시 쓰시오.

(1) The airplane has been flying an hour ago.

➡ _____

(2) The government has been stealing our public funds since a long time.

➡ _____

_____

(3) I have been knowing him ever since he was a boy.

➡ _____

(4) The room is large enough of all of us to stay in.

➡ _____

(5) I think it is nice for you to give books to your brother.

➡ _____

(6) The bands played music for many people dance to.

➡ _____

[07~09] 다음 글을 읽고 물음에 답하시오.

Lin Wang, Ecologist
Tsingy, the Stone Forest of Madagascar
I've been visiting the stone forest of Madagascar to study plants and animals for over 20 years. The spiky stones of this place are true miracles of nature. This (A)[amazing / amazed] shape has been created by rainfall. Rain has cut down the stones and made them (B)[sharp / sharply] and spiky over a long

period of time. The environment is harsh for animals to live in, but they have found ways to survive. ___ⓐ___ example, lemurs, which only live in Madagascar, have frog-like legs that help them jump from one stone tower to another. For me, the stone forest is (C)[like / alike] a jack-in-the-box. It always surprises me and keeps me ___ⓑ___ my toes!

07 위 글의 괄호 (A)~(C)에서 어법상 알맞은 낱말을 골라 쓰시오.

➡ (A)_____ (B)_____ (C)_____

08 위 글의 빈칸 ⓐ와 ⓑ에 각각 들어갈 알맞은 말을 쓰시오.

➡ ⓐ _____ , ⓑ _____

09 How can lemurs live in the stone forest of Tsingy? Fill in the blanks with suitable words.

They can live there because they have _____ _____ that help them jump from one stone tower to another.

01 대화의 흐름에 맞게 빈칸에 주어진 단어를 이용하여 자신의 기대에 관해 쓰시오.

> A: I'm going to go to the preview tonight.
> B: Wow, that's amazing.
> A: _____ (film, wait, see, meet, actors, director)

02 다음 그림을 보고, 주어진 조건에 맞게 영작하시오.

(1) 2:00 p.m. ~ 4:00 p.m.(now) (2) 3:00 p.m.~now

조건

(1) 사진 속 인물의 행동을 묘사할 것.
(2) since 또는 for를 이용하여 현재완료진행형으로 쓸 것.

(1) _____
(2) _____

03 다음 내용을 바탕으로 여러분이 기획한 테마 여행을 소개하는 글을 쓰시오.

> Q1 For whom is your trip designed?
> A1 My trip is designed for people who are interested in hiking.
>
> Q2 Which places will the tourists visit? Write two places.
> A2 They will visit Mt. Jiri and Mt. Seorak.
>
> Q3 What will the tourists do during the trip?
> A3 They will be able to walk along beautiful hiking routes. They will also learn how to get in shape and keep fit.

> Are you a hiking fan? Then join my trip. It is designed for those who are interested in (A)_____. You'll visit (B)_____. These are the best places for hiking fans to visit. You'll be able to walk along beautiful (C)_____. Also, you'll learn how to (D)_____ and (E)_____. This trip will be the most memorable one!

단원별 모의고사

01 다음 영영풀이가 나타내는 말을 주어진 철자로 시작하여 쓰시오.

> very many, especially more than you think is reasonable

➡ c_____

02 다음 빈칸을 〈보기〉에 있는 어휘를 이용하여 채우시오.

┌─ 보기 ─┐
cut get keep walk

(1) She gets up at six every morning to _____ along the beach.

(2) If you want to _____ in shape, you should do more exercise.

(3) People do not need to _____ down trees and produce paper.

(4) With a test every Friday, she _____ her students on their toes.

03 다음 밑줄 친 부분의 의미로 알맞지 않은 것은?

① The movie has won a number of <u>awards</u>. (상)

② <u>Hundreds of</u> people were killed or wounded. (수백의)

③ I got more <u>insights</u> about him from reading his books than from talking to him. (시야)

④ She bought a few items of <u>clothing</u>. (의류, 옷)

⑤ The <u>glowing</u> blue color is created by X-rays. (빛나는)

04 다음 우리말에 맞도록 빈칸에 알맞은 말을 쓰시오. (철자가 주어진 경우 주어진 철자로 시작할 것.)

(1) 원할 때 언제라도 날 방문해도 좋다.
➡ You can visit me w_____ you want.

(2) 당신을 만나서 정말 영광입니다.
➡ I'm really h_____ to meet you.

(3) 섬유소가 많고 칼로리가 적은 음식을 골라라.
➡ Choose foods that are h_____ in fiber and low in calories.

[05~06] 다음 대화를 읽고 물음에 답하시오.

W: ⓐLook at this picture on Jake's blog. ⓑHe went indoor rock climbing!

M: ⓒOh, it looks interesting but seems too hard.

W: Actually, 지역문화회관에 다른 수준의 코스들이 있다고 들었어. (hear, that, course, at, there, level, center)

M: Really? ⓓThen, maybe I should visit the center and find out more about the courses.

W: ⓔLet me to know how does it turn out.

05 밑줄 친 우리말과 일치하도록 주어진 단어를 이용해 문장을 쓰시오.

➡ _____
_____

06 ⓐ~ⓔ 중 어법상 어색한 것을 골라 바르게 고치시오.

➡ _____
_____

[07~08] 다음 대화를 읽고 물음에 답하시오.

M: Do you want to watch the new 3D movie?

W: Which one?

M: The one about adventures under the sea. It was shot near Australia's Great Barrier Reef.

W: Oh, I've heard of it. It has the most beautiful sea life.

M: Right. 나는 빨리 그 영화를 보고 싶어. Let's go and get the ticket.

07 위 대화에서 다음 영영풀이에 해당하는 단어를 찾아 쓰시오.

an exciting experience in which dangerous or unusual things happen

➡ _____

08 밑줄 친 우리말과 일치하도록 주어진 단어를 이용하여 영작하시오.

➡ _____

(wait, watch, to, 7 단어)

[09~10] 다음 대화를 읽고 물음에 답하시오.

M: Jisu, (A)_____ the sun never sets in Norway during summer?

W: No, I didn't know that. How interesting!

M: Yeah, and (B)_____ people go hiking and even cycling at night because it isn't dark.

W: I'd love to go hiking and cycling in the middle of the night!

M: Me, too. I hope we get the chance to try it someday.

09 다음 빈칸 (A)와 (B)에 들어갈 말이 알맞게 짝지어진 것은?

    (A)   (B)

① do you know why – I've heard that

② do you know why – I've heard about

③ did you know that – I've heard that

④ did you know that – I didn't know that

⑤ did you know that – I've heard about

10 위 대화의 내용에 맞게 빈칸에 알맞은 말을 쓰시오.

In Norway, people go _____ _____ the night during summer because _____.

[11~13] 다음 대화를 읽고 물음에 답하시오.

W: David, what's your summer plan? (①)

M: My family is going to China. (②)

W: The Rainbow Mountains? (③)

M: They are some mountains (A)that look like canvases in rainbow colors. (④)

W: That sounds amazing! (⑤) Take lots of pictures!

11 ①~⑤ 중 주어진 문장이 들어갈 곳은?

I can't wait to visit the Rainbow Mountains.

①   ②   ③   ④   ⑤

12 위 대화에서 다음 영영풀이에 해당하는 단어를 찾아 쓰시오.

a large curve of different colors that can appear in the sky when there is both sun and rain

➡ _____

13 밑줄 친 (A)that과 쓰임이 같은 것을 고르시오.

① I heard that he was very sick.
② Do you know that ice cream is from China?
③ Do you know the girl that is standing there?
④ I've heard that the school tennis team won the match.
⑤ People didn't know that the earth is round.

14 다음 중 〈보기〉의 문장과 의미가 같은 것을 고르시오.

┌─── 보기 ────
He is working now. He began working at 7 p.m.
└───────────

① He is working at 7 p.m.
② He worked at 7 p.m.
③ He has been working since 7 p.m.
④ He has been worked for 7 p.m.
⑤ He had worked since 7 p.m.

15 다음 중 어법상 옳은 문장을 모두 고르시오.

① Isn't it necessary of us to help them?
② Iceland is the best place for many location scouts to visit.
③ She has been listening to the music since two hours.
④ Alex has been having his father's watch since his father passed away.
⑤ They have been waiting for a doctor for two hours.

16 다음 두 문장의 의미가 같도록 빈칸에 알맞은 말을 쓰시오.

(1) It's important that we should have a sense of belonging.
= It's important _____.
(2) It's reasonable that employees should be properly paid.
= It's reasonable _____.

17 주어진 표현을 사용하여 질문에 대한 대답을 완성하시오.

(1) Q: How long have both of you been living together?
A: We _____.
(5 years)
(2) Q: Since when has Christine been reading the book?
A: She _____.
(yesterday)

18 다음 문장에서 어법상 어색한 것을 바르게 고쳐 다시 쓰시오.

(1) The greenhouse in the Ice Cube is warm enough of Mathew to grow fresh vegetables.
➡ _____
_____

(2) It was wise for Solomon to make such a careful decision.
➡ _____

(3) Jason has been taking horse-riding lessons since three months.
➡ _____
_____

(4) Ashley has been learning to play the flute 5 months ago.
➡ _____
_____

(5) Lily has been liking Gino since she first met him.
➡ _____

[19~21] 다음 글을 읽고 물음에 답하시오.

"①The beauty of nature inspires us all. Let's find out how people from different fields of work get inspired by nature."

Lin Wang, Ecologist
②Tsingy, the Stone Forest of Madagascar

I've been visiting the stone forest of Madagascar to study plants and animals for ③over 20 years. The spiky stones of this place are true miracles of nature. This amazing shape has been created by rainfall. Rain has cut down the stones and made them sharp and spiky ④over a long period of time. ⓐThe environment is harsh for animals to live in, but they have found ways to survive. For example, lemurs, which only live in Madagascar, have frog-like legs ⓑthat help them jump from one stone tower to another. For me, the stone forest ⑤is like a jack-in-the-box. It always surprises me and keeps me on my toes!

19 다음 중 위 글의 밑줄 친 ①~⑤에 대한 설명을 옳게 하지 <u>못한</u> 사람을 고르시오.

① 수미: 수동태로 고치면 Us all are inspired by the beauty of nature.야.
② 혜경: 콤마는 동격을 나타내서, 'Madagascar에 있는 석림인 Tsingy'라는 뜻이야.
③ 영호: '… 이상'이라는 뜻으로, more than으로 바꿔 쓸 수 있어.
④ 철규: '…에 걸쳐'라는 뜻이야.
⑤ 진성: is similar to로 바꿔 쓸 수 있지.

20 위 글의 밑줄 친 ⓐ처럼 말한 이유를 우리말로 쓰시오.

➡ _____

_____

21 위 글의 밑줄 친 ⓑthat과 문법적 쓰임이 같은 것을 <u>모두</u> 고르시오.

① She said that the story was true.
② I can't walk that far.
③ The people that he spoke to were very helpful.
④ It's the best novel that I've ever read.
⑤ It's true that he was a little late.

[22~24] 다음 글을 읽고 물음에 답하시오.

Danny Mehta, Location Scout
Vatnajökull National Park, Frozen Beauty of Iceland

I'm a location scout and my job is finding perfect places to ⓐshoot movies. Iceland is the best place for many location scouts to visit due to its unusual beauty. My personal favorite is the Vatnajökull National Park. The sharp cliffs, blue glacier caves, and long mountain ranges can stand in for any place in the world or the universe. In fact, the recent sci-fi movie we shot here was produced without using computer graphics! ⓑIceland can help make our wildest dreams come true on the movie screen.

22 위 글의 밑줄 친 ⓐshoot와 같은 의미로 쓰인 것을 고르시오.

① Don't shoot beams of light at him.
② The police rarely shoot to kill people.
③ He likes to shoot his film in Hollywood.
④ He tried to shoot the ball to first base.
⑤ This is just a toy gun — it doesn't shoot real bullets.

23 위 글의 밑줄 친 ⓑ를 다음과 같이 바꿔 쓸 때 빈칸에 들어갈 알맞은 말을 두 단어로 쓰시오.

➡ Iceland can help _____ _____ our wildest dreams come true on the movie screen.

24 Which question CANNOT be answered after reading the passage?

① What is Danny Mehta's job?

② Where is the Vatnajökull National Park?

③ Why is Iceland the best place for many location scouts to visit?

④ What place is Danny Mehta's personal favorite?

⑤ How many sci-fi movies were produced in the Vatnajökull National Park?

[25~27] 다음 글을 읽고 물음에 답하시오.

Are you a hiking fan? Then join my trip. It is designed for those who are interested in hiking. You'll visit Mt. Jiri and Mt. Seorak. These are the best places for hiking fans to visit. You'll be able to walk along beautiful hiking routes. Also, you'll learn how to get in shape and keep fit. This trip will be the most memorable @one!

25 위 글의 종류로 알맞은 것을 고르시오.

① article ② essay ③ PR poster

④ review ⑤ book report

26 위 글의 밑줄 친 @one이 가리키는 것을 본문에서 찾아 쓰시오.

➡ _____

27 위 글을 읽고 알 수 없는 것을 고르시오.

① For whom is the trip designed?

② How long will it take to go hiking?

③ Which places will the tourists visit?

④ What will the tourists do during the trip?

⑤ Will this trip be unforgettable?

[28~29] 다음 글을 읽고 물음에 답하시오.

Danny Mehta, Location Scout
Vatnajökull National Park, Frozen Beauty of Iceland

I'm a location scout and my job is finding perfect places to shoot movies. Iceland is the best place for many location scouts to visit due to its unusual beauty. My personal favorite is the Vatnajökull National Park. The sharp cliffs, blue glacier caves, and long mountain ranges can stand in for any place in the world or the universe.   @ , the recent sci-fi movie we shot here was produced without using computer graphics! Iceland can help make our wildest dreams come true on the movie screen.

28 위 글의 빈칸 @에 들어갈 알맞은 말을 고르시오.

① Moreover ② In fact

③ Therefore ④ However

⑤ In other words

29 According to the passage, which is NOT true?

① Danny Mehta is a location scout.

② Vatnajökull National Park is located in Iceland.

③ Iceland is the best place for many location scouts to visit due to its unusual beauty.

④ The recent action movie Danny Mehta's team shot here was produced without using computer graphics.

⑤ Iceland can help make our wildest dreams become realized on the movie screen.

[30~31] 다음 글을 읽고 물음에 답하시오.

Amber Smith, Fashion Colorist
Caño Cristales, the River of Five Colors of Colombia
The world is filled with millions of different colors. It is my job to mix, develop, and create colors for clothing. Over the years, I've been gaining insights from the beautiful colors of Caño Cristales. You cannot see the wonderful mixed colors of this river anywhere else in the world. ⓐ물속의 화려한 식물들과 햇빛의 결합은 그 색깔을 더 생생하고 밝게 만든다. Whenever I visit the Caño Cristales, it makes me think that maybe there are still countless colors that are waiting to be created.

30 위 글의 밑줄 친 ⓐ의 우리말에 맞게 한 단어를 보충하여, 주어진 어휘를 알맞게 배열하시오.

> sunlight / of colorful plants / and / under the water / the / makes / more alive and bright / the colors

➡ _____
_____
_____

31 다음 빈칸 (A)와 (B)에 알맞은 단어를 넣어 Amber Smith에 대한 소개를 완성하시오.

> Amber Smith is a (A)_____ _____ who has been gaining insights from the beautiful colors of (B)_____ _____.

[32~34] 다음 글을 읽고 물음에 답하시오.

I'm a location scout and my job is finding perfect places to shoot movies. ⓐ아이슬란드는 비범한 아름다움 때문에 많은 장소 섭외가들이 방문하기에 최고의 장소이다. My personal favorite is the Vatnajökull National Park. The sharp cliffs, blue glacier caves, and long mountain ranges can stand ___ⓑ___ for any place in the world or the universe. In fact, the recent sci-fi movie we shot here was produced without using computer graphics! Iceland can help make our wildest dreams come true on the movie screen.

32 위 글의 밑줄 친 ⓐ의 우리말에 맞게 한 단어를 보충하여, 주어진 어휘를 알맞게 배열하시오.

> the best place / is / to visit / Iceland / its unusual beauty / due to / for many location

➡ _____
_____

33 위 글의 빈칸 ⓑ에 알맞은 것은?

① in   ② to   ③ at
④ for   ⑤ with

34 What makes the Vatnajökull National Park stand in for any place in the world or the universe? Fill in the blanks (A) and (B) with suitable words.

> Its sharp cliffs, blue (A)_____ _____, and long (B)_____ _____.

Lesson 3

For the Love of Our Country

 의사소통 기능

- 알고 있는 내용 진술하기

  A: Wasn't Jeong Yakyong a scholar in the
  Joseon Dynasty?

  B: Yeah, but it is said that he was also a detective.

- 허락 요청하기

  A: Is it okay if I take pictures in the museum?

  B: Sure. Go ahead.

언어 형식

- 접속사 if

  I was not sure **if** he was telling the truth.

- 과거완료

  When I was sixteen years old, my family **had**
  already **made** an arrangement for me to marry
  him.

교과서

Words & Expressions

Key Words

- **afterwards** [ǽftərdz] 분 나중에, 그 뒤에
- **already** [ɔːlrédi] 분 이미, 벌써
- **article** [áːrtikl] 명 기사
- **biography** [baiágəfi] 명 자서전, 전기
- **bring** [briŋ] 동 가져오다
- **chest** [tʃest] 명 서랍장, 큰 상자, 장롱
- **clinic** [klínik] 명 병원, 진료소
- **detective** [ditékiv] 명 형사, 탐정
- **disappointing** [dìsəpɔ́intiŋ] 형 실망시키는
- **Dynasty** [dáinəsti] 명 왕조
- **embarrassing** [imbǽrəsiŋ] 형 부끄러운, 당황스러운
- **female** [fíːmeil] 명 여자 형 여자의, 여성의
- **fight** [fait] 동 싸우다
- **fortress** [fɔ́ːrtris] 명 요새
- **fortune** [fɔ́ːrtʃən] 명 재산, 행운
- **gamble** [gǽmbl] 동 도박하다, ~을 도박으로 잃다
- **gambling house** 도박장
- **general** [dʒénərəl] 명 장군
- **horrible** [hɔ́ːrəbl] 형 끔찍한
- **husband** [hʌ́zbənd] 명 남편
- **include** [inklúːd] 동 ~을 포함하다
- **independence** [ìndipéndəns] 명 독립, 광복
- **invention** [invénʃən] 명 발명품, 발명
- **Japanese** [dʒæpəníːz] 형 일본의 명 일본어
- **leave** [liːv] 동 맡기다, 남기다
- **locker** [lάkər] 명 사물함
- **machine** [məʃíːn] 명 기계, 기구
- **Manchuria** [mæntʃúərə] 명 만주 형 만주의

- **marriage** [mǽridʒ] 명 결혼, 혼인
- **marry** [mǽri] 동 결혼하다, 혼인하다
- **merchant** [mɔ́ːrtʃənt] 명 상인
- **move** [muːv] 동 이동시키다, 이동하다
- **movement** [múːvmənt] 명 (정치적·사회적) 운동
- **museum** [mjuːzíːəm] 명 박물관, 기념관
- **musical instrument** 악기
- **object** [άbdʒikt] 명 물건
- **odd** [ɑd] 형 이상한
- **officer** [ɔ́ːfisər] 명 경찰관, 장교
- **pilot** [páilət] 명 조종사, 비행사
- **realistic** [rìːəlístik] 형 진짜 같은, 사실적인
- **realize** [ríːəlàiz] 동 깨닫다
- **ruin** [rúːin] 동 망치다, 파산시키다
- **save** [seiv] 동 구하다
- **scholar** [skάlər] 명 학자
- **since** [sins] 접 ~이기 때문에, ~한 이래로
- **social studies** 사회
- **solve** [sɑlv] 동 해결하다, 풀다
- **strange** [streindʒ] 형 낯선, 모르는
- **Sudan** [suːdǽn] 명 수단 (민주 공화국)
- **truth** [truːθ] 명 진실, 사실
- **village** [vílidʒ] 명 마을, 농촌
- **whenever** [hwenévər] 접 ~할 때마다, ~하면
- **whisper** [hwíspər] 동 속삭이다, (사람·일에 대하여) 소곤소곤 이야기하다
- **wonder** [wʌ́ndər] 동 궁금하다
- **wooden** [wúdn] 형 나무로 된, 목재의
- **would** [wəd] 동 (과거에 있어서의 습관·습성·반복적 동작) ~(하곤) 했다

Key Expressions

- **ask for**: 청구하다, 청하다
- **at that moment**: 그 순간에
- **at this hour**: 이 시간에
- **be used to (동)명사**: ~하는 데 익숙하다
- **behind one's back**: ~ 몰래, ~의 등 뒤에서
- **by 동사ing**: ~함으로써
- **devote one's life to 명사**: ~에 일생을 바치다
- **hear of[about]** ~: ~에 대해 듣다
- **instead of**: ~ 대신에

- **Is it okay if I** ~?: 제가 ~해도 될까요?
- **It is said that 주어+동사** ~: (사람들이) ~라고 한다
- **keep a secret**: 비밀을 지키다
- **make an arrangement**: ~을 결정하다
- **so+형용사/부사+that 주어+동사**: 너무 ~해서 …하다
- **take a look at** ~: ~을 보다
- **try on**: 입어 보다, 신어 보다
- **yell at**: ~에게 고함치다, ~에게 호통치다

Word Power

※ 명사형 어미 -age(~하는 행위, 상태)
- □ **marry**(결혼하다)+**-age**(~의 상태) → **marriage**(결혼)
- □ **pack**(싸다)+**-age**(~한 것) → **package**(꾸러미, 하나로 묶음)
- □ **use**(사용하다)+**-age**(법) → **usage**(사용법)
- □ **cour**(마음)+**-age**(~의 상태) → **courage**(용기, 용감)
- □ 라틴어 **damnum**(손해)+**-age**(상태, 요금) → **damage**(손해, 손상)
- □ 라틴어 **ab**(~으로)+**ante**(앞)+**-age**(상태) → **advantage**(우위, 우세)

※ 부사형 접미어 -ward(s)(방향, ~쪽으로)
- □ **after**(뒤에, 후에)+**-ward**(~쪽으로) → **afterwards**(후에, 나중에)
- □ **back**(뒤)+**-ward**(~쪽으로) → **backwards**(뒤로)
- □ **up**(위)+**-ward**(~쪽으로) → **upwards**(위로)
- □ **fore**(앞)+**-ward**(~쪽으로) → **forwards**(앞으로)
- □ **in**(안)+**-ward**(~쪽으로) → **inward**(안으로)
- □ **out**(바깥에)+**-ward**(~쪽으로) → **outward**(밖으로)

English Dictionary

- □ **article** 기사
  → a piece of writing about a particular subject that is published in a newspaper or magazine
  신문이나 잡지에 발행되는 특정한 주제에 대해 쓴 글

- □ **biography** 자서전, 전기
  → a book that someone writes about someone else's life
  누군가가 다른 누군가의 삶에 대해 쓴 책

- □ **chest** 서랍장, 큰 상자, 장롱
  → a large strong heavy box used for storing things
  물건을 보관하기 위해 사용되는 크고 무거운 상자

- □ **female** 여자의, 여성의
  → relating to women or girls
  여자나 여자아이와 관련된

- □ **fortress** 요새
  → a large strong building used for defending an important place
  중요한 장소를 방어하기 위해 사용되는 크고 튼튼한 건물

- □ **fortune** 재산
  → a very large amount of money
  매우 많은 돈

- □ **general** 장군
  → an officer of very high rank in the army or air force
  육군이나 공군에서 높은 계급을 가진 장교

- □ **include** ~을 포함하다
  → to contain someone or something as a part
  사람이나 사물을 어떤 것의 일부로 내포하다

- □ **independence** 독립
  → freedom from control by another country or organization
  다른 나라나 조직에 의한 통제로부터 벗어난 자유

- □ **merchant** 상인
  → someone who buys and sells goods in large quantities
  많은 양의 물건을 사고파는 사람

- □ **movement** (정치적 · 사회적) 운동
  → a gradual development or change of an attitude, opinion, or policy
  태도, 의견 또는 정책의 점진적인 발전 또는 변화

- □ **ruin** 망치다, 파산시키다
  → to make someone lose all their money or power
  누군가로 하여금 그들의 돈이나 권력을 모두 잃게 만들다

- □ **scholar** 학자
  → someone who studies a particular subject and knows a lot about it, especially a subject that is not scientific
  특히 과학적인 주제가 아닌 특정 주제에 대해 공부하고 많이 아는 사람

- □ **save** 구하다
  → to make someone or something safe from danger, harm, or destruction
  위험, 해로움, 또는 파괴로부터 사람이나 사물을 안전하게 만들다

[01~02] 다음 밑줄 친 부분과 바꿔 쓸 수 있는 말을 고르시오.

01
We were <u>rescued</u> from the sinking ship by a passing fishing boat.

① trapped ② protected ③ saved
④ rushed ⑤ searched

02
Buffett made <u>a lot of money</u> through intelligent investments.

① a move ② a result ③ a chance
④ a fortune ⑤ a poverty

03 중요 다음 밑줄 친 부분의 의미로 알맞지 <u>않은</u> 것은?

① He is a writer rather than a <u>scholar</u>. (학자)
② She was clearly speaking the <u>truth</u>. (진실)
③ The soldiers were ready to defend the <u>fortress</u>. (요새)
④ Have you ever been to the War <u>Memorial</u> Museum of Korea? (기념관)
⑤ He was recently promoted to <u>general</u>. (일반적인 것)

04 다음 빈칸에 들어갈 말을 고르시오.

It was really _____ to find all our money stolen.

① terrific ② confident ③ boring
④ horrible ⑤ exciting

05 다음 제시된 단어를 사용하여 자연스러운 문장을 만들 수 없는 것은? (형태 변화 가능)

hear make take try

① Let's _____ an arrangement of our destination.
② She said she would _____ her life to public service.
③ Do you have any jackets I could _____ on?
④ It's an interesting place. Do you want to _____ a look around?
⑤ Have you _____ about the garage sale?

06 서답형 두 문장이 같은 의미가 되도록 빈칸을 채우시오. (주어진 철자로 시작할 것)

You should talk to Karen because she's the one responsible for it.
= You should talk to Karen s_____ she's the one responsible for it.

07 중요 다음 영영풀이가 나타내는 말을 고르시오.

a gradual development or change of an attitude, opinion, or policy

① movement ② culture
③ model ④ volunteer
⑤ activity

01 우리말 해석에 맞게 주어진 단어를 알맞게 배열하시오.

(1) 그는 새로운 안경에 익숙해지려고 노력하면서 늙은이처럼 걸었다.

➡ He walked like an old man _____ _____. (glasses, be, to, trying, to, new, used)

(2) 사람들은 그녀가 전 세계를 다녀왔다고 말한다.

➡ _____

(that, all, said, world, she, is, the, been, over, it, has)

(3) 나는 그의 등 뒤에서 이렇게 얘기하는 것을 싫어한다.

➡ _____

(talking, behind, like, back, his, hate, this, I)

(4) 내가 사진을 찍어도 괜찮을까요?

➡ _____

(a, okay, picture, I, if, it, take, is)

02 빈칸에 적절한 말을 주어진 단어를 변형하여 채우시오.

She took part in the March 1st Movement for Korea's _____. (depend)

03 두 문장이 같은 의미가 되도록 주어진 단어를 이용하여 빈칸을 채우시오.

He was strong enough to lift it.
= He was _____ strong _____ _____ _____ lift it. (can)

04 다음 제시된 의미에 맞는 단어를 주어진 철자로 시작하여 빈칸에 쓰고, 알맞은 것을 골라 문장을 완성하시오.

- i_____ : to contain someone or something as a part
- r_____ : to make someone lose all their money or power
- s_____ : to make someone or something safe from danger, harm, or destruction

(1) Some say spoilers _____ the story.

(2) Wearing a seat belt can help _____ your life.

(3) The price for the hotel _____s breakfast.

05 다음 빈칸에 공통으로 들어갈 말을 쓰시오.

- The building was destroyed _____ fire in 2004.
- She earns extra money _____ babysitting.

06 다음 우리말에 맞도록 빈칸에 알맞은 말을 쓰시오.

(1) LA Times에 직장 내 괴롭힘에 대한 흥미로운 기사가 있었다.

➡ There was an interesting _____ in the LA Times about bullying at work.

(2) 우리는 자주 저녁 산책을 하곤 했다.

➡ We _____ often have a walk of an evening.

Conversation

1 알고 있는 내용 진술하기

> **A:** Wasn't Jeong Yakyong a scholar in the Joseon Dynasty?
> 정약용이 조선왕조 때의 학자가 아니었나요?
>
> **B:** Yeah, but it is said that he was also a detective.
> 네, 하지만 그는 또한 탐정이었다는 말이 있어요.

■ 'It is said that 주어+동사 ~.'는 '(사람들이) ~라고 한다.'라는 뜻으로 that절의 내용에 대해 진술할 때 사용한다. 'is said'가 수동태 형태임에 주의한다.

■ 'It is said that 주어+동사 ~.'는 말하는 사람이 구체적으로 정해져 있지 않고 '(사람들이) ~라고 말했다'라는 의미로 사용하므로, 일반인인 'they[people]'를 주어로 'They[People] say that 주어+동사'.로 바꿔 쓸 수 있다.

알고 있는 내용 진술하기

- It is said that 주어+동사 ~. (~라고 한다.)
- It is believed that 주어+동사 ~. (~라고 믿어진다.)
- It is thought that 주어+동사 ~. (~라고 생각된다.)
- They[People] say (that) 주어+동사 ~. (사람들이 ~라고 말한다.)

핵심 Check

1. 우리말과 일치하도록 주어진 단어를 알맞게 배열하여 문장을 만드시오.

   A: _____ in front of the City Hall this weekend.
   (that, is, will, a, said, it, there, be, festival, big)
   B: I'm interested in that. How about going there?

2. 다음 문장과 같은 의미가 되도록 주어진 단어를 이용하여 쓰시오.

They say that he is a liar.

   ➡ _____ (said)

3. 다음 우리말과 일치하도록 빈칸에 알맞은 말을 쓰시오.

   보라색은 클레오파트라가 가장 좋아하는 색이었다고 한다.
   ➡ _____ a favorite color of Cleopatra.

② 허락 요청하기

A: Is it okay if I take pictures in the museum? 박물관에서 사진을 찍어도 괜찮나요?

B: Sure. Go ahead. 물론이죠. 그렇게 하세요.

- 'Is it okay if I ~?'는 '제가 ~해도 될까요?'라는 뜻으로 어떤 행동을 하기 전에 허가를 요청할 때 사용하는 표현이다. if 다음에는 허락을 구하는 내용을 쓴다.

- 허가를 묻는 다른 표현으로 'Can I ~?', 'Are we allowed to 동사원형 ~?', I'm wondering if I ~. 등이 있다.

허락 요청하기

• Is it okay if I ~?	• Is it possible that I ~?
• Can[May] I ~?	• I'm wondering if I ~.
• Would it be all right if I ~?	• Are we allowed to 동사원형 ~?

허락을 요청하는 질문에 답하기

〈허락하기〉

• Sure.   • Of course.   • Certainly.   • Why not?   • No problem.

〈거절하기〉

• I'm sorry, but you can't[may not].	• I'm afraid you can't.
• I'm afraid not.	• No way!
• You're not allowed to 동사원형.	• You're not permitted to do that.
• You can't do that.	• Not right now.

핵심 Check

4. 다음 우리말과 일치하도록 주어진 말을 이용해 빈칸을 완성하시오.

> **A:** _____ (okay, if, the guitar) (제가 기타를 연습해도 될까요?)
> **B:** OK, but you're not allowed to practice after 10 p.m.

5. 우리말과 일치하도록 주어진 단어를 배열하여 영작하시오.

> **A:** _____ (okay, to, it, you, if, is, next, sit, I)
> (내가 당신 옆에 앉아도 될까요?)
> **B:** No problem.

Listen & Talk 1 A-1

M: Lisa, ❶what are you reading?

W: I'm reading a ❷biography of Gwon Giok.

M: ❸I haven't heard about her. Who is she?

W: She was the first ❹female pilot in Korea. ❺It is said that she had over 7,000 hours of flying time.

M: Wow, I didn't know that.

M: Lisa, 너 뭐 읽고 있니?

W: 권기옥의 전기를 읽고 있어.

M: 그녀에 대해 들어본 적이 없어. 그녀는 누구니?

W: 그녀는 한국의 첫 번째 여성 조종사야. 그녀는 비행시간이 7,000 시간이 넘는다고 해.

M: 와, 난 몰랐어.

❶ 무엇을 읽고 있는지 현재진행형(be동사+동사ing)을 이용해 질문하고 있다.

❷ biography: 자서전, 전기

❸ hear about ~: ~에 대해 듣다

❹ female: 여자; 여자의, 여성의 pilot: 조종사, 비행사

❺ 'It is said that 주어+동사 ~.'는 '(사람들이) ~라고 한다.'라는 뜻으로 that절의 내용에 대해 진술할 때 사용한다. over: ~을 넘어, ~보다 많은

Check(√) True or False

(1) Lisa is reading a novel about Gwon Giok. T ☐ F ☐

(2) The man didn't know who Gwon Giok was. T ☐ F ☐

(3) Gwon Giok was the first female pilot in Korea. T ☐ F ☐

 Listen & Talk 2 A-1

W: Excuse me, you ❶can't take your backpack ❷inside the museum.

M: Oh, I didn't know that. Is it okay if I ❸bring in my water bottle?

W: ❹Yes, that's fine. You can ❺leave your bag in the locker.

M: Okay, thank you.

W: 죄송합니다만, 박물관에 가방을 가지고 들어갈 수 없어요.

M: 아, 몰랐어요. 물병은 가지고 들어가도 괜찮나요?

W: 네, 그건 괜찮아요. 가방은 라커에 두시면 돼요.

M: 알았어요. 감사합니다.

❶ 어떤 일이 가능한지 묻고 답할 때 조동사 can을 사용할 수 있다.

❷ inside: ~ 안에

❸ bring in: 들여가다

❹ 'that's fine.'은 '그것은 괜찮다.'라는 의미로 상대방이 허락을 구하는 말을 했을 때 허락하는 표현이다. 이외의 허락의 표현에는 'Of course.', 'Certainly.', 'No problem.' 등이 있다.

❺ leave: 남기다, 맡기다

Check(√) True or False

(4) The museum allows people to take their backpack inside it. T ☐ F ☐

(5) The woman can't bring in her water bottle. T ☐ F ☐

Listen & Talk 1 B

W: Hey, Mark, ❶do you know about Father Lee Taeseok?

M: Yeah, ❷I've heard of him. Why?

W: ❸Take a look at this article. He is going to ❹be included in the social studies textbook in South Sudan.

M: Wow, that's great.

W: Yeah, he helped the children ❺by building a clinic and a school. ❻It is said that such stories will be included in the textbook.

M: It is good to hear ❼that students will learn about such a great person.

W: 어이, Mark, 너 이태석 신부에 대해 아니?

M: 응, 그에 대해 들어본 적이 있어. 왜?

W: 이 기사를 봐. 그는 남수단의 사회 교과서에 실릴 거야.

M: 와, 그거 대단하구나.

W: 그래, 그는 병원과 학교를 지어 아이들을 도와주었어. 그런 이야기들이 교과서에 실릴 거라고 해.

M: 학생들이 그토록 훌륭한 사람에 대해 배울 거라는 말을 들으니 좋군.

❶ 'Do you know about ∼?'은 '∼에 대해서 알고 있어?'라는 의미로 상대방에게 알고 있는지 묻는 표현이다. 'Have you heard about ∼?'이나 'Are you aware of ∼?'로 바꿔 쓸 수 있다.

❷ 'I've heard of[about] ∼'은 '∼에 대해 들었다'라는 뜻으로 알고 있거나 들은 것에 대해 말할 때 쓰는 표현이다. 일반적으로 현재완료의 형태로 쓰지만 'I heard of[about] ∼'라고 할 수도 있다

❸ take a look at ∼: ∼을 보다 article: 기사 ❹ include: ∼을 포함하다 ❺ by 동사ing: ∼함으로써

❻ 'It is said that 주어+동사 ∼.'는 말하는 사람이 구체적으로 정해져 있지 않고 '(사람들이) ∼라고 말한다'라는 의미로 사용하므로, 일반인인 'they[people]'를 주어로 'They[People] say that 주어+동사 ∼.'로 바꿔 쓸 수 있다. (= They[People] say that such stories will be included in the textbook.)

❼ 동사 hear 뒤에 명사절을 이끄는 접속사 that이 사용되고 있다.

Check(√) True or False

(6) The woman read the article about how to be a great person. T ☐ F ☐

(7) Mark wasn't aware of Father Lee Taeseok. T ☐ F ☐

 Communication Step B

A: This ❶is called the *Geojunggi*.

B: Wow, this ❷looks interesting.

A: This is a machine ❸that moves heavy objects. It is said that ❹it helped to build the Hwaseong Fortress only in 28 months.

B: How amazing! Is it okay if I take a closer look at it?

A: Sure.

A: 이것은 거중기라고 불려.

B: 와, 이거 흥미 있어 보이는데.

A: 이것은 무거운 물체들을 옮기는 기계야. 그것은 화성 요새를 겨우 28개월 만에 짓는 데 도움이 되었다고 해.

B: 정말 놀랍다! 그걸 더 자세히 봐도 괜찮겠니?

A: 물론이지.

❶ call이 5형식으로 사용하여 '[사람·물건을] (어떤 이름으로) 부르다, 이름을 붙이다'로 쓰일 수 있다. 원래는 'People call this the *Geojunggi*.'인 문장을 수동태로 바꾼 것이다.

❷ look+형용사: ∼하게 보이다 / interesting은 현재분사형의 형용사로 '∼하게 하는'의 뜻으로 감정을 유발하는 대상에 쓰인다.

❸ that은 주격 관계대명사로 which와 바꿔 쓸 수 있다. 주격 관계대명사는 생략할 수 없다.

❹ help (to+) 동사원형: ∼ 하는 데 도움이 되다

Check(√) True or False

(8) They are looking at the *Geojunggi*. T ☐ F ☐

(9) *B* is interested in *Geojunggi*. T ☐ F ☐

Listen & Talk 1 Get Ready

A: Kim Deuksin was a painter.

B: ❶No! I read a book and ❷it is said that he was a scholar.

C: Don't fight. You are ❸both right.

❶ 다음에 'He was not a painter.'가 생략되어 있다.
❷ scholar: 학자 ❸ both: 둘 다

Listen & Talk 1 A-2

M: I watched an interesting movie yesterday. Jeong Yakyong was a ❶detective in it.

W: Jeong Yakyong? Wasn't he a scholar in the Joseon ❷Dynasty?

M: Yeah, but it is said that he was also a detective. He ❸solved ❹about 90 cases.

W: Oh, I didn't know that he was also a detective.

❶ detective: 형사, 탐정 in it에서 it은 남자가 어제 본 영화를 의미한다.
❷ Dynasty: 왕조 ❸ solve: 해결하다, 풀다
❹ 숫자 앞의 about은 '대략, 약'의 의미를 가진다.

Listen & Talk 2 A-2

W: Hi, ❶welcome to the National Museum. How can I help you?

M: Hi, is it okay if I ❷take pictures in the museum?

W: Yes, but please ❸don't use a flash.

M: Oh, I see. Thank you.

❶ welcome to 장소: (장소에) 오신 것을 환영합니다
❷ take pictures: 사진 찍다
❸ 명령문은 동사로 시작한다. 하지 말라고 할 때는 그 앞에 'Don't'를 붙인다.
flash: (카메라) 플래시

Listen & Talk 2 B

M: Hello, Ms. Jackson. How was your tour of the *Hanok Village*?

W: It was wonderful. The houses were really beautiful.

M: That's great.

W: Actually, I didn't ❶get the chance to have dinner. Is it okay if I cook in the kitchen at this hour?

M: Yes, but please remember ❷that the kitchen ❸closes at 10 p.m.

W: Okay. The kitchen is on the 5th floor, right?

M: Yes, it is. ❹Let me know if you need anything.

❶ get a chance: 기회를 가지다(= have a chance) 'to have dinner'는 앞의 the chance를 수식하는 형용사적 용법이다. ❷ that은 remember의 목적어인 명사절을 이끄는 접속사이다. ❸ 반복되는 사실에 대해서 현재시제를 사용할 수 있다. ❹ 상대방에게 어떤 일을 나에게 알려 달라고 부탁할 때 'let me know'를 이용해 말할 수 있다. let은 사역동사이므로 목적격보어 자리에 동사원형인 know를 사용한다.

Wrap Up 1

W: James, ❶what are you watching?

M: Oh, I'm watching a video about Yi Sunsin.

W: Isn't he the one ❷that saved Joseon from Japan?

M: Right. It is said that he won the war only with twelve wooden ships.

W: Wow, ❸how can that be possible?

M: He was a wise general who made creative plans.

❶ 무엇을 읽는 중인지 현재진행형(be동사+ing)을 사용하여 질문하고 있다. ❷ 주격 관계대명사(= who) ❸ '그것이 어떻게 가능하겠어요?'의 의미로 놀람을 나타내는 표현이며, 여기서는 가능하게 된 이유를 물어보고 있다.

● 다음 우리말과 일치하도록 빈칸에 알맞은 말을 쓰시오.

Listen & Talk 1 Get Ready

A: Kim Deuksin _____ a painter.

B: No! I _____ a book and _____ _____ _____ that he was a scholar.

C: Don't fight. You are _____ right.

Listen & Talk 1 A-1

M: Lisa, _____ are you _____?

W: I'm reading a _____ of Gwon Giok.

M: I _____ _____ about her. Who is she?

W: She was _____ _____ _____ pilot in Korea. _____ _____ _____ _____ she had _____ 7,000 hours of flying time.

M: Wow, I didn't know that.

Listen & Talk 1 A-2

M: I watched an _____ movie yesterday. Jeong Yakyong was a _____ in it.

W: Jeong Yakyong? Wasn't he a _____ in the Joseon Dynasty?

M: Yeah, _____ _____ _____ _____ _____ _____ _____ _____ a detective. He _____ about 90 cases.

W: Oh, I _____ _____ _____ he was also a detective.

Listen & Talk 1 B

W: Hey, Mark, do you _____ _____ Father Lee Taeseok?

M: Yeah, I've _____ of him. Why?

W: _____ _____ _____ _____ _____ this article. He is going _____ _____ _____ in the social studies textbook in South Sudan.

M: Wow, that's great.

W: Yeah, he _____ the children _____ _____ _____ _____ and a school. It is said _____ _____ _____ will _____ _____ the textbook.

M: It is good _____ hear that students will learn about _____ a great person.

 해석

A: 김득신은 화가였어.
B: 아니야! 내가 책을 읽었는데 그는 학자였다고 해.
C: 싸우지 마. 너희 둘 다 옳아.

M: Lisa, 너 뭐 읽고 있니?
W: 권기옥의 전기를 읽고 있어.
M: 그녀에 대해 들어본 적이 없어. 그녀는 누구니?
W: 그녀는 한국의 첫 번째 여성 조종사야. 그녀는 비행시간이 7,000시간이 넘는다고 해.
M: 와, 난 몰랐어.

M: 난 어제 흥미 있는 영화를 보았어. 그 영화에서 정약용이 탐정이었어.
W: 정약용? 그는 조선 왕조의 학자 아니었니?
M: 응, 하지만 그는 탐정이기도 했다고 해. 그는 약 90개의 사건을 해결했어.
W: 아, 그가 또한 탐정이었다는 건 몰랐어.

W: 어이, Mark, 너 이태석 신부에 대해 아니?
M: 응, 그에 대해 들어본 적이 있어. 왜?
W: 이 기사를 봐. 그는 남수단의 사회 교과서에 실릴 거야.
M: 와, 그거 대단하구나.
W: 그래, 그는 병원과 학교를 지어 아이들을 도와주었어. 그런 이야기들이 교과서에 실릴 거라고 해.
M: 학생들이 그토록 훌륭한 사람에 대해 배울 거라는 말을 들으니 좋군.

Listen & Talk 2 A-1

W: Excuse me, you _____ _____ your backpack inside the _____.
M: Oh, I didn't know that. _____ _____ _____ if I bring in my water bottle?
W: Yes, that's fine. You can _____ your bag _____ the locker.
M: Okay, thank you.

W: 죄송합니다만, 박물관에 가방을 가지고 들어갈 수 없어요.
M: 아, 몰랐어요. 물병은 가지고 들어가도 괜찮나요?
W: 네, 그건 괜찮아요. 가방은 라커에 두시면 돼요.
M: 알았어요. 감사합니다.

Listen & Talk 2 A-2

W: Hi, welcome _____ the National Museum. _____ can I help you?
M: Hi, _____ _____ _____ _____ _____ _____ _____ _____ the museum?
W: Yes, but please _____ use a flash.
M: Oh, I see. Thank you.

W: 안녕하세요, 국립박물관에 오신 걸 환영합니다. 무엇을 도와드릴까요?
M: 안녕하세요. 박물관에서 사진을 찍어도 괜찮나요?
W: 네, 하지만 플래시는 사용하지 마세요.
M: 아, 알겠습니다. 감사합니다.

Listen & Talk 2 B

M: Hello, Ms. Jackson. _____ _____ your tour of the *Hanok Village*?
W: It was wonderful. The houses _____ really beautiful.
M: That's great.
W: Actually, I didn't _____ _____ _____ _____ have dinner. Is it _____ _____ _____ cook in the kitchen at this hour?
M: Yes, but please _____ _____ the kitchen closes _____ 10 p.m.
W: Okay. The kitchen is _____ the 5th floor, right?
M: Yes, it is. _____ _____ _____ _____ you need anything.

M: 안녕하세요. Jackson 씨. 한옥 마을 관광은 어땠어요?
W: 굉장했어요. 집들이 정말 아름다웠습니다.
M: 대단하네요.
W: 사실 전 저녁식사를 할 기회가 없었어요. 이 시간에 부엌에서 요리해도 괜찮나요?
M: 네, 하지만 부엌이 오후 10시에 문을 닫는 걸 기억하세요.
W: 알겠습니다. 부엌은 5층에 있죠, 맞나요?
M: 네, 그래요. 무언가 필요하시면 제게 말씀해 주세요.

Communication Step A

M: All right, everyone! This way, please. Now, we _____ _____ _____ the Joseon Dynasty. _____ _____ _____ _____, there were _____ interesting _____. This one _____ _____ the *Jagyeongnu*.

W: Is it a _____ _____?

M: Actually, this is a water clock. _____ _____ _____ _____ _____ the oldest and the _____ water clock in Korea.

W: _____ amazing! _____ _____ _____ _____ I take a picture of it?

M: Sure.

M: 좋아요, 여러분! 이쪽으로 오세요. 이제, 우리는 조선 왕조로 옮겨갑니다. 보시다시피, 많은 흥미 있는 발명품들이 있습니다. 이것은 자격루라고 불립니다.

W: 그것은 악기인가요?

M: 사실은 이것은 물시계입니다. 그것은 한국에서 가장 오래되고, 가장 큰 물시계라고 합니다.

W: 정말 놀랍군요. 그것을 사진 찍어도 괜찮나요?

M: 물론입니다.

Wrap Up 1

W: James, _____ are you watching?

M: Oh, I'm _____ a video about Yi Sunsin.

W: _____ _____ the one that saved Joseon from Japan?

M: Right. _____ _____ _____ _____ _____ _____ the war only with twelve wooden ships.

W: Wow, _____ can that be _____?

M: He was a wise _____ _____ _____ _____ plans.

W: James, 뭘 보고 있니?

M: 아, 이순신에 관한 비디오를 보고 있어.

W: 그는 일본으로부터 조선을 구한 사람 아니니?

M: 맞아. 그는 겨우 12척의 목선으로 전쟁에 이겼다고 해.

W: 와, 그게 어떻게 가능할 수 있지?

M: 그는 창의적인 계획을 세운 현명한 장군이었어.

Wrap Up 2

W: Excuse me, sir. _____ _____ _____ _____ _____ have curry or *bibimbap*?

M: _____ _____ _____ have *bibimbap*, please.

W: _____ you are.

M: Thank you. Oh, _____ _____ _____ I use the bathroom now?

W: Sure, but _____ the seat light is _____, you should _____ in your seat.

M: Okay, thank you.

W: 실례합니다, 선생님. 카레를 드시겠어요 아니면 비빔밥을 드시겠어요?

M: 비빔밥을 먹고 싶습니다.

W: 여기 있습니다.

M: 고마워요. 아, 지금 화장실을 이용해도 괜찮나요?

W: 그럼요, 하지만 좌석 불이 켜져 있으면 선생님 좌석에 있으셔야 합니다.

M: 알았어요, 감사합니다.

01 주어진 문장 이후에 올 대화의 순서를 바르게 배열한 것을 고르시오.

> Lisa, what are you reading?

> (A) Wow, I didn't know that.
> (B) She was the first female pilot in Korea. It is said that she had over 7,000 hours of flying time.
> (C) I'm reading a biography of Gwon Giok.
> (D) I haven't heard about her. Who is she?

① (B) – (A) – (C) – (D)   ② (B) – (C) – (A) – (D)

③ (C) – (A) – (B) – (D)   ④ (C) – (B) – (A) – (D)

⑤ (C) – (D) – (B) – (A)

[02~03] 다음 대화를 읽고 물음에 답하시오.

W: Hi, welcome to the National Museum. How can I help you?
M: Hi, is it okay (A)_____ I take pictures in the museum?
W: (B)_____, but please don't use a flash.
M: Oh, I see. Thank you.

02 빈칸 (A)에 알맞은 말을 고르시오

① that   ② if   ③ while

④ what   ⑤ though

03 빈칸 (B)에 알맞은 말을 모두 고르시오.

① No, you can't   ② Okay   ③ Of course not

④ Sure, go ahead   ⑤ Yes

04 밑줄 친 우리말을 주어진 단어를 이용해 영작하시오.

> A: <u>내가 창문을 열어도 되나요?</u>
> B: Sorry, you can't.

➡ _____ (if, okay)

[01~02] 다음 대화를 읽고 물음에 답하시오.

M: I watched an interesting movie yesterday. (①) Jeong Yakyong was a (A)_____ in it. (②)
W: Jeong Yakyong? (③)
M: Yeah, but it is said that he was also a (B)_____. (④) He solved about 90 cases. (⑤)
W: Oh, I didn't know that he was also a (C)_____.

01 위 대화의 ①~⑤ 중 주어진 문장이 들어갈 알맞은 곳은?

> Wasn't he a scholar in the Joseon Dynasty?

①　　　②　　　③　　　④　　　⑤

02 밑줄 친 부분을 근거로 (A)~(C)에 알맞은 말을 고르시오.

① diplomat　　② detective
③ reporter　　④ victim
⑤ painter

[03~04] 다음 대화를 읽고 물음에 답하시오.

M: Lisa, what are you reading? (①)
W: I'm reading a biography of Gwon Giok. (②)
M: I haven't heard about her. (③)
W: She was the first female pilot in Korea. (④) It is said that she had over 7,000 hours of flying time.
M: Wow, I didn't know that. (⑤)

03 위 대화의 ①~⑤ 중 주어진 문장이 들어갈 알맞은 곳은?

> Who is she?

①　　　②　　　③　　　④　　　⑤

04 위 대화를 읽고 답할 수 없는 질문을 모두 고르시오.

① What kind of book is Lisa reading?
② How many hours of flying time did Gwon Giok have?
③ Who was the first male pilot in Korea?
④ Why is Lisa reading the book about Gwon Giok?
⑤ Has the man heard about Gwon Giok?

05 다음 중 짝지어진 대화가 어색한 것은?

① A: Is it okay if I turn on the air conditioning?
　 B: I'm afraid not. I feel so cold now.
② A: You didn't hand in the homework?
　 B: I'm sorry. Is it okay if I submit it tomorrow?
③ A: May I turn on the heater?
　 B: Sure. Go ahead.
④ A: Is it possible that I use your cellphone?
　 B: Certainly. I didn't bring it today.
⑤ A: Is it okay if I go out and play?
　 B: I'm sorry, but it's too late.

06 대화가 자연스럽게 연결되도록 (A)~(D)를 순서대로 가장 적절하게 배열한 것은?

> M: Hello, Ms. Jackson. How was your tour of the *Hanok Village*?
> W: _____
> M: _____
> W: _____
> M: _____
> W: Okay. The kitchen is on the 5th floor, right?
> M: Yes, it is. Let me know if you need anything.

> (A) That's great.
> (B) Actually, I didn't get the chance to have dinner. Is it okay if I cook in the kitchen at this hour?
> (C) It was wonderful. The houses were really beautiful.
> (D) Yes, but please remember that the kitchen closes at 10 p.m.

① (B) – (A) – (C) – (D)
② (B) – (C) – (A) – (D)
③ (C) – (A) – (B) – (D)
④ (C) – (B) – (A) – (D)
⑤ (C) – (D) – (B) – (A)

[07~09] 다음 대화를 읽고 물음에 답하시오.

> W: Hey, Mark, (A)_____
> M: Yeah, I've heard of him. (①) Why?
> W: (B)_____ a look at this article. (②) He is going to be included in the social studies textbook in South Sudan. (③)
> M: Wow. that's great. (④)
> W: Yeah, he helped the children by building a clinic and a school. (⑤)
> M: It is good to hear that students will learn about such a great person.

07 위 대화의 ①~⑤ 중 주어진 문장이 들어갈 알맞은 곳은?

> It is said that such stories will be included in the textbook.

①   ②   ③   ④   ⑤

08 빈칸 (A)에 알맞지 <u>않은</u> 말을 <u>모두</u> 고르시오.

① what do you think about Father Lee Taeseok?
② do you know about Father Lee Taeseok?
③ are you reading about Father Lee Taeseok?
④ have you heard of Father Lee Taeseok?
⑤ do you know who Father Lee Taeseok is?

09 빈칸 (B)에 알맞은 말을 고르시오.

① Take   ② See   ③ Make
④ Stay   ⑤ Find

10 빈칸 (A)에 알맞지 <u>않은</u> 말을 <u>모두</u> 고르시오.

> A: Do you know who Kim Deuksin is?
> B: Yes. Isn't he a scholar from the Joseon Dynasty?
> A: Right. I saw a TV show and it is (A)_____ that he read one book over 10,000 times.

① said   ② allowed
③ thought   ④ possible
⑤ believed

[01~02] 다음 대화를 읽고 물음에 답하시오.

A: Do you know (A)_____?
B: Yes. Isn't she an artist from the Joseon Dynasty?
A: Right. I saw a TV show and (B)_____ _____. (that, painted, so, paintings, gathered, were, birds, is, the, that, realistic, her, tree, said, around, it)

01 Who is Shin Saimdang?을 빈칸 (A)에 어법에 맞게 써 넣으시오.

➡ _____

02 빈칸 (B)를 괄호 안에 주어진 단어를 알맞게 배열하여 채우시오.

➡ _____
_____

[03~04] 다음 대화를 읽고 물음에 답하시오.

W: Hi, welcome to the National Museum. How can I help you?
M: Hi, is it okay (A)_____ I take pictures in the museum?
W: (B)_____, but please don't use a flash.
M: Oh, I see. Thank you.

03 빈칸 (A)에 알맞은 말을 쓰시오.

➡ _____

04 빈칸 (B)에 알맞은 말을 3개 이상 쓰시오.

➡ _____

[05~07] 다음 대화를 읽고 물음에 답하시오.

W: Hey, Mark, do you know about Father Lee Taeseok?
M: Yeah, I've heard of him. Why?
W: Take a look at this article. He is going to be included in the social studies textbook in South Sudan.
M: Wow. that's great.
W: Yeah, he helped the children (A)_____ building a clinic and a school. It is said that (B)_____ stories will be included in the textbook.
M: It is good to hear that students will learn about (C)_____ a great person.

05 빈칸 (A)에 알맞은 전치사를 쓰시오.

➡ _____

06 빈칸 (B)와 (C)에 공통으로 들어갈 말을 쓰시오.

➡ _____

07 위 대화의 내용에 맞게 빈칸에 알맞은 말을 쓰시오.

Father Lee Taeseok's story that he _____ a clinic and a school to help the children _____ _____ _____ in the social studies textbook in _____ _____.

08 밑줄 친 우리말과 일치하도록 주어진 단어를 이용하여 영작하시오.

A: 내가 너의 모자를 써 보아도 될까?
B: Yes, go ahead.

➡ _____ (okay, try, on)

Grammar

① 접속사 if

> • I was not sure **if** he was telling the truth. 나는 그가 진실을 말하고 있는지 확신할 수 없었다.
>
> • I don't know **if** Sarah will like the idea. 사라가 그 아이디어를 좋아할지 모르겠어요.

■ '~인지 (아닌지)'라는 의미의 접속사로 어떠한 사실의 여부를 확인하거나 불확실함을 나타낼 때 쓰이며, 주로 ask, find out, know, see, tell, wonder, be not sure 등의 동사의 목적어 역할을 하는 명사절을 이끈다. if 뒤에 오는 절은 의문사가 없는 간접의문문으로 'if[whether]+주어+동사'의 어순으로 쓴다.

- I asked him **if** I could borrow his car. 나는 그에게 차를 빌려 달라고 부탁했다.
- I wonder **if** he is at home. 그가 집에 있을지 모르겠다.
- I can't tell **if** it will rain or not. 비가 올지 안 올지 모르겠다.
- I'm not sure. + Can I ask this kind of question?
  → I'm not sure **if** I can ask this kind of question. 이런 질문해도 될까 모르겠네요.

■ if가 명사절을 이끄는 접속사로 그 명사절이 문장 내에서 동사의 목적어로 쓰일 때는 whether로 바꿔 쓸 수 있다. whether가 이끄는 절이 주어 역할을 할 경우에는 if로 바꿔 쓸 수 없으며, whether 다음에는 or not을 바로 붙여 쓸 수 있지만, if는 바로 붙여 쓸 수 없다.

- When they asked me **if** I wanted the job, I said yes. 그들이 나에게 그 직장을 원하느냐고 물었을 때 난 그렇다고 대답했다. [목적어]

  = When they asked me **whether** I wanted the job, I said yes.

- **Whether** it's true or not doesn't matter. 그것이 진실이든 아니든 중요하지 않다. [주어]

  = If it's true or not doesn't matter. (✕)

- It's questionable **whether** or not that will be true. 그게 사실일지 어쩔지는 의심스럽다.

  = It's questionable if or not that will be true. (✕)

cf. if가 조건의 부사절을 이끌 때는 '만약 ~라면'이라는 의미로 쓰이며, whether가 부사절을 이끌 경우에는 '~이든 (아니든)'이라는 '양보'의 의미로 쓰인다.

- **If** anyone calls, tell them I'm not at home. 누구든 전화하면 나 집에 없다고 해. [조건]
- I'm going **whether** you like it or not. 네가 좋아하든 안 하든 난 갈 거야. [양보]

핵심 Check

1. 다음 〈보기〉에서 알맞은 말을 골라 빈칸을 채우시오.

┌─ 보기 ┤

whether, if

(1) I wonder _____ he is at home.

(2) Tell me _____ or not you are willing to believe it.

(3) I don't know _____ you can help me.

❷ 과거완료

- When I was sixteen years old, my family **had** already **made** an arrangement for me to marry him. 내가 열여섯 살 때 나의 가족은 이미 내가 그와 결혼하기로 합의했다.
- I was in a hotel, and I **had** just **finished** shaving. 전 그때 호텔에 있었는데 막 면도를 끝냈어요.

■ 과거완료는 과거 이전에 일어난 일이 과거의 어느 시점까지 영향을 미칠 때 쓰며, 'had+과거분사'의 형태로 쓴다. 과거완료도 현재완료처럼 완료, 경험, 계속, 결과의 용법이 있다. 또한 과거의 어느 시점보다 먼저 일어난 일이나 상태를 나타낼 때도 쓰이며 이것을 보통 '대과거'라고 한다.

- A young businessman **had** just **started** his own firm. (한 젊은 사업가가 막 자신의 회사를 열었다.) 〈완료〉
- He **had** never **learned** to read and write. (그는 읽고 쓰기를 전혀 배우지 못했다.) 〈경험〉
- She **had written** the letter for two hours. (그녀는 2시간 동안 그 편지를 쓰고 있었다.) 〈계속〉
- He **had gone** to America leaving his family in Korea. (그는 가족을 한국에 남겨 두고 미국으로 가버렸다.) 〈결과〉
- She wasn't recognizable after she **had had** plastic surgery. (성형 수술 후 그녀를 알아볼 수 없었다.) 〈대과거〉

■ 한 문장에 두 가지 과거의 일이 나올 때, 두 동작이 거의 동시에 일어났거나 시간차가 거의 없이 연속적으로 일어났을 경우에는 단순과거로 표현한다. 또, 접속사 after나 before가 쓰여 두 동작의 전후 관계가 명백할 때도 단순과거로 표현할 수 있다.

- He **closed** the door and **went** away. (그는 문을 닫고 가버렸다.) 〈시간차가 거의 없는 연속 동작〉
- His father **died** before he **was** born. (그의 아버지는 그가 태어나기 전에 돌아가셨다.) 〈전후 관계가 명백함〉

핵심 Check

2. 괄호 안에서 알맞은 말을 고르시오.

(1) She couldn't believe what she (has just heard / had just heard).

(2) Their friends knew that they (had lost / lost) their son a week before.

(3) His face grew dark after he (has heard / heard) the news.

01 다음 빈칸에 들어갈 말로 알맞은 것은?

> He remembered that he _____ them onto the table.

① toss   ② tosses   ③ tossed
④ has tossed   ⑤ had tossed

02 다음 괄호 안에서 알맞은 말을 고르시오.

(1) When I arrived at the station, the train (already left / had already left).

(2) He confessed to me that he (broke / had broken) the vase.

(3) I don't know (if / that) he will be able to come.

(4) Decide (if / whether) or not the answer is correct.

03 다음 빈칸에 알맞은 것은?

> I asked her _____ she was ready to go, and she nodded.

① that   ② what   ③ which
④ if   ⑤ unless

04 다음 우리말에 맞게 주어진 어휘를 바르게 배열하시오.

(1) 제 딸은 그때까지 아팠던 적이 한 번도 없어요.
  (my daughter, been, then, sick, had, until, never)

  ➡ _____

(2) 잠이 막 들었을 때 누군가가 문을 노크했다. (I로 시작할 것)
  (I, someone, the door, asleep, fallen, knocked, had, when, just, at)

  ➡ _____

(3) 그녀는 자신이 미래에 돌아올지 여부에 대해 확신하지 못한다.
  (she, she, the future, will, is, return, sure, not, if, in)

  ➡ _____

01 다음 중 어법상 <u>어색한</u> 것은?

① I was so excited because I had never played yut before.
② When she arrived at the station, the first train already left.
③ They described a bear that had threatened them.
④ Tom has lived in LA for 12 years.
⑤ This was the first gold medal that Korea had ever won.

02 다음 중 어법상 바르지 <u>않은</u> 것은?

① I am not sure if he had lunch already.
② I asked her if she wanted to join our meeting.
③ If my guess is right, he must be about forty.
④ He asked her nicely that he could see her license.
⑤ Let your friends know that Thursday's the deadline.

03 다음 빈칸에 알맞은 말이 바르게 짝지어진 것은?

> • I wonder _____ my child expresses himself well in English.
> • I came across a pen that I _____ last week.

① if – had lost
② because – had lost
③ if – lost
④ because – lost
⑤ whether – have lost

04 다음 괄호 안에서 알맞은 말을 고르시오.

(1) She was the most remarkable woman he had ever (encounters / encountered).
(2) I walked the dog which Dad (had bought / bought) for me.
(3) Sartre (had practiced / practiced) playing the piano since childhood.
(4) Please tell me (whether / that) he is at home.
(5) Carol wants to know (if / that) the seat is vacant.
(6) We're debating (whether / if) or not to go skiing this winter.

05 주어진 문장의 <u>틀린</u> 부분을 찾아, 올바르게 고친 것을 고르시오.

> When Dave got there, Juliet already entered the theater by herself.

① When Dave got there, Juliet already enters the theater by herself.
② When Dave got there, Juliet has already entered the theater by herself.
③ When Dave got there, Juliet had already entered the theater by herself.
④ When Dave had got there, Juliet already entered the theater by herself.
⑤ When Dave had got there, Juliet already had entered the theater by herself.

06 다음 문장의 밑줄 친 부분 중 어법상 어색한 것은?

> I ⓐhave been, I ⓑthought, a ⓒbalanced reporter ⓓfor ⓔ26 years.

① ⓐ   ② ⓑ   ③ ⓒ

④ ⓓ   ⑤ ⓔ

07 빈칸 (A)와 (B)에 알맞은 것으로 바르게 짝지어진 것은?

> Sara wanted to know ___(B)___ the bag ___(A)___ away or not.

      (A)   (B)

① whether   was thrown

② that   was thrown

③ if   has been thrown

④ that   had been thrown

⑤ if   had been thrown

서답형

08 〈보기〉에서 알맞은 접속사를 골라 다음 빈칸을 채우시오. (한 번씩만 쓸 것.)

> ┌── 보기 ──┐
>
> whether, though, if, when, unless

(1) We will go on a picnic _____ it rains.

(2) She will forgive you _____ you apologize to her.

(3) Cross the road carefully _____ there is no car coming.

(4) Alicia put on a mask _____ working as a spy.

(5) They have never decided _____ or not he was killed.

[09~10] 다음 문장의 빈칸에 알맞은 말을 고르시오.

09

> When I got back home, my parents _____ out for a walk.

① goes   ② went   ③ going

④ has gone   ⑤ had gone

10

> I wonder _____ this soup will keep till tomorrow.

① since   ② unless   ③ if

④ after   ⑤ though

11 다음 우리말을 바르게 영작한 것을 고르시오.

> 그 일을 끝냈는지 물어봐도 될까요?

① May I ask though you finished the work?

② May I ask if you finished the work?

③ May I ask unless you finished the work?

④ May I ask as you finished the work?

⑤ May I ask since you finished the work?

서답형

12 다음 두 문장을 한 문장으로 바꿔 쓰고자 한다. 빈칸에 들어갈 알맞은 말을 쓰시오.

> • Cathy started to play the violin when she was 6.
>
> • Cathy played the violin successfully at the contest yesterday.
>
> = Cathy played the violin successfully at the contest yesterday as she _____ it since she was 6.

13 다음 밑줄 친 과거완료의 용법이 〈보기〉와 같은 것은?

> ┌─ 보기 ─┐
> Kim <u>had been</u> ill for a couple of years.

① He <u>had</u> just <u>arrived</u> from the countryside.
② It was the best chicken soup I <u>had</u> ever <u>had</u>.
③ When you hired him, how long <u>had</u> he <u>practiced</u> law?
④ The people <u>had lost</u> faith in their politicians and faith in their government.
⑤ He realized that it <u>had been</u> a bad decision on his part.

14 다음 문장에서 어법상 어색한 것을 바르게 고쳐 다시 쓰시오.

(1) Please tell me what your sister is in her room.

➡ _____

(2) If he wants or not isn't that important.

➡ _____

(3) I suddenly remembered that I left the windows open.

➡ _____
_____

(4) I had never been to the big city ago.

➡ _____

(5) I found out that someone broke the lamp.

➡ _____

[15~16] 다음 우리말에 맞게 영작한 것을 고르시오.

15

> 그는 내게 고전 음악을 좋아하느냐고 물었다.

① He asked me that I liked classic music.
② He asked me what I liked classic music.
③ He asked me which I liked classic music.
④ He asked me if I liked classic music.
⑤ He asked me if or not I liked classic music.

16

> 나는 네게 얘기했던 카메라를 샀다.

① I bought the camera that I told you about.
② I bought the camera that I told you.
③ I bought the camera that I have told you about.
④ I bought the camera that I had told you.
⑤ I bought the camera that I had told you about.

17 다음 중 어법상 어색한 것을 고르시오. (2개)

① He asked me if or not the book was boring.
② I remembered that I turned the stove on.
③ He had never been to any foreign countries.
④ When I arrived at the theater, the movie had already begun.
⑤ John wants to ask if you are going to go on a world tour this year.

Grammar 서술형 시험대비

01 시간 흐름에 따른 사건 전개에 맞게 빈칸을 채워 문장을 완성하시오.

> (1) My boy friend bought a ring for me the day before. → Yesterday I lost the ring.
> (2) Clare received flowers last Saturday. → Today her little brother threw them away.

(1) Yesterday I lost the ring that my boy friend _____ the day before.

(2) Today Clare's little brother threw away the flowers that _____ last Saturday.

02 다음을 when을 이용하여 한 문장으로 연결할 때 빈칸을 알맞게 채우시오. (시제에 유의할 것.)

(1) I went to the restaurant to have lunch with my friends. I arrived there. I remembered that I did not lock the door.
→ When I arrived at the restaurant to have lunch with my friends, I remembered that I _____ the door.

(2) I was supposed to meet Harry at the library. I went there very late. He already went back to his home. So, I couldn't meet him.
→ When I got to the library to meet Harry, _____ back to his home.

03 다음 우리말에 맞게 주어진 단어를 바르게 배열하시오.

(1) 이 음식들이 입맛에 맞으실지 모르겠군요. (I, your taste, these dishes, suit, wonder, will, if)

➡ _____

(2) 그가 집에 있는지 사무실에 있는지 모른다. (I, he, at the office, at home, is, don't, know, whether, or)

➡ _____

(3) 우리는 우리가 같은 학교에 다녔다는 걸 알게 되었다. (we, we, school, found, been, had, the, that, same, out, at)

➡ _____
_____

(4) 내가 파리에 한 번도 못 가 보았다는 것에 그녀가 몹시 놀라는 눈치였다. (I, she, Paris, had, astonished, seemed, been, that, never, to)

➡ _____
_____

04 다음 문장에서 잘못된 것을 알맞게 고치시오.

(1) If you said so or not doesn't matter now.

➡ _____

(2) This approach may be useful in assessing if or not the programme was of value.

➡ _____

(3) I couldn't decide if to have pizza or a hamburger.

➡ _____

05 그림을 보고, 주어진 어휘를 이용하여 빈칸을 알맞게 채우시오.

(1) The elderly man was afraid of skiing because he ＿＿＿＿＿＿ skiing before. (never, learn)

(2) He wonders ＿＿＿＿＿＿ about the appointment. (she, forgot)

06 알맞은 접속사를 이용하여 주어진 두 문장을 하나의 문장으로 쓰시오.

(1) • The man isn't sure.
   • He can help her.
   ➡ ＿＿＿＿＿＿＿＿＿

(2) • They don't know.
   • Will he be promoted?
   ➡ ＿＿＿＿＿＿＿＿＿

(3) • Would you tell me?
   • He needs surgery or not.
   ➡ ＿＿＿＿＿＿＿＿＿

07 다음 두 문장을 because를 사용하여 한 문장으로 연결하시오. (두 사건의 시간차가 드러나도록 할 것.)

(1) • He won the contest.
   • He practiced a lot for the contest.
   ➡ ＿＿＿＿＿＿＿＿＿

(2) • I couldn't take the class.
   • The class was canceled.
   ➡ ＿＿＿＿＿＿＿＿＿

08 다음 문장에서 어법상 어색한 것을 바르게 고쳐 다시 쓰시오.

(1) He told me that he stole the money the other day.
   ➡ ＿＿＿＿＿＿＿＿＿

(2) No computer won even one game against a human player until then.
   ➡ ＿＿＿＿＿＿＿＿＿

(3) I found my bag that I lost on the bus.
   ➡ ＿＿＿＿＿＿＿＿＿

(4) I asked the lady that I could use the bathroom.
   ➡ ＿＿＿＿＿＿＿＿＿

(5) I'm not sure if Santa gives me a nice gift or not.
   ➡ ＿＿＿＿＿＿＿＿＿

(6) I couldn't decide if to buy it.
   ➡ ＿＿＿＿＿＿＿＿＿

Reading

The Secret of My Father

In 1946, a strange man visited me and asked, "Are you Mr. Kim Yonghwan's daughter?"

For me, this was an odd question because I was more used to being
= Are you Mr. Kim Yonghwan's daughter?   be used to ~ing: ~하는 데 익숙하다
called the daughter of a *parakho*.

"I'm your father's friend. You may wonder if it is true, but your
                                                    = whether
father...," the man said.

At that moment, I was expecting disappointing news since I did not
                                    disappointed(×)   이유를 나타내는 접속사
have good memories of my father.

Back in the 1920's, whenever people saw me in the village, they
      과거 1920년대에
would say, "There goes the *parakho*'s daughter."
과거의 불규칙적 습관을 나타내는 조동사(~하곤 했다)
My father was a son from a very rich family. Instead of living the life
                                                ~하는 대신에   동명사
of a *seonbi*, he was always at the gambling house. That is why he was
                                                                because(×)
called a *parakho*, which means someone who ruins his family's fortune.
              계속적 용법의 관계대명사(= and it)   = that
"Your father has gambled away all of the money, and now he's asking
          gamble away: 도박으로 ~을 다 날리다[잃다]   요청하다
for more. Go and tell him that we have no more money left," my
                                      더 이상 돈이 남아 있지 않다
mother would tell me whenever she sent me to the gambling house.
      과거의 불규칙적 습관을 나타내는 조동사(~하곤 했다)
Then, my father would yell at me angrily, "Why did you come empty-
                                              주격 보어로 쓰인 유사분사(명사+ed)
handed? Bring me more money!"

strange 이상한, 낯선
odd 이상한
moment 순간
disappointing 실망스러운
back 돌아가서, 과거로 거슬러
whenever ~할 때마다
instead of ~하는 대신에
gambling 도박
ruin 망치다, 파산시키다
fortune 재산
yell 소리치다
angrily 화가 나서
empty-handed 빈손으로

 확인문제

● 다음 문장이 본문의 내용과 일치하면 T, 일치하지 <u>않으면</u> F를 쓰시오.

1   The writer was more used to being called the daughter of a *parakho* than Mr. Kim Yonghwan's daughter. ☐

2   The writer was expecting terrific news though she did not have good memories of her father. ☐

3   The writer's father lived the life of a *seonbi*. ☐

When I was sixteen years old, my family had already made an
arrangement for me to marry Mr. Seo. As part of the wedding
tradition, Mr. Seo's family sent my family some money to buy a new
chest for clothes.

Right before the wedding day, my mother came into my room and
said, "Your father has taken the money for the chest."

I asked angrily, "How could he do such a horrible thing? What
should we do now?"

"We have no choice. You'll have to take your aunt's old chest," my
mother said.

"How embarrassing for the family," people would whisper behind
my back.

Since the first day of marriage, life at my husband's house had been
difficult for me.

"Your father, my dear friend...," my father's friend continued his
story. "He was not a gambler. Your father sent the family money to
the independence fighters in Manchuria. He made himself look like a
gambler to keep this a secret from the Japanese officers."
At first, I was not sure if he was telling the truth. But afterwards,
I found out the truth about my father and I realized that I had been
wrong about him. Ever since that moment, I have been proud to be the
daughter of a *parakho* who had devoted his life to the independence
movement.

arrangement 협의, 합의
wedding 결혼, 결혼식
tradition 전통
chest 상자, 장롱
horrible 지긋지긋한, 끔찍한
choice 선택
embarrassing 난처한, 당혹스러운
behind one's back ~ 몰래, ~의 등 뒤에서
whisper 속삭이다
continue 계속하다
officer 경찰관
at first 처음에
truth 사실
afterwards 나중에, 그 후에
realize 깨닫다, 알아차리다

 확인문제

● 다음 문장이 본문의 내용과 일치하면 T, 일치하지 <u>않으면</u> F를 쓰시오.

1 Mr. Seo's family sent the writer's family some money to buy a new chest for
   clothes. ☐

2 The writer's father sent the family money to the independence fighters in
   Manchuria. ☐

3 The writer's father devoted his life to gambling. ☐

● 우리말을 참고하여 빈칸에 알맞은 말을 쓰시오.

1 The _____ of My Father

2 In 1946, _____ _____ _____ visited me and asked, "Are you Mr. Kim Yonghwan's daughter?"

3 For me, this was _____ _____ _____ because I _____ _____ _____ _____ _____ the daughter of a *parakho*.

4 "I'm _____ _____ _____.

5 You may _____ _____ it is true, but your father...," the man said.

6 At that moment, I was expecting _____ news since I did not have _____ _____ of my father.

7 _____ in the 1920's, _____ people saw me in the village, they would say, "_____ _____ the *parakho*'s daughter."

8 My father was a son _____ a very rich family.

9 _____ _____ the life of a *seonbi*, he was always at the gambling house.

10 _____ _____ _____ he was called a *parakho*, _____ means someone who _____ his family's fortune.

11 "Your father _____ _____ _____ all of the money, and now he's asking for more.

12 Go and tell him that we _____ _____ _____ _____ _____," my mother _____ tell me _____ she sent me to the gambling house.

13 Then, my father _____ _____ _____ me angrily, "Why did you come _____?

14 _____ me more money!"

1	아버지의 비밀
2	1946년에, 낯선 남자가 나를 찾아와 물었다. "당신이 김용환 씨의 딸입니까?"
3	나는 파락호의 딸이라고 불리는 것이 더 익숙했으므로 나에게 이것은 이상한 질문이었다.
4	"나는 당신 아버지의 친구입니다.
5	당신은 이것이 사실인지 의아하겠지만, 당신의 아버지는…,"이라고 그 남자는 말했다.
6	나는 내 아버지에 대해 좋은 기억을 가지고 있지 않았으므로 그 순간에 실망스러운 소식을 예상하고 있었다.
7	1920년대에 마을에서 사람들이 나를 볼 때마다 그들은 "저기에 파락호의 딸이 가네."라고 말하곤 했다.
8	나의 아버지는 매우 부유한 집안의 아들이었다.
9	선비의 삶을 사는 대신, 아버지는 항상 도박장에 계셨다.
10	그것이 그가 집안의 재산을 탕진하는 사람이라는 뜻의 파락호로 불린 이유이다.
11	"네 아버지는 도박으로 모든 돈을 써 버리고 지금 더 요구하고 계신다.
12	가서 더 이상 남아 있는 돈이 없다고 말씀드려라."라고 나의 어머니는 나를 도박장으로 보낼 때마다 말씀하시곤 했다.
13	그러면, 아버지는 나에게 화를 내시며 소리치셨다. "왜 빈손으로 왔니?
14	돈을 더 가져와!"

15 When I was sixteen years old, my family _____ _____ _____ _____ _____ for me to marry Mr. Seo.

16 _____ _____ _____ the wedding tradition, Mr. Seo's family sent my family some money to buy _____ _____ _____ _____ _____ .

17 _____ _____ the wedding day, my mother came into my room and said, "Your father _____ _____ _____ _____ for the chest."

18 I asked angrily, "How could he do _____ _____ _____ _____ ?

19 _____ should we do now?"

20 "We have _____ _____ .

21 _____ _____ _____ _____ your aunt's old chest," my mother said.

22 " _____ _____ for the family," people would whisper _____ _____ _____ .

23 Since the first day of marriage, life at my husband's house _____ _____ _____ _____ _____ .

24 "Your father, my dear friend...," my father's friend _____ _____ _____ .

25 "He was not _____ _____ .

26 Your father sent the family money to the _____ _____ in Manchuria.

27 He _____ _____ look like a gambler to _____ _____ _____ _____ _____ the Japanese officers."

28 At first, I was not sure _____ he was telling the truth.

29 But _____ , I found out the truth about my father and I realized that I _____ _____ _____ about him.

30 Ever since that moment, I have been proud to be the daughter of a *parakho* who _____ _____ _____ _____ the independence movement.

15 내가 16살이 되었을 때, 나의 가족은 나를 서 씨와 결혼시키기로 이미 결정을 했었다.

16 결혼 풍습의 일부로, 서 씨네 가족은 새 장롱을 사라고 우리 가족에게 돈을 보냈다.

17 결혼식 바로 전날, 나의 어머니는 내 방에 들어오셔서 말씀하셨다. "네 아버지가 장롱을 살 돈을 가져가 버렸다."

18 나는 화가 나서 물었다 "어떻게 그리 끔찍한 일을 하실 수 있나요?

19 우린 이제 어떡해요?"

20 "우리에게 선택권은 없구나.

21 큰어머니의 옛 장롱을 가져가야겠구나."라고 어머니가 말씀하셨다.

22 "가문에 부끄러운 일이야."라고 사람들이 내 뒤에서 속삭이곤 했다.

23 결혼 첫날부터, 남편의 집에서의 생활은 나에게 힘겨웠다.

24 "당신의 아버지, 나의 친애하는 친구…," 나의 아버지의 친구분은 그의 이야기를 이어가셨다.

25 "그는 도박꾼이 아니었어요.

26 당신의 아버지는 가족의 돈을 만주에 있는 독립운동가들에게 보냈답니다.

27 그는 이것을 일본 순사들에게 비밀로 하기 위해 그 자신을 도박꾼처럼 보이게 했어요."

28 처음엔, 나는 그분이 사실을 얘기하시는 건지 확신할 수 없었다.

29 그러나 나중에, 나는 나의 아버지에 대한 진실을 알게 되었고 내가 아버지에 관해 오해하고 있었다는 것을 깨달았다.

30 그 순간부터, 나는 독립운동에 그의 인생을 헌신하신 파락호의 딸인 것이 자랑스러웠다.

● 우리말을 참고하여 본문을 영작하시오.

1 ▶ 아버지의 비밀

➡ _____

2 ▶ 1946년에, 낯선 남자가 나를 찾아와 물었다. "당신이 김용환 씨의 딸입니까?"

➡ _____

3 ▶ 나는 파락호의 딸이라고 불리는 것이 더 익숙했으므로 나에게 이것은 이상한 질문이었다. .

➡ _____

4 ▶ "나는 당신 아버지의 친구입니다.

➡ _____

5 ▶ 당신은 이것이 사실인지 의아하겠지만, 당신의 아버지는…,"이라고 그 남자는 말했다.

➡ _____

6 ▶ 나는 내 아버지에 대해 좋은 기억을 가지고 있지 않았으므로 그 순간에 실망스러운 소식을 예상하고 있었다.

➡ _____

7 ▶ 1920년대에 마을에서 사람들이 나를 볼 때마다 그들은 "저기에 파락호의 딸이 가네."라고 말하곤 했다.

➡ _____

_____

8 ▶ 나의 아버지는 매우 부유한 집안의 아들이었다.

➡ _____

9 ▶ 선비의 삶을 사는 대신, 아버지는 항상 도박장에 계셨다.

➡ _____

10 ▶ 그것이 그가 집안의 재산을 탕진하는 사람이라는 뜻의 파락호로 불린 이유이다.

➡ _____

11 ▶ "네 아버지는 도박으로 모든 돈을 써 버리고 지금 더 요구하고 계신다.

➡ _____

12 ▶ 가서 더 이상 남아 있는 돈이 없다고 말씀드려라."라고 나의 어머니는 나를 도박장으로 보낼 때마다 말씀하시곤 했다.

➡ _____

_____

13 ▶ 그러면, 아버지는 나에게 화를 내시며 소리치셨다. "왜 빈손으로 왔니?

➡ _____

14 ▶ 돈을 더 가져와!"

➡ _____

15 내가 16살이 되었을 때, 나의 가족은 나를 서 씨와 결혼시키기로 이미 결정을 했었다.

➡ _____

16 결혼 풍습의 일부로, 서 씨네 가족은 새 장롱을 사라고 우리 가족에게 돈을 보냈다.

➡ _____
_____

17 결혼식 바로 전날, 나의 어머니는 내 방에 들어오셔서 말씀하셨다. "네 아버지가 장롱을 살 돈을 가져가 버렸다."

➡ _____
_____

18 나는 화가 나서 물었다 "어떻게 그리 끔찍한 일을 하실 수 있나요?

➡ _____

19 우린 이제 어떡해요?"

➡ _____

20 "우리에게 선택권은 없구나.

➡ _____

21 큰어머니의 옛 장롱을 가져가야겠구나."라고 어머니가 말씀하셨다.

➡ _____

22 "가문에 부끄러운 일이야."라고 사람들이 내 뒤에서 속삭이곤 했다.

➡ _____

23 결혼 첫날부터, 남편의 집에서의 생활은 나에게 힘겨웠다.

➡ _____

24 "당신의 아버지, 나의 친애하는 친구…," 나의 아버지의 친구분은 그의 이야기를 이어가셨다.

➡ _____

25 "그는 도박꾼이 아니었어요.

➡ _____

26 당신의 아버지는 가족의 돈을 만주에 있는 독립운동가들에게 보냈답니다.

➡ _____

27 그는 이것을 일본 순사들에게 비밀로 하기 위해 그 자신을 도박꾼처럼 보이게 했어요."

➡ _____

28 처음엔, 나는 그분이 사실을 얘기하시는 건지 확신할 수 없었다.

➡ _____

29 그러나 나중에, 나는 나의 아버지에 대한 진실을 알게 되었고 내가 아버지에 관해 오해하고 있었다는 것을 깨달았다.

➡ _____
_____

30 그 순간부터, 나는 독립운동에 그의 인생을 헌신하신 파락호의 딸인 것이 자랑스러웠다.

➡ _____
_____

[01~03] 다음 글을 읽고 물음에 답하시오.

In 1946, a strange man visited me and asked, "Are you Mr. Kim Yonghwan's daughter?"

For me, ⓐthis was a(n) (A)[familiar / odd] question because I was more used to (B)[be / being] called the daughter of a *parakho*.

"I'm your father's friend. You may wonder (C)[if / that] it is true, but your father...," the man said.

At that moment, I was expecting disappointing news ⓑsince I did not have good memories of my father.

서답형
01 위 글의 밑줄 친 ⓐthis가 가리키는 것을 본문에서 찾아 쓰시오.

➡ _____

서답형
02 위 글의 괄호 (A)~(C)에서 문맥이나 어법상 알맞은 낱말을 골라 쓰시오.

➡ (A)_____ (B)_____ (C)_____

03 위 글의 밑줄 친 ⓑsince와 같은 의미로 쓰인 것을 모두 고르시오.

① She's been off work since Tuesday.
② Since you're already here, you might as well stay.
③ We've lived here since 1994.
④ Since then, I had wondered where he lived.
⑤ Since we're not very busy just now, I can get away from the office.

[04~05] 다음 글을 읽고 물음에 답하시오.

"Your father, my dear friend...," my father's friend continued his story. "He was not a gambler. Your father sent the family money to the independence fighters in Manchuria. He made himself look like a gambler to keep this a secret from the Japanese officers."

At first, I was not sure ⓐif he was telling the truth. But afterwards, I found out the truth about my father and I realized that I had been wrong about him. Ever since that moment, I have been proud to be the daughter of a *parakho* who had devoted his life to the independence movement.

04 위 글의 밑줄 친 ⓐif와 문법적 쓰임이 같은 것을 모두 고르시오.

① If necessary, I can come at once.
② If you run all the way, you'll get there in time.
③ I don't care if you agree with me.
④ He asked me if I knew Spanish.
⑤ I will tell him if he comes.

05 위 글을 읽고 알 수 없는 것을 고르시오.

① Was the writer's father a gambler?
② To whom did the writer's father send the family money?
③ Why did the writer's father make himself look like a gambler?
④ How much money did the writer's father send to the independence fighters?
⑤ How did the writer find out the truth about her father?

[06~08] 다음 글을 읽고 물음에 답하시오.

Back in the 1920's, whenever people saw me in the village, they would say, "There goes the *parakho*'s daughter." (①)

My father was a son from a very rich family. (②) That is why he was called a *parakho*, which means someone who ruins his family's fortune. (③)

"Your father has gambled away all of the money, and now he's asking ⓐ more. (④) Go and tell him that we have no more money left," my mother would tell me whenever she sent me to the gambling house. (⑤)

Then, my father would yell ⓑ me angrily, "Why did you come empty-handed? Bring me more money!"

06 위 글의 빈칸 ⓐ와 ⓑ에 들어갈 전치사가 바르게 짝지어진 것은?

	ⓐ	ⓑ		ⓐ	ⓑ
①	for	at	②	in	to
③	in	for	④	on	at
⑤	for	for			

07 위 글의 흐름으로 보아, 주어진 문장이 들어가기에 가장 적절한 곳은?

Instead of living the life of a *seonbi*, he was always at the gambling house.

①　　②　　③　　④　　⑤

08 According to the passage, which is NOT true?

① The writer's father was a son from a very rich family.

② The writer's father lived the life of a *seonbi*.

③ A *parakho* means someone who ruins his family's fortune.

④ The writer's father gambled away all of the money.

⑤ The writer's family had no more money left.

09 주어진 글 다음에 이어질 글의 순서로 가장 적절한 것은?

"Your father, my dear friend...," my father's friend continued his story.

(A) "He was not a gambler. Your father sent the family money to the independence fighters in Manchuria. He made himself look like a gambler to keep this a secret from the Japanese officers."

(B) Ever since that moment, I have been proud to be the daughter of a *parakho* who had devoted his life to the independence movement.

(C) At first, I was not sure if he was telling the truth. But afterwards, I found out the truth about my father and I realized that I had been wrong about him.

① (A)–(C)–(B)　　② (B)–(A)–(C)

③ (B)–(C)–(A)　　④ (C)–(A)–(B)

⑤ (C)–(B)–(A)

[10~12] 다음 글을 읽고 물음에 답하시오.

When I was sixteen years old, my family had (A)[already / yet] made an arrangement for me to marry Mr. Seo. ⓐAs part of the wedding tradition, Mr. Seo's family sent my family some money to buy a new chest for clothes.

Right before the wedding day, my mother came into my room and said, "Your father has taken the money for the chest."

I asked angrily, "How could he do such a horrible thing? (B)[How / What] should we do now?"

"We have no choice. You'll have to take your aunt's old chest," my mother said.

(C)[For / Since] the first day of marriage, life at my husband's house had been difficult for me.

10 위 글의 괄호 (A)~(C)에서 어법상 알맞은 낱말을 골라 쓰시오.

➡ (A)_____ (B)_____ (C)_____

11 위 글의 밑줄 친 ⓐAs와 같은 의미로 쓰인 것을 고르시오.

① She came up as I was speaking.
② Her anger grew as she talked.
③ This is twice as large as that.
④ Leave it as it is.
⑤ This box will be used as a table.

12 Which question CANNOT be answered after reading the passage?

① Whom did the writer's family make an arrangement for the writer to marry?
② Why did Mr. Seo's family send the writer's family some money?
③ Could the writer buy a new chest for clothes?
④ Where did the writer's father spend the money for the chest?
⑤ Was the writer's life at Mr. Seo's house easy for her?

[13~15] 다음 글을 읽고 물음에 답하시오.

Back in the 1920's, whenever people saw me in the village, they would say, "There goes ①the *parakho*'s daughter."

My father was a son from a very rich family. __ⓐ__ living the life of a *seonbi*, ②he was always at the gambling house. That is why he was called a *parakho*, which means someone who ruins ③his family's fortune.

"Your father has gambled away all of the money, and now he's asking for more. Go and tell ④him that we have no more money left," my mother ⓑwould tell me whenever she sent me to the gambling house.

Then, my father would yell at me angrily, "Why did you come empty-handed? Bring ⑤me more money!"

13 위 글의 빈칸 ⓐ에 들어갈 알맞은 말을 고르시오.

① In spite of   ② Because of
③ As well as   ④ Instead of
⑤ In addition to

14 밑줄 친 ①~⑤ 중에서 가리키는 대상이 나머지 넷과 다른 것은?

①   ②   ③   ④   ⑤

15 위 글의 밑줄 친 ⓑwould와 문법적 쓰임이 같은 것을 고르시오.

① He said he would be here at eight o'clock.
② Would you open the door for me, please?
③ I would rather come with you.
④ When my parents were away, my grandmother would take care of me.
⑤ Would you like a sandwich?

[16~17] 다음 글을 읽고 물음에 답하시오.

"Your father, my dear friend...," my father's friend continued his story. "He was not a gambler. Your father sent the family money to the independence fighters in Manchuria. He made himself look like a gambler to keep this a secret from the Japanese officers."

At first, ⓐ그분이 사실을 얘기하시는 건지 확신할 수 없었다. But afterwards, I found out the truth about my father and I realized that I had been wrong about him. Ever since that moment, I have been proud to be the daughter of a *parakho* who had devoted his life to the independence movement.

서답형

16 위 글의 밑줄 친 ⓐ의 우리말에 맞게 한 단어를 보충하여, 주어진 어휘를 알맞게 배열하시오.

> the truth / not / telling / was / sure / I / was / he

➡ _____

중요

17 위 글의 제목으로 알맞은 것을 고르시오.

① The Miserable Life of a *Parakho*
② Not a *Parakho* But a Secret Independence Fighter
③ The Secret Independence Fighters in Manchuria
④ History of Independence Movement
⑤ The Life as a Daughter of a *Parakho*

[18~21] 다음 글을 읽고 물음에 답하시오.

Back in the 1920's, whenever people saw me in the village, they (A)[should / would] say, "There goes the *parakho*'s daughter."

My father was a son from a very rich family. Instead of living the life of a *seonbi*, he was always at the gambling house. That is __ⓐ__ he was called a *parakho*, ⓑwhich means someone who (B)[increases / ruins] his family's fortune.

"Your father has gambled away all of the money, and now he's asking for more. Go and tell him that ⓒ우리는 더 이상 남아 있는 돈이 없다," my mother would tell me whenever she sent me to the gambling house.

Then, my father would yell at me angrily, "Why did you come (C)[empty-hand / empty-handed]? Bring me more money!"

18 위 글의 빈칸 ⓐ에 들어갈 알맞은 말을 모두 고르시오.

① how
② the reason
③ why
④ when
⑤ where

서답형

19 위 글의 괄호 (A)~(C)에서 문맥이나 어법상 알맞은 낱말을 골라 쓰시오.

➡ (A) _____ (B) _____ (C) _____

서답형

20 위 글의 밑줄 친 ⓑ를 접속사를 사용하여 두 단어로 바꿔 쓰시오.

➡ _____

서답형

21 위 글의 밑줄 친 ⓒ의 우리말에 맞게 주어진 어휘를 이용하여 6 단어로 영작하시오.

> more, left

➡ _____

[01~03] 다음 글을 읽고 물음에 답하시오.

Back in the 1920's, (A)whenever people saw me in the village, they would say, "There goes the *parakho*'s daughter."

My father was a son from a very rich family. Instead of living the life of a *seonbi*, he was always at the gambling house. (B)That is why he was called a *parakho*, which means someone who ruins his family's fortune.

"Your father has gambled away all of the money, and now he's asking for more. Go and tell him that we have no more money ⓐ_____," my mother would tell me whenever she sent me to the gambling house.

Then, my father would yell at me angrily, "Why did you come empty-handed? Bring me more money!"

01 위 글의 빈칸 ⓐ에 leave를 알맞은 형태로 쓰시오.

➡ _____

02 위 글의 밑줄 친 (A)whenever와 바꿔 쓸 수 있는 말을 쓰시오.

➡ _____

03 위 글의 밑줄 친 (B)That이 가리키는 것을 본문에서 찾아 쓰시오.

➡ _____
_____

[04~07] 다음 글을 읽고 물음에 답하시오.

"Your father, my dear friend...," my father's friend continued his story. "He was not a gambler. (A)Your father sent the family money to the independence fighters in Manchuria. He

made himself look like a gambler to keep this a secret from the Japanese officers."

(B)At first, I was not sure if he was telling the truth. But afterwards, I found out the truth about my father and I realized that I had been wrong about him. Ever since that moment, I have been proud to be the daughter of a *parakho* who ⓐ___ his life to the independence movement.

04 위 글의 빈칸 ⓐ에 devote를 알맞은 형태로 쓰시오.

➡ _____

05 위 글의 밑줄 친 (A)를 4형식 문장으로 고치시오.

➡ _____
_____

06 위 글의 밑줄 친 (B)를 다음과 같이 바꿔 쓸 때 빈칸에 들어갈 알맞은 단어를 쓰시오.

➡ At first, I was not sure _____ he was telling the truth.

07 다음 빈칸 (A)와 (B)에 알맞은 단어를 넣어 필자가 아버지에 대해 오해한 내용을 완성하시오.

The writer mistook her father for a *parakho* but in fact he sent the family money to the (A)_____ _____ in Manchuria and made himself look like a gambler to keep this (B)_____ _____ from the Japanese officers.

[08~10] 다음 글을 읽고 물음에 답하시오.

When I was sixteen years old, my family had already made an arrangement for me to marry Mr. Seo. As ⓐpart of the wedding tradition, Mr. Seo's family sent my family some money to buy a new chest for (A)[cloths / clothes].

Right before the wedding day, my mother came into my room and said, "Your father has taken the money for the chest."

I asked angrily, "How could he do such a (B)[horrible / terrific] thing? What should we do now?"

"We have no choice. You'll have to take your aunt's old chest," my mother said.

"How (C)[embarrassing / embarrassed] for the family," people would whisper behind my back.

Since the first day of marriage, life at my husband's house had been difficult for me.

08 다음 빈칸에 알맞은 말을 넣어 위 글의 밑줄 친 ⓐ에 대한 설명을 완성하시오.

> The family of the bridegroom sent (A)_____ _____ to buy a (B)_____ _____ for clothes to the family of the bride.

09 위 글의 괄호 (A)~(C)에서 문맥이나 어법상 알맞은 낱말을 골라 쓰시오.

➡ (A) _____ (B) _____ (C) _____

10 주어진 영영풀이에 해당하는 단어를 본문에서 찾아 쓰시오.

> a large, heavy box used for storing things

➡ _____

[11~13] 다음 글을 읽고 물음에 답하시오.

Back in the 1920's, whenever people saw me in the village, they would say, "ⓐ저기에 파락호의 딸이 간다."

My father was a son from a very rich family. Instead of living the life of a *seonbi*, he was always at the gambling house. ⓑThat is why he was called a *parakho*, that means someone who ruins his family's fortune.

"Your father has gambled away all of the money, and now he's asking for more. Go and tell him that we have no more money left," my mother would tell me whenever she sent me to the gambling house.

Then, my father would yell at me angrily, "Why did you come empty-handed? Bring me more money!"

11 위 글의 밑줄 친 ⓐ의 우리말에 맞게 주어진 어휘를 알맞게 배열하시오.

> there / the *parakho*'s daughter / goes

➡ _____

12 위 글의 밑줄 친 ⓑ에서 어법상 틀린 부분을 찾아 고치시오.

➡ _____

13 다음 빈칸 (A)와 (B)에 알맞은 단어를 넣어 글쓴이의 아버지에 대한 소개를 완성하시오.

> The writer's father was called a (A)_____ because he (B)_____ away his family's fortune.

교과서

구석구석

Grammar in Real Life A

Mary Jane, your fans have many questions about your plans.

1. Are you going to release a new song this month?

2. Are you interested in various music genres?
              = a variety of

3. Do you have any plans to work with other artists?
              부정사의 형용사적 용법

4. Are you going to go on a world tour this year?

구문해설 • release: 발표[발매]하다 • genre: 유형(類型), 양식, 장르

Mary Jane. 너의 팬들은 너의 계획에 대해 많은 질문들을 가지고 있어.

1. 넌 이 달에 새 노래를 발표할 거니?

2. 넌 다양한 음악 장르에 관심이 있니?

3. 넌 다른 아티스트들과 일할 계획을 가지고 있니?

4. 넌 금년에 월드 투어를 떠날 거니?

Grammar in Real Life B

When I got back home, my parents had gone out for a walk. The house was
때를 나타내는 접속사   대과거

dark and quiet, but it seemed a little bit strange. I remembered that I had left
            strangely(×)   대과거

the door in my room open. I saw that someone had broken the lamp. I found
            대과거

out that someone had eaten my cookies on the table. At last I knew who did it!
      대과거   간접의문문

I found small footprints of my dog, Lucy, and the cat next door.
           (footprints of) the cat

구문해설 • a little bit: 조금 (a bit에 little이 붙은 말; 뜻은 a bit과 같음) • at last: 마침내
• next door: 옆집에

내가 집에 돌아왔을 때 나의 부모님은 산보를 나가셨다. 집은 어둡고 조용했지만, 조금 이상해 보였다. 나는 내 방문을 열어둔 것이 기억났다. 나는 누군가가 램프를 깨뜨린 것을 알았다. 나는 누군가가 식탁 위에 있던 내 쿠키를 먹은 것을 알아냈다. 마침내 나는 누가 그런 일을 했는지 알았다! 나는 내 개 Lucy와 옆집 고양이의 작은 발자국들을 발견했다.

After You Read: Read and Write A

The Secret of My Father
I thought my father was ...
My father was known as a *parakho*. He was born into a rich family but he
         be known as: ～로 알려지다

gambled away all of the money. He even took the money for a new chest for
   노름으로 모든 돈을 탕진했다

clothes.
cloth의 복수: 의복

Actually my father was ...
My father was not a gambler. He sent the family money to the independence
            send는 to를 사용하여 3형식으로 고친다.

fighters in Manchuria. He made himself look like a gambler to keep this a
         him(×)   to부정사의 부사적 용법(목적)

secret from the Japanese officers.

구문해설 • secret: 비밀 • gamble away: 도박으로 ～을 다 날리다 • chest: 궤 • gambler: 노름꾼
• independence fighter: 독립 운동가 • keep+O+O.C.+from A: A로부터 ～을 …로 지키다

나의 아버지의 비밀
나는 아버지가 …라고 생각했다.
나의 아버지는 '파락호'라고 알려져 있었다. 그는 부잣집에 태어났지만, 모든 돈을 노름으로 날렸다. 그는 심지어 새 장롱을 살 돈도 가져갔다.

사실 나의 아버지는 …이었다.
나의 아버지는 노름꾼이 아니었다. 그는 가족의 돈을 만주에 있는 독립 운동가들에게 보냈다. 그는 일본 경찰들로부터 이것을 비밀로 지키려고 스스로를 노름꾼처럼 보이게 했다.

영역별 핵심문제

01 다음 밑줄 친 부분의 의미로 알맞지 <u>않은</u> 것을 <u>모두</u> 고르시오.

① The <u>odd</u> thing was that he didn't recognize me. (이상한)
② The country has made great advances since <u>independence</u>. (독립)
③ He followed the impressionist <u>movement</u>. (이동)
④ Did you <u>leave</u> the kids with Grandma on Saturday? (떠나다)
⑤ Don't <u>whisper</u> with your neighbors. (속삭이다)

02 다음 짝지어진 두 단어의 관계가 같도록 빈칸에 알맞은 말을 쓰시오.

solve : solution = marry : _____

[03~04] 다음 빈칸에 공통으로 들어갈 말을 쓰시오.

03

• Have you ever heard _____ a band called Big Star?
• Could I have tuna instead _____ ham?

04

• Most humans are not very good at _____ secrets.
• Paul was _____ awake by drinking lots of strong black coffee.

[05~07] 다음 대화를 읽고 물음에 답하시오.

A: This (A)[called / is called] the *Geojunggi*.
B: Wow, this looks interesting.
A: This is a machine that moves heavy objects. It is said that it helped to build the Hwaseong Fortress only in 28 months.
B: How amazing! Is it okay (B)[that / if / what] I take a closer look at it?
A: Sure.

05 위 대화의 괄호 (A)와 (B)에서 적절한 것을 골라 쓰시오.

➡ (A) _____, (B) _____

06 위 대화에서 다음 영영풀이에 해당하는 단어를 찾아 쓰시오.

a large strong building used for defending an important place

➡ _____

07 위 대화의 내용과 일치하는 것은 <u>모두</u> 몇 개인지 고르시오.

ⓐ *Geojunggi* was used for building the Hwaseong Fortress.
ⓑ *B* wants to watch Hwaseong Fortress closely.
ⓒ Hwaseong Fortress was built in 28 months.
ⓓ *Geojunggi* is a kind of machine.
ⓔ *A* knows about what *Geojunggi* is.

① 1개   ② 2개   ③ 3개   ④ 4개   ⑤ 5개

[08~09] 다음 대화를 읽고 물음에 답하시오.

M: Hello, Ms. Jackson. (①)

W: It was wonderful. (②) The houses were really beautiful.

M: That's great.

W: Actually, I didn't get the chance ⓐ_____ have dinner. (③) Is it okay ⓑ_____ I cook in the kitchen at this hour?

M: Yes, but please remember ⓒ_____ the kitchen closes ⓓ_____ 10 p.m. (④)

W: Okay. The kitchen is on the 5th floor, right? (⑤)

M: Yes, it is. Let me know ⓔ_____ you need anything.

08 ①~⑤ 중 주어진 문장이 들어갈 곳은?

> How was your tour of the *Hanok Village*?

①   ②   ③   ④   ⑤

09 빈칸 ⓐ~ⓔ에 들어가지 <u>않는</u> 말을 고르시오.

① for   ② at   ③ if   ④ that   ⑤ to

[10~12] 다음 대화를 읽고 물음에 답하시오.

W: James, what are you watching?

M: Oh, I'm watching a video about Yi Sunsin.

W: Isn't he the one that saved Joseon from Japan?

M: (A)[No, he isn't. / Right.] It is said that he won the war only with twelve (a)_____ (wood) ships.

W: Wow, how can that be possible?

M: He was a wise general (B)[who / which] (C)[made / is made] creative plans.

10 괄호 안의 단어를 문맥에 맞게 고쳐 빈칸 (a)에 쓰시오.

➡ _____

11 위 대화의 괄호 (A)~(C)에서 적절한 것을 골라 쓰시오.

➡ (A)_____ (B)_____ (C)_____

12 위 대화에서 다음 영영풀이에 해당하는 단어를 찾아 쓰시오.

> an officer of very high rank in the army or air force

➡ _____

Grammar

13 다음 밑줄 친 부분과 바꿔 쓸 수 있는 것은?

> You were the one who asked me <u>if</u> I had anything to say.

① unless   ② that   ③ what

④ which   ⑤ whether

14 다음 문장 중에서 어법상 <u>어색한</u> 문장을 고르시오.

① When I got home, Mom had already prepared our dinner.

② I found out that someone had eaten my cookies on the table.

③ Cathy lost the necklace that I had bought for her.

④ When Megan had arrived at the station, the train already left for London.

⑤ He had gone out for a walk when I arrived at his home.

15 다음 그림을 보고 주어진 어휘를 이용하여 빈칸을 알맞게 채우시오.

➡ A man visited his teacher, and asked him

_____.

(his fault, forgive, will)

16 다음 ⓐ~ⓖ 중 어법상 옳은 것을 <u>모두</u> 고르시오.

> ⓐ The movie has been over when I arrived at the theater.
> ⓑ I realized that I had been wrong about him.
> ⓒ I had eaten the sandwich which Mom made the night before.
> ⓓ David would like to know if you have any plans to work with other artists.
> ⓔ Can you tell me if she's a new student in our class?
> ⓕ Let me ask you which you want to buy something nice.
> ⓖ I wonder that the dress looks good on me.

➡ _____

17 다음 문장의 빈칸에 들어갈 수 <u>없는</u> 말은?

> When Scott arrived at the station, _____
> _____.

① the train had already left for London
② the train had just arrived at the platform
③ he had already his lunch
④ he remembered that he had left his smart phone at the restaurant
⑤ Lily had already gone

18 다음 두 문장을 한 문장으로 쓰시오.

(1) • I was not sure.
　　• He was telling the truth.
　　➡ _____

(2) • Rob wants to know.
　　• More men than women like gardening.
　　➡ _____
　　_____

(3) • I asked her.
　　• I could have a drink.
　　➡ _____

19 다음 빈칸에 들어갈 말이 <u>다른</u> 하나는?

① Try this food and see _____ you like it.
② I wonder _____ the movie is still showing on the theater.
③ Lucy wants to know _____ you are going to release a new song this month.
④ I am not sure _____ Rachel can play the cello.
⑤ I can't believe _____ it will be New Year's Day soon.

Reading

[20~21] 다음 글을 읽고 물음에 답하시오.

Back in the 1920's, whenever people saw me in the village, they would say, "There goes the *parakho*'s daughter."

ⓐMy father was a son from a very rich family. Instead of living the life of a *seonbi*, he was always at the gambling house. ⓑThat is because he was called a *parakho*, which means someone who ruins his family's fortune.

"Your father has gambled away all of the money, and now he's asking for more. Go and tell him that we have no more money left," my mother would tell me whenever she sent me to the gambling house.

Then, my father would yell at me angrily, "Why did you come empty-handed? Bring me more money!"

20 위 글의 ⓐMy father에 관한 내용으로 옳지 <u>않은</u> 것은?

① He was born into a rich family.
② He didn't live the life of a *seonbi*.
③ He was always at the gambling house.
④ He was called a *parakho*.
⑤ He won a lot of money by gambling.

21 위 글의 밑줄 친 ⓑ에서 흐름상 어색한 부분을 찾아 고치시오.

➡ _____

[22~24] 다음 글을 읽고 물음에 답하시오.

When I was sixteen years old, my family had already made an arrangement for me to marry Mr. Seo. (①)
ⓐRight before the wedding day, my mother came into my room and said, "Your father has taken the money for the chest." (②) I asked angrily, "How could he do such a horrible thing? (③) What should we do now?" (④)
"We have no choice. (⑤) You'll have to take your aunt's old chest," my mother said.
"How embarrassing for the family," people would whisper behind my back.
Since the first day of marriage, life at my husband's house had been difficult for me.

22 위 글의 흐름으로 보아, 주어진 문장이 들어가기에 가장 적절한 곳은?

As part of the wedding tradition, Mr. Seo's family sent my family some money to buy a new chest for clothes.

①   ②   ③   ④   ⑤

23 위 글의 밑줄 친 ⓐRight과 같은 의미로 쓰인 것을 고르시오.

① What gives you the <u>right</u> to do that?
② The bus came <u>right</u> on time.
③ You were quite <u>right</u> to criticize him.
④ Next time we'll get it <u>right</u>.
⑤ I don't feel quite <u>right</u> today.

24 본문의 내용과 일치하도록 다음 빈칸 (A)와 (B)에 알맞은 단어를 쓰시오.

The writer got married to Mr. Seo, but because of (A)_____ _____, she couldn't buy a (B)_____ _____ for clothes.

[25~27] 다음 글을 읽고 물음에 답하시오.

"Your father, my dear friend...," my father's friend continued his story. "He was not a gambler. Your father sent the family money to the independence fighters in Manchuria. He made (A)[him / himself] look like a gambler to (B)[keep / stop] this a secret from the Japanese officers."

(C)[At first / For the first time], I was not sure if he was telling the truth. But afterwards, I found out the truth about my father and I realized that I had been wrong about him. Ever since that moment, I ⓐhave been proud to be the daughter of a *parakho* who had devoted his life to the independence movement.

25 위 글의 괄호 (A)~(C)에서 문맥이나 어법상 알맞은 낱말을 골라 쓰시오.

➡ (A)_____ (B)_____ (C)_____

26 위 글의 밑줄 친 ⓐhave been과 현재완료 용법이 다른 것을 모두 고르시오.

① I have worn these jeans for 3 years.
② I have never met a student like him.
③ How long has Jim been here?
④ She has gone to Paris.
⑤ He hasn't eaten his hamburger yet.

27 위 글에서 알 수 있는 아버지에 대한 'I'의 심경 변화로 가장 알맞은 것을 고르시오.

① ashamed → surprised
② respectful → satisfied
③ bored → disappointed
④ ashamed → respectful
⑤ surprised → proud

[28~30] 다음 글을 읽고 물음에 답하시오.

Have you heard of Nam Jahyun? She was a female independence fighter. When her husband died during the war, she decided to fight for independence. In 1919, Nam Jahyun moved to Manchuria. Then, she built schools and educated women there. When she was arrested by the Japanese in 1933, she had tried to kill Japanese officers. After she ⓐ_____ in prison for six months, she was released and died shortly after. In 1962, to honor her work fighting for independence, the government gave her an award.

28 위 글의 빈칸 ⓐ에 be동사를 알맞은 형태로 쓰시오.

➡ _____

29 위 글의 종류로 알맞은 것을 고르시오.

① e-mail   ② biography
③ diary   ④ article
⑤ autobiography

30 위 글의 남자현에 관한 내용으로 옳지 않은 것은?

① 여성 독립 운동가였다.
② 그녀의 남편이 죽은 뒤에 만주로 갔다.
③ 만주에서 학교를 세우고 여성들을 가르쳤다.
④ 일본 경찰에 체포된 뒤에 감옥에서 죽었다.
⑤ 1962년 정부가 그녀에게 상을 주었다.

01 출제율 90%

접미사 -ward(s)를 붙여 부사로 만들 수 <u>없는</u> 것을 고르시오.

① in   ② over   ③ after

④ back   ⑤ fore

02 출제율 100%

다음 빈칸에 알맞은 단어를 〈보기〉에서 골라 쓰시오.

┌─── 보기 ┐
    any   most   so   some   such

(1) Everything has changed _____ much that I can hardly recognize the place.

(2) He came to _____ a sudden stop that we almost hit him.

03 출제율 95%

빈칸 (A)와 (B)에 들어갈 말로 알맞은 것끼리 짝지어진 것을 고르시오.

• He's always unwilling to ask (A)_____ anyone's help.

• She announced that she would devote her life (B)_____ art.

    (A)   (B)   (A)   (B)

① out – for   ② out – to

③ for – for   ④ for – to

⑤ around – for

04 출제율 90%

다음 주어진 우리말에 맞게 빈칸을 채우시오. (철자가 주어진 경우 주어진 철자로 시작할 것.)

(1) 그녀는 포기하지 않고 유명한 중국 장군을 만나러 갔다.

➡ She did not give up and went to see a famous Chinese g_____.

(2) 너무 많은 결혼들이 이혼으로 끝난다.

➡ Too many _____ end in divorce.

(3) 하늘에 이상한 물체가 있다.

➡ There's a strange o_____ in the sky.

(4) 내가 휴가 갈 것이기 때문에, 그 회의에 참석할 수 없을 것 같다.

➡ I won't be able to attend the meeting s_____ I'll be on vacation.

[05~07] 다음 대화를 읽고 물음에 답하시오.

W: Excuse me, sir. (①)

M: I'd like to have *bibimbap*, please. (②)

W: Here you are. (③)

M: Thank you. (④) Oh, 지금 화장실을 이용해도 될까요?

W: Sure, but if the seat light is on, you should stay in your seat. (⑤)

M: Okay, thank you.

05 출제율 90%

①~⑤ 중 주어진 문장이 들어갈 곳은?

Would you like to have curry or *bibimbap*?

①   ②   ③   ④   ⑤

06 출제율 90%

Where is this conversation taking place?

① bus   ② train   ③ hotel

④ airplane   ⑤ factory

07 출제율 95%

밑줄 친 우리말과 일치하도록 주어진 단어를 이용해 문장을 만드시오.

➡ _____

    (okay, bathroom, use)

M: Lisa. (A)_____

W: I'm reading a biography of Gwon Giok.

M: I haven't heard about her. (B)_____

W: She was the first ⓐ[male / female] pilot in Korea. It ⓑ[says / said / is said] ⓒ[which / what / that] she had over 7,000 hours of flying time.

M: Wow, I didn't know that.

08 위 대화의 빈칸 (A)와 (B)에 알맞은 것을 〈보기〉에서 골라 쓰시오.

┌─── 보기 ───┐

• Is it okay if I take a picture of it?

• Who is she?

• Why did she become a pilot?

• What are you reading?

• How was your reading?

• How can it be possible?

➡ (A) _____

(B) _____

09 위 대화의 괄호 ⓐ~ⓒ에서 적절한 것을 골라 쓰시오.

➡ ⓐ_____ ⓑ_____ ⓒ_____

10 위 대화에서 다음 영영풀이에 해당하는 단어를 찾아 쓰시오.

a book that someone writes about someone else's life

➡ _____

M: All right, everyone! This way, please. Now, we are moving onto the Joseon Dynasty. (A)_____, there were many interesting (B)_____ (invent). This one is called the *Jagyeongnu.*

W: Is it a musical instrument?

M: Actually, this is a water clock. It is said that it is the oldest and the largest water clock in Korea.

W: How amazing! Is it okay if I take a picture of it?

M: Sure.

11 빈칸 (A)에 알맞은 말을 고르시오.

① Besides   ② However

③ Instead   ④ As it is

⑤ As you can see

12 괄호 안의 단어를 문맥에 맞게 고쳐 빈칸 (B)에 쓰시오.

➡ _____

13 다음 그림을 보고 주어진 어휘를 사용하여 빈칸을 알맞게 채우시오.

Jonathan asked Bells _____

_____ with him. (go, she, can, out)

14 다음 중 밑줄 친 if의 쓰임이 다른 하나는?

① It does not matter if you answer yes or no.

② I'm not sure if I'm well prepared.

③ I asked him if he was sorry for what he had done.

④ Please let me know if he comes.

⑤ You may wonder if it is true or not.

15 다음 중 어법상 적절한 문장은?

① I had told the story that I have read in the book.

② I couldn't find the pen which Dad had gave to me.

③ After she was in prison for 6 months, she had been released and died short after.

④ I couldn't meet him because he had left the town when I got back.

⑤ It was proved that the officials took bribes from him months before.

[16~17] 다음 글을 읽고 물음에 답하시오.

Back in the 1920's, whenever people saw me in the village, they would say, "There goes the *parakho*'s daughter."

My father was a son from a very rich family. Instead of ⓐliving the life of a *seonbi*, he was always at the gambling house. That is why he was called a *parakho*, which means someone who ruins his family's fortune.

"Your father has gambled away all of the money, and now he's asking for more. Go and tell him that we have no more money left," my mother would tell me whenever she sent me to the gambling house.

Then, my father would yell at me angrily, "Why did you come empty-handed? Bring me more money!"

16 위 글의 밑줄 친 ⓐliving과 문법적 쓰임이 다른 것을 모두 고르시오.

① He is good at playing tennis.

② We enjoy swimming after school.

③ She is cooking in the kitchen.

④ They stopped eating the food.

⑤ They sat studying in the room.

17 Why was the writer's father called a *parakho*? Fill in the blanks below with suitable words. (2 words)

Because he was always at the _____ _____ instead of living the life of a *seonbi*.

[18~20] 다음 글을 읽고 물음에 답하시오.

ⓐWhen I was sixteen years old, my family has already made an arrangement for me to marry Mr. Seo. As part of the wedding tradition, Mr. Seo's family sent my family some money to buy a new chest for clothes.

Right before the wedding day, my mother came into my room and said, "Your father has taken the money for the chest."

I asked angrily, "How could he do ⓑ그런 끔찍한 일? What should we do now?"

"We have no choice. You'll have to take your aunt's old chest," my mother said.

"How embarrassing for the family," people would whisper ⓒ나 몰래.

Since the first day of marriage, life at my husband's house had been difficult for me.

18 위 글의 밑줄 친 ⓑ와 ⓒ의 우리말에 맞게 주어진 어휘를 이용하여, 각각 4 단어와 3 단어로 영작하시오.

ⓑ horrible ⓒ back

➡ ⓑ _____ ⓒ _____

19 위 글의 밑줄 친 ⓐ에서 어법상 틀린 부분을 찾아 고치시오.
출제율 90%

➡ _____

20 According to the passage, which is NOT true?
출제율 100%

① The writer's husband's family name was Seo.

② As part of the wedding tradition, the writer received some money from Mr. Seo's family.

③ The money that Mr. Seo's family sent was for buying a new chest for clothes.

④ The writer's father took the money for the chest on the wedding day.

⑤ The writer had to take her aunt's old chest.

[21~23] 다음 글을 읽고 물음에 답하시오.

"Your father, my dear friend...," my father's friend continued his story. "He was not a gambler. Your father sent the family money to the independence fighters in Manchuria. He made himself look like a gambler (A)to keep this a secret ___ⓐ___ the Japanese officers."

At first, I was not sure if he was telling the truth. But afterwards, I found out (B)the truth about my father and I realized that I had been wrong about him. Ever since that moment, I have been proud to be the daughter of a parakho who had devoted his life ___ⓑ___ the independence movement.

21 위 글의 빈칸 ⓐ와 ⓑ에 들어갈 전치사가 바르게 짝지어진 것은?
출제율 90%

       ⓐ   ⓑ   ⓐ   ⓑ
① from – on   ② to – at
③ to – on   ④ for – to
⑤ from – to

22 위 글의 밑줄 친 (A)to keep과 to부정사의 용법이 **다른** 것을 **모두** 고르시오.
출제율 95%

① I don't have any friends to talk with.

② He went to Africa in 1990, never to return.

③ He can't be rich to ask me for some money.

④ She encouraged me to try once again.

⑤ She came here to ask a question.

23 다음 빈칸 (A)와 (B)에 알맞은 단어를 넣어 (B)the truth에 대한 설명을 완성하시오.
출제율 95%

> The writer's father was not a *parakho* but he made himself (A)_____ _____ a gambler to keep the fact that he sent the family money to the independence fighters in Manchuria a secret from the (B)_____ _____.

[24~25] 다음 글을 읽고 물음에 답하시오.

I thought my father was ...

My father was known as a *parakho*. He was born into a rich family but he gambled away all of the money. He even took the money for a new chest for clothes.

Actually my father was ...

My father was not a gambler. He sent the family money to the independence fighters in Manchuria. ⓐHe made himself to look a gambler to keep ⓑthis a secret from the Japanese officers.

24 위 글의 밑줄 친 ⓐ에서 어법상 틀린 부분을 찾아 고치시오.
출제율 100%

➡ _____

25 위 글의 밑줄 친 ⓑthis가 가리키는 것을 본문에서 찾아 쓰시오.
출제율 95%

➡ _____

_____

서술형 실전문제

[01~02] 다음 대화를 읽고 물음에 답하시오.

> W: Hey, Mark, do you know about Father Lee Taeseok?
> M: Yeah, I've heard of him. ⓐWho?
> W: ⓑTake a look at this article. ⓒHe is going to include in the social studies textbook in South Sudan.
> M: Wow. that's great.
> W: Yeah, ⓓhe helped the children by building a clinic and a school. 사람들이 그러한 이야기들이 교과서에 포함된다고 말했어.
> M: ⓔIt is bad to hear that students will learn about such a great person.

01 밑줄 친 ⓐ~ⓔ 중 문맥상 또는 어법상 어색한 것을 모두 골라 바르게 고치시오.

➡ _____
_____
_____
_____

02 밑줄 친 우리말을 주어진 단어를 이용하여 영작하시오.

➡ _____
_____ (say, it)

➡ _____
_____ (people)

03 주어진 단어를 이용하여 빈칸에 알맞은 말을 쓰시오.

(1) I remembered that I _____ the door of my room open. (leave)

(2) The library _____ when I got there. (closed)

04 밑줄 친 우리말을 주어진 단어를 이용하여 영작하시오.

> W: Excuse me, you can't take your backpack inside the museum.
> M: Oh, I didn't know that. 물병을 가지고 들어가도 될까요?
> W: Yes, that's fine. You can leave your bag in the locker.
> M: Okay, thank you.

➡ _____ (okay)

➡ _____ (can)

05 다음 문장에서 틀린 것을 고쳐 다시 쓰시오.

(1) It was the most interesting game that I ever played.

➡ _____
_____

(2) His wife was surprised to learn that he was already fired without any warning.

➡ _____
_____

(3) He could not decide that this was a fairy tale or a nightmare.

➡ _____
_____

(4) I'm considering if to accept his offer.

➡ _____

06 다음 우리말을 주어진 어휘를 이용하여 영작하시오.

(1) 나는 그가 그녀에게 추천서를 줄 수 있는지 알고 싶다. (give her a recommendation, 11 단어)

➡ _____

_____

(2) 그녀는 열쇠를 학교에 두고 왔기 때문에 문을 열 수가 없었다. (at school, leave, the door, the key, because, open, 14 단어)

➡ _____

_____

[07~08] 다음 글을 읽고 물음에 답하시오.

Back in the 1920's, whenever people saw me in the village, they would say, "There goes the *parakho*'s daughter."

My father was a son from a very rich family. ⓐInstead of living the life of a *seonbi*, he was always at the gambling house. That is why he was called a *parakho*, which means someone who ruins his family's fortune.

"Your father has gambled away all of the money, and now he's asking for more. Go and tell him that we have no more money left," my mother would tell me whenever she sent me to the gambling house.

Then, my father would yell at me angrily, "Why did you come empty-handed? ⓑBring me more money!"

07 위 글의 밑줄 친 ⓐ를 다음과 같이 바꿔 쓸 때 빈칸에 들어갈 알맞은 단어를 쓰시오.

➡ He did _____ live the life of a *seonbi*, _____ he was always at the gambling house.

08 위 글의 밑줄 친 ⓑ를 3형식 문장으로 고치시오.

➡ _____

[09~11] 다음 글을 읽고 물음에 답하시오.

ⓐWhen I was sixteen years old, my family had already made an arrangement for me to marry with Mr. Seo. As part of the wedding tradition, Mr. Seo's family sent my family some money to buy a new chest for clothes.

Right before the wedding day, my mother came into my room and said, "Your father has taken the money for the chest."

I asked angrily, "How could he do ⓑsuch a horrible thing? What should we do now?"

"We have no choice. You'll have to take your aunt's old chest," my mother said.

"How embarrassing for the family," people would whisper behind my back.

Since the first day of marriage, life at my husband's house had been difficult for me.

09 위 글의 밑줄 친 ⓐ에서 어법상 틀린 부분을 찾아 고치시오.

➡ _____

10 위 글의 밑줄 친 ⓑsuch a horrible thing이 가리키는 내용을 우리말로 쓰시오.

➡ _____

11 Why did people whisper behind the writer's back that it was very embarrassing for the family? Fill in the blanks below with suitable words.

Because _____ _____ took the _____ for the chest.

01 그림을 보고 허락을 요청하는 말을 이용해 문장을 완성하시오. 괄호 안에 주어진 말을 이용하시오.

A: _____

_____

(borrow, 2개 이상)

B: _____

(sorry, broken)

02 그림을 참고하고, 주어진 어휘를 이용하여 대화를 완성하시오.

(1)   (2)

(1) A: Do you know _____ a comic book? (she, read)

　　B: I'm not sure, but she likes to read comic books.

(2) A: How was your play yesterday?

　　B: It was terrible. I forgot the lines that I _____ during our practice. (memorize)

03 다음 내용을 바탕으로 독립운동가 남자현의 전기문을 쓰시오.

Biography of Nam Jahyun, a female independence fighter

1873: born in Yeongyang

1919: Her husband died during the war.

　　• moved to Manchuria • built schools and educated women there

1919: decided to fight for independence

1924~1933: tried to kill Japanese officers

1933: • arrested by the Japanese • had been in prison for six months

　　• died on Aug 22nd

1962: The government gave her an award.

Have you heard of Nam Jahyun? She was a (A)_____. When her husband died during the war, she decided (B)_____. In 1919, Nam Jahyun moved to Manchuria. Then, she (C)_____ there. When she was arrested by the Japanese in 1933, she had tried to kill Japanese officers. After she had been in prison for (D)_____, she was released and died shortly after. In 1962, to honor her work fighting for independence, the government gave her (E)_____.

단원별 모의고사

01 다음 문장 중 자연스럽지 <u>않은</u> 것을 찾아 고치시오.

ⓐ The road surface became so hot that it melted.
ⓑ Children are used to spend much of their free time watching TV.
ⓒ I wanted to buy a new car by selling my house.

➡ _____

02 다음 빈칸에 공통으로 들어갈 말을 고르시오.

• Right _____ that moment, you came up to me and issued a ticket without giving me a chance to explain.
• Don't yell _____ me like that!

03 다음 빈칸을 〈보기〉에 있는 어휘를 이용하여 채우시오.

┌─ 보기 ─┐
biography detective female locker
└──────┘

(1) I have read a _____ of Abraham Lincoln.
(2) Oh Eun-sun is a Korean _____ mountaineer.
(3) Where can I get a key for my _____?
(4) The _____ found some evidence.

04 다음 우리말에 맞도록 빈칸에 알맞은 말을 쓰시오. (철자가 주어진 경우 주어진 철자로 시작할 것)

(1) 미국의 많은 가정, 호텔, 학교에서 이 운동에 참여했습니다.
➡ Many American families, hotels, and schools participated in this _____.
(2) 그의 많은 발명품 덕분에 그는 많은 돈을 벌었습니다.
➡ He made a lot of money thanks to his many _____.
(3) 그는 일찍 일어나는 데 익숙하다.
➡ He is used to _____ up early.

[05~06] 다음 대화를 읽고 물음에 답하시오.

W: Excuse me, you can't ⓐ_____ your backpack inside the museum.
M: Oh, I didn't ⓑ_____ that. Is it okay if I ⓒ_____ in my water bottle?
W: Yes, that's fine. You can ⓓ_____ your bag in the locker.
M: Okay, thank you.

05 빈칸 ⓐ～ⓔ에 들어가지 <u>않는</u> 말을 고르시오.

① know   ② help   ③ leave
④ bring   ⑤ take

06 위 대화를 읽고 답할 수 <u>없는</u> 질문을 고르시오.

① Can the man carry the water bottle inside the museum?
② Where is the man now?
③ Is there a locker in the museum?
④ Can the man take pictures inside the museum?
⑤ Can the man take his backpack inside the museum?

[07~09] 다음 대화를 읽고 물음에 답하시오.

M: All right, everyone! This way, please. Now, we are moving onto the Joseon Dynasty. As you can see, there were many interesting inventions. This one (A)[called / is called] the *Jagyeongnu*.
W: Is it a musical instrument?
M: (a)<u>Actually</u>, this is a water clock. (b)<u>그것은 한국에서 가장 오래되고 가장 큰 물시계라고 합니다.</u>
W: How amazing! Is it okay if I take a picture of (B)[it / them]?
M: Sure.

07 위 대화의 괄호 (A)와 (B)에서 적절한 것을 고르시오.

➡ (A)_____ (B)_____

08 밑줄 친 (a)Actually와 바꿔 쓸 수 있는 말을 고르시오.

① However   ② Rather
③ In fact   ④ In the end
⑤ On the other hand

09 밑줄 친 (b)의 우리말과 일치하도록 주어진 단어를 이용하여 영작하시오.

➡ _____

_____

(large, say, in, old)

[10~13] 다음 대화를 읽고 물음에 답하시오.

M: I watched an interesting movie yesterday. (①)
W: Jeong Yakyong? (②) Wasn't he a scholar in the Joseon Dynasty? (③)
M: Yeah, but (A)<u>그는 또한 탐정이었다고 한다.</u> (④) He solved about 90 cases. (⑤)
W: Oh, I didn't know (B)_____ he was also a detective.

10 ①~⑤ 중 주어진 문장이 들어갈 곳은?

Jeong Yakyong was a detective in it.

①   ②   ③   ④   ⑤

11 위 대화에서 다음 영영풀이에 해당하는 단어를 찾아 쓰시오.

someone who studies a particular subject and knows a lot about it, especially a subject that is not scientific

➡ _____

12 밑줄 친 (A)의 우리말과 일치하도록 영작하시오. (9 단어)

➡ _____

13 빈칸 (B)에 알맞은 말을 고르시오.

① how   ② what   ③ which
④ that   ⑤ if

14 Which is grammatically WRONG?

① The woman wants to know if there is a bank near here.
② I want to ask Wendy if she likes ice cream or not.
③ Try this food and see if or not you like it.
④ Can you tell me whether you will go shopping tonight?
⑤ I'm not sure whether Mina can join the picnic or not.

15 다음 두 문장을 한 문장으로 바꿔 쓸 때 빈칸에 알맞은 말을 쓰시오.

(1) • I want to know.
   • Is the school lunch delicious?
   ➡ I want to know _____
   _____.

(2) • I'll ask Sarah.
   • It's all right to sit next to her.
   ➡ I'll ask Sarah _____
   _____.

(3) • Jim didn't feel hungry.
   • Jim ate lunch already.
   ➡ Jim didn't feel hungry because he
   _____ lunch.

16 다음 문장에서 어법상 어색한 것을 바르게 고쳐 다시 쓰시오.

(1) Would you please check that I filled out this card right?
   ➡ _____
   _____

(2) I don't know that my mom likes potato pizza.
   ➡ _____
   _____

(3) I am not sure that Mike will meet Judy at 3 o'clock.
   ➡ _____
   _____

(4) He insisted that he never heard a girl crying that night.
   ➡ _____
   _____

(5) I decided to come home earlier than I planned.
   ➡ _____

17 다음 중 어법상 어색한 문장을 고르시오.

① I knew that Mike had won first prize at the singing contest.
② Lisa doesn't know whether I can ride a bike.
③ Whether Juliet likes Romeo is not certain.
④ Lily wonders if you are interested in various music genres.
⑤ I'm not sure if or not she made a mistake.

18 다음 두 문장의 뜻이 같도록 빈칸에 알맞은 말을 쓰시오.

(1) I went to the store, but all the flowers were sold out.
   = All the flowers _____
   when I went to the store.

(2) I didn't know who she was. I never met her.
   = I didn't know who she was since I
   _____ her.

[19~20] 다음 글을 읽고 물음에 답하시오.

In 1946, a strange man visited me and asked, "Are you Mr. Kim Yonghwan's daughter?"

For me, this was an odd question because I was more used to ⓐbeing called the daughter of a *parakho*.

"I'm your father's friend. You may wonder if it is true, but your father...," the man said.

At that moment, I was expecting disappointing news since I did not have good memories of my father.

19

위 글의 밑줄 친 ⓐbeing과 문법적 쓰임이 같은 것을 모두 고르시오.

① His hobby is collecting stamps.
② Playing the piano is fun.
③ I finished doing my homework.
④ Kirl was playing chess.
⑤ Look at the smiling girl.

20

When the writer heard the man's words, why was she expecting disappointing news? Fill in the blanks below with suitable words. (2 words)

> Because she did not have _____ _____ of her father.

21

위 글의 밑줄 친 ⓐ를 능동태로 고치시오.

➡ _____

22

아래 〈보기〉에서 위 글의 밑줄 친 ⓑwho와 문법적 쓰임이 다른 것의 개수를 고르시오.

보기
① Anyone who wants to come is welcome.
② There's a student who wants to see you.
③ This is the person who made me a kite yesterday.
④ Nobody knew who he was.
⑤ He was the only one who trusted me.

① 1개 ② 2개 ③ 3개 ④ 4개 ⑤ 5개

[21~22] 다음 글을 읽고 물음에 답하시오.

Back in the 1920's, whenever people saw me in the village, they would say, "There goes the *parakho*'s daughter."

My father was a son from a very rich family. Instead of living the life of a *seonbi*, he was always at the gambling house. That is why ⓐhe was called a *parakho*, which means someone ⓑwho ruins his family's fortune.

"Your father has gambled away all of the money, and now he's asking for more. Go and tell him that we have no more money left," my mother would tell me whenever she sent me to the gambling house.

Then, my father would yell at me angrily, "Why did you come empty-handed? Bring me more money!"

[23~24] 다음 글을 읽고 물음에 답하시오.

When I was sixteen years old, my family (A)had already made an arrangement for me to marry Mr. Seo. As part of the wedding tradition, Mr. Seo's family sent my family some money to buy a new chest for clothes.

Right before the wedding day, my mother came into my room and said, "Your father has taken the money for the chest."

I asked angrily, "How could he do such a horrible thing? What should we do now?"

"We have no choice. You'll have to take your aunt's old chest," my mother said.

"How ⓐ _____ for the family," people would whisper behind my back.

Since the first day of marriage, life at my husband's house had been difficult for me.

23 위 글의 빈칸 ⓐ에 들어갈 알맞은 말을 고르시오.

① exciting   ② satisfying

③ boring   ④ embarrassing

⑤ amazing

24 위 글의 밑줄 친 (A)had made와 과거완료의 용법이 같은 것을 모두 고르시오.

① I found that I had lost my watch.

② When she came, I had not finished my homework yet.

③ When I called on her, she had been ill for two weeks.

④ The train had just left when he got to the station.

⑤ I did not tell him at first, for I had never seen him before.

[25~28] 다음 글을 읽고 물음에 답하시오.

"Your father, my dear friend...," my father's friend continued his story. "He was not a gambler. Your father sent the family money to the independence fighters in Manchuria. He made ⓐhim look like a gambler to keep this a secret from the Japanese officers."

  ⓑ   first, I was not sure if he was telling the truth. But afterwards, I found out the truth about my father and I realized that I had been wrong about him. Ever since that moment, I have been proud to be the daughter of a *parakho* ⓒ독립운동에 그의 인생을 헌신하신.

25 밑줄 친 ⓐhim을 알맞은 형으로 고치시오.

➡ _____

26 빈칸 ⓑ에 알맞은 것은?

① In   ② At

③ For   ④ With

⑤ From

27 위 글의 밑줄 친 ⓒ의 우리말에 맞게 주어진 어휘를 이용하여 9 단어로 영작하시오.

had devoted, life, movement

➡ _____

    _____

28 According to the passage, which is NOT true?

① The writer's father was not a gambler.

② The writer's father sent the family money to the independence fighters in Manchuria.

③ The writer's father wanted to look like a gambler to keep his secret identity from the independence fighters.

④ The writer realized that she had been wrong about her father.

⑤ The writer's father was a *parakho* who had devoted his life to the independence movement.

MEMO

INSIGHT
on the textbook

교과서 파헤치기

Lesson **1** **The Art of Communication**

Lesson **2** **Wonderful Nature**

Lesson **3** **For the Love of Our Country**

※ 다음 영어를 우리말로 쓰시오.

01 prevent _____

02 demand _____

03 detail _____

04 argument _____

05 careless _____

06 concentrate _____

07 actually _____

08 direct _____

09 uncomfortable _____

10 effectively _____

11 argue _____

12 express _____

13 prepare _____

14 hide _____

15 solve _____

16 mad _____

17 mean _____

18 consider _____

19 probably _____

20 request _____

21 disappointed _____

22 reason _____

23 relationship _____

24 simply _____

25 trouble _____

26 instead _____

27 long face _____

28 upset _____

29 somewhere _____

30 helpful _____

31 pick _____

32 seem _____

33 focus _____

34 loudly _____

35 work out _____

36 cut ~ off _____

37 keep ~ in mind _____

38 be ready to 동사원형 _____

39 get cold feet _____

40 free from _____

41 be upset about ~ _____

42 let the cat out of the bag _____

43 point the finger at _____

※ 다음 우리말을 영어로 쓰시오.

01	주장, 논쟁		22	단순히
02	부주의한, 조심성 없는		23	사실은
03	딱 부러지는, 단도직입적인		24	막다, 예방하다
04	어딘가에		25	요구
05	아마도		26	요청
06	집중하다		27	구체적 내용, 자세한 내용
07	도움이 되는, 유용한		28	이유
08	화난, 기분 나쁜		29	관계
09	숨기다, 감추다		30	두려워하는, 겁먹은
10	그 대신에		31	표현하다, 나타내다
11	말다툼하다, 언쟁하다		32	감정, 느낌
12	불편한		33	(~처럼) 보이다, ~인 듯하다
13	시험		34	고민, 문제
14	못된, 심술궂은		35	~에게 자꾸 이래라저래라 하다
15	배려하다, 고려하다		36	요구하다
16	실망한, 낙담한		37	먼저, 무엇보다도
17	해결하다		38	~할 준비가 되다
18	효과적으로		39	~을 명심하다
19	우울한 얼굴		40	정시에, 제때에
20	선택하다, 고르다		41	~의 도중에, ~의 중간에
21	준비하다		42	결국 ~하게 되다
			43	~을 중단시키다, ~을 잘라내다

※ 다음 영영풀이에 알맞은 단어를 <보기>에서 골라 쓴 후, 우리말 뜻을 쓰시오.

1 _____ : cruel or not kind: _____

2 _____ : frightened, or worried: _____

3 _____ : feeling sad or upset: _____

4 _____ : useful, or providing help: _____

5 _____ : an angry disagreement between people: _____

6 _____ : very sad, worried, or angry about something: _____

7 _____ : to give all your attention to the thing you are doing: _____

8 _____ : a sad, disappointed, or serious expression on someone's face: _____

9 _____ : to think about someone's feelings or reactions: _____

10 _____ : to put something in a place so that no one can find or see it: _____

11 _____ : to find a solution to something that is causing difficulties: _____

12 _____ : to stop something from happening or existing: _____

13 _____ : to tell someone about a feeling, opinion, or goal by speaking or writing
about it: _____

14 _____ : one of many small facts or pieces of information relating to a situation:
_____

15 _____ : unhappy because something that you hoped for or expected did not
happen or because someone or something was not as good as you
expected: _____

16 _____ : a fact, situation, or intention that explains why something happened,
why someone did something, or why something is true: _____

보기			
disappointed	concentrate	hide	helpful
detail	long face	express	scared
reason	upset	consider	unhappy
prevent	argument	solve	mean

※ 다음 우리말과 일치하도록 빈칸에 알맞은 말을 쓰시오.

Listen & Talk 1 Get Ready

A: _____ do you _____ so _____?

B: I'm upset _____ Roy. He always _____ me.

A: Don't _____ _____ so _____.

A: 너는 왜 침울해 보이니?
B: 나는 Roy한테 화가 나. 그는 항상 나를 따라 해.
A: 너무 속상해 하지 마.

Listen & Talk 1 A-1

M: Sally, _____ _____ you don't talk much _____ Anna _____ _____?

W: Well, I'm _____ _____ _____ _____ we had.

M: _____ are you _____?

W: She kept _____ _____ _____ _____ the middle of my sentences, so I got _____. We argued and I _____ _____ _____ her.

M: Oh, I'm _____ _____ _____ that.

M: Sally야, 요즘에 왜 Anna와 별로 대화를 하지 않니?
W: 음, 나는 우리가 한 논쟁 때문에 화가 나.
M: 왜 화가 난 거야?
W: 그녀가 계속해서 내가 말을 하고 있는 도중에 끊어서 화가 났어. 우리는 논쟁을 했고, 나는 그녀와 이야기를 하지 않았어.
M: 오, 그거 유감이구나.

Listen & Talk 1 A-2

W: _____ is your science homework _____?

M: Not good. _____ _____ _____ my science group.

W: What's _____?

M: The group members only speak and never listen. _____ _____ _____ _____ we can finish the homework _____ _____.

W: That's _____ _____.

W: 너의 과학 숙제는 어떻게 되어 가고 있니?
M: 좋지 않아. 나는 나의 과학 그룹에 화가 나.
W: 뭐가 문제인데?
M: 그룹 구성원들이 말만 하고 전혀 듣지 않아. 나는 우리가 숙제를 제시간에 끝낼 수 있을 거라고 생각하지 않아.
W: 그것 참 안 되었구나.

Listen & Talk 1 B

M: _____ the _____ _____, Julie?

W: I got _____ _____ my sister yesterday and _____ _____ _____ things to her.

M: Oh, _____ were you _____?

W: I was really tired and I wanted _____ _____. _____ she was _____ _____ _____ _____ _____. I was really _____ about that.

M: 왜 그렇게 우울한 얼굴이니, Julie?
W: 어제 여동생한테 화가 나서 그녀에게 심술궂은 말을 했어.
M: 오, 왜 화가 났니?
W: 정말 피곤해서 자고 싶었어. 하지만 여동생은 전화로 큰 소리로 이야기하고 있었어. 나는 그것에 대해 정말 화가 났어.

M: I see. And you two _____ _____ _____ _____ yet?

W: No, not yet. I want to say I'm sorry _____ I was _____ to her,

_____ _____ _____ _____ _____.

M: _____ _____ you write her a note or _____ her a text message?

W: Hmm, that's a good idea. Thanks.

M: 그렇구나. 그리고 너희 둘은 아직 화해하지 않았니?

W: 아니, 아직이야. 내가 여동생에게 심술궂게 굴어서 미안하다고 말하고 싶지만, 방법을 모르겠어.

M: 그녀에게 편지를 쓰거나 문자 메시지를 보내는 게 어때?

W: 음, 좋은 생각이야. 고마워.

Listen & Talk 1 Get Ready

A: Don't _____ _____ _____ _____ _____

_____ about Clara's _____ _____.

B: A cat? I don't have a cat.

A: _____ _____ _____ I meant. _____ her party _____

_____.

A: Clara의 깜짝 파티에 대해 비밀을 누설하지 마.

B: 고양이? 나는 고양이가 없어.

A: 그건 그런 뜻이 아니야. 그녀의 파티를 비밀로 해.

Listen & Talk 2 A-1

W: Mr. Brown, I want to _____ a good _____ _____ English.

_____ _____ I do?

M: Well, Sujin, you should _____ in class, _____ _____ _____.

I see you often _____ _____ _____ _____

_____.

W: Clouds? I can't _____ _____ _____ from inside the

classroom.

M: _____ _____ _____ _____ _____. I _____ you

don't _____ in class.

W: Brown 선생님, 저는 영어에서 좋은 점수를 받고 싶어요. 어떻게 해야 하죠?

M: 음, 수진아, 너는 우선 수업에 집중해야 해. 난 네가 종종 공상에 잠겨 있는 것을 본단다.

W: 구름이요? 교실 안에서는 하늘을 볼 수 없어요.

M: 그건 그런 뜻이 아니야. 내 말은 네가 수업에 집중하지 않는다는 거야.

Listen & Talk 2 A-2

W: Did you finally _____ _____ yesterday, Nick?

M: _____, I _____ _____ _____, Mina.

W: That's too bad. How did you _____ _____ _____?

M: No, Mina. That's not _____ I meant. _____ _____ _____
I got _____, so I didn't dive.

W: Nick, 어제 드디어 다이빙하러 갔니?

M: 미나야, 사실 난 겁이 났어.

W: 그거 안 됐구나. 어떻게 감기에 걸렸니?

M: 아니, 미나야. 그건 그런 뜻이 아니야. 내가 겁을 먹어서 다이빙을 안 했다는 뜻이야.

Listen & Talk 2 B

W: I'm so _____ _____ _____ my exams, Jinsu.

M: Yeah, me, too. We have _____ _____ _____ _____.

W: After _____ my exams, I want to _____ _____ _____ trip
and just let my _____ _____.

M: You want to change your _____ _____?

W: No, that's not _____ _____ _____. I want to go somewhere
and _____ _____ _____ all my _____.

W: 진수야, 나는 시험에 대해 너무 스트레스를 받아.

M: 그래, 나도. 우리는 볼 시험이 두 개 더 있어.

W: 시험을 마친 후, 나는 여행을 가서 느긋하게 쉬고 싶어.

M: 머리 스타일을 바꾸고 싶다고?

W: 아니, 그런 뜻이 아니야. 난 어디 가서 내 모든 고민에서 벗어나고 싶어.

Communication

W: Hey, Jason. You _____ upset. Anything _____?

M: People _____ _____ _____ _____ I'm too _____. I'm
_____ about that.

W: Hmm…. I kind of know _____ _____ _____ _____.

M: _____ do you _____?

W: Well, sometimes you _____ _____ _____ _____ _____
your mind too _____.

M: _____ I just _____ _____, then?

W: _____ _____ _____ _____ _____ _____. You can _____
_____ _____ others' _____.

M: I see. I'll _____ that.

W: 안녕, Jason. 화나 보여. 무슨 문제라도 있니?

M: 사람들은 내가 너무 단도직입적이라고 계속 말해. 나는 그것에 대해 화가 나.

W: 흠…. 난 그들이 무슨 이야기를 하는지 어느 정도 알아.

M: 무슨 의미야?

W: 음, 가끔 넌 네 마음에 있는 것을 너무 강하게 말하는 경향이 있어.

M: 그럼, 그냥 조용히 있어야 하니?

W: 내 말은 그게 아니야. 너는 다른 사람의 감정을 고려하도록 노력하면 돼.

M: 알겠어. 그렇게 해 보도록 할게.

※ 다음 우리말에 맞도록 대화를 영어로 쓰시오.

Listen & Talk 1 Get Ready

A: _____

B: _____

A: _____

A: 너는 왜 침울해 보이니?
B: 나는 Roy한테 화가 나. 그는 항상 나를 따라 해.
A: 너무 속상해 하지 마.

Listen & Talk 1 A-1

M: _____

W: _____

M: _____

W: _____

_____

M: _____

M: Sally야, 요즘에 왜 Anna와 별로 대화를 하지 않니?
W: 음, 나는 우리가 한 논쟁 때문에 화가 나.
M: 왜 화가 난 거야?
W: 그녀가 계속해서 내가 말을 하고 있는 도중에 끊어서 화가 났어. 우리는 논쟁을 했고, 나는 그녀와 이야기를 하지 않았어.
M: 오, 그거 유감이구나.

Listen & Talk 1 A-2

W: _____

M: _____

W: _____

M: _____

_____

W: _____

W: 너의 과학 숙제는 어떻게 되어 가고 있니?
M: 좋지 않아. 나는 나의 과학 그룹에 화가 나.
W: 뭐가 문제인데?
M: 그룹 구성원들이 말만 하고 전혀 듣지 않아. 나는 우리가 숙제를 제시간에 끝낼 수 있을 거라고 생각하지 않아.
W: 그것 참 안 되었구나.

Listen & Talk 1 B

M: _____

W: _____

M: _____

W: _____

_____

M: 왜 그렇게 우울한 얼굴이니, Julie?
W: 어제 여동생한테 화가 나서 그녀에게 심술궂은 말을 했어.
M: 오, 왜 화가 났니?
W: 정말 피곤해서 자고 싶었어. 하지만 여동생은 전화로 큰 소리로 이야기하고 있었어. 나는 그것에 대해 정말 화가 났어.

M: _____

W: _____

_____

M: _____

W: _____

M: 그렇구나. 그리고 너희 둘은 아직 화
해하지 않았니?

W: 아니, 아직이야. 내가 여동생에게 심
술궂게 굴어서 미안하다고 말하고 싶
지만, 방법을 모르겠어.

M: 그녀에게 편지를 쓰거나 문자 메시
지를 보내는 게 어때?

W: 음, 좋은 생각이야. 고마워.

Listen & Talk 1 Get Ready

A: _____

B: _____

A: _____

A: Clara의 깜짝 파티에 대해 비밀을 누
설하지 마.

B: 고양이? 나는 고양이가 없어.

A: 그건 그런 뜻이 아니야. 그녀의 파티
를 비밀로 해.

Listen & Talk 2 A-1

W: _____

M: _____

_____

W: _____

M: _____

W: Brown 선생님, 저는 영어에서 좋은 점
수를 받고 싶어요. 어떻게 해야 하죠?

M: 음, 수진아, 너는 우선 수업에 집중
해야 해. 난 네가 종종 공상에 잠겨
있는 것을 본단다.

W: 구름이요? 교실 안에서는 하늘을 볼
수 없어요.

M: 그건 그런 뜻이 아니야. 내 말은 네
가 수업에 집중하지 않는다는 거야.

Listen & Talk 2 A-2

W: _____

M: _____

W: _____

M: _____

W: Nick, 어제 드디어 다이빙하러 갔니?
M: 미나야, 사실 난 겁이 났어.
W: 그거 안 됐구나. 어떻게 감기에 걸렸니?
M: 아니, 미나야. 그건 그런 뜻이 아니야. 내가 겁을 먹어서 다이빙을 안 했다는 뜻이야.

Listen & Talk 2 B

W: _____

M: _____

W: _____

M: _____

W: _____

W: 진수야, 나는 시험에 대해 너무 스트레스를 받아.
M: 그래, 나도. 우리는 볼 시험이 두 개 더 있어.
W: 시험을 마친 후, 나는 여행을 가서 느긋하게 쉬고 싶어.
M: 머리 스타일을 바꾸고 싶다고?
W: 아니, 그런 뜻이 아니야. 난 어디 가서 내 모든 고민에서 벗어나고 싶어.

Communication

W: _____

M: _____

W: _____

M: _____

W: _____

M: _____

W: _____

M: _____

W: 안녕, Jason. 화나 보여. 무슨 문제라도 있니?
M: 사람들은 내가 너무 단도직입적이라고 계속 말해. 나는 그것에 대해 화가 나.
W: 흠…. 난 그들이 무슨 이야기를 하는지 어느 정도 알아.
M: 무슨 의미야?
W: 음, 가끔 넌 네 마음에 있는 것을 너무 강하게 말하는 경향이 있어.
M: 그럼, 그냥 조용히 있어야 하니?
W: 내 말은 그게 아니야. 너는 다른 사람의 감정을 고려하도록 노력하면 돼.
M: 알겠어. 그렇게 해 보도록 할게.

Step1

※ 다음 우리말과 일치하도록 빈칸에 알맞은 것을 골라 쓰시오.

1 _____ Your _____ _____
A. Mind　　　　　B. Speak　　　　　C. Effectively

2 _____ _____ "All about _____."
A. Teens　　　　　B. to　　　　　C. welcome

3 I'm _____ _____.
A. Carter　　　　　B. Dr.

4 Today, we're going to talk about _____ good communication _____ to _____ ourselves more _____.
A. skills　　　　B. using　　　　C. effectively　　　　D. express

5 _____ start _____ our first _____ about Brian.
A. with　　　　　B. let's　　　　　C. clip

6 When he _____ to talk to his brother, he always _____ _____ _____ with his brother.
A. up　　　　B. tries　　　　C. arguing　　　　D. ends

7 Let's _____ _____ the _____ _____ he has this problem.
A. out　　　　B. reason　　　　C. find　　　　D. why

8 **Brian: *You _____ my earphones again. _____ are you _____ _____?***
A. careless　　　　B. lost　　　　C. why　　　　D. so

9 Brian is starting a _____ _____ "you" to _____ his _____.
A. feelings　　　　B. sentence　　　　C. express　　　　D. with

10 _____, he should _____ the "_____."
A. use　　　　　B. instead　　　　　C. I-message

11 Starting with "I" can help him _____ _____ what he feels or thinks _____ _____ point the finger at his brother.
A. on　　　　B. than　　　　C. rather　　　　D. focus

12 **Brian: I'm *really* _____ _____ my _____ earphones *are* _____.**
A. lost　　　　B. upset　　　　C. favorite　　　　D. because

13 _____ is _____.
A. Calli　　　　　B. next

14 She is _____ to talk to her mother, but she is _____ _____ to go to _____.
A. work　　　　B. trying　　　　C. preparing　　　　D. busy

15 Let's _____ _____ _____.
A. look　　　　　B. a　　　　　C. have

1 당신의 마음을 효과적으로 말하라

2 '십 대들의 모든 것'에 오신 걸 환영합니다.

3 저는 Carter 박사입니다.

4 오늘 우리는 자신을 더 효과적으로 표현하기 위해 적절한 의사소통 기술을 사용하는 것에 대해 이야기해 보겠습니다.

5 Brian에 대한 첫 번째 동영상으로 시작해 보죠.

6 Brian이 남동생과 이야기하려고 할 때, 그는 결국 동생과 항상 말다툼을 하게 돼요.

7 그에게 이런 문제가 있는 이유를 알아봅시다.

8 Brian: "너 또 내 이어폰 잃어버렸지. 너는 왜 그렇게 조심성이 없니?"

9 Brian은 그의 감정을 표현하기 위해 '너'로 문장을 시작하고 있군요.

10 대신에 그는 '나 메시지'를 써야 해요.

11 '나'로 시작하는 것은 그가 남동생을 비난하기보다는 자신이 느끼거나 생각하는 것에 집중하도록 도울 수 있답니다.

12 Brian: "내가 가장 좋아하는 이어폰이 없어서 난 정말 속상해."

13 다음은 Calli입니다.

14 그녀는 어머니와 이야기하려고 하지만, 어머니는 출근 준비로 바쁘시군요.

15 한번 보시죠.

16 **Calli:** *Hey, Mom.* _____ *I* _____ *to you about* _____?
　　A. something　　B. talk　　C. could

17 Calli _____ to _____ the _____ _____ to talk to her mom.
　　A. right　　B. needs　　C. find　　D. time

18 Maybe Calli's mom _____ to listen _____ _____ Calli was _____ to say.
　　A. what　　B. going　　C. wanted　　D. to

19 But she didn't have _____ _____ _____ talk _____ her daughter.
　　A. time　　B. with　　C. enough　　D. to

20 Calli should _____ a time when her mom is _____ _____ _____.
　　A. ready　　B. pick　　C. listen　　D. to

21 **Calli:** *Hey, Mom.* _____ *I talk to you* _____ _____?
　　A. about　　B. could　　C. something

22 _____ : _____.
　　A. sure　　B. Mom

23 Now, let's _____ a _____ _____ our last clip.
　　A. at　　B. take　　C. look

24 Anna and Julie are best friends, but Anna _____ _____ Julie's _____.
　　A. feelings　　B. hurts　　C. often

25 **Anna:** _____ _____ *your bag* _____ *my desk!*
　　A. put　　B. don't　　C. on

26 Julie probably _____ _____ because Anna made a _____ _____ the word "don't."
　　A. using　　B. uncomfortable　　C. demand　　D. felt

27 People _____ don't like _____ _____.
　　A. orders　　B. simply　　C. taking

28 Anna should _____ _____ use words _____ _____ "can," "could," or "please."
　　A. as　　B. to　　C. such　　D. try

29 Then, _____ she says will sound _____ a _____ rather than a _____.
　　A. like　　B. demand　　C. what　　D. request

30 **Anna:** _____ *you* _____ *your bag* _____ *your desk?*
　　A. put　　B. on　　C. could

31 As we saw in the video clips, a small _____ in the way we _____ ourselves can _____ or even _____ communication problems.
　　A. express　　B. prevent　　C. change　　D. solve

32 Let's _____ these tips _____ _____!
　　A. mind　　B. keep　　C. in

16 Calli: "저기, 엄마. 엄마랑 뭔가에 대해 이야기 좀 할 수 있을까?"

16 Calli는 어머니와 이야기를 나눌 적절한 때를 찾아야 해요.

16 Calli의 어머니도 아마 Calli가 말하려고 했던 것을 듣고 싶어 하셨을 거예요.

16 그러나 어머니에게는 딸과 이야기할 시간이 충분하지 않았어요.

20 Calli는 어머니가 들으실 준비가 된 때를 골라야 해요.

21 Calli: "저기, 엄마. 엄마랑 뭔가에 대해 이야기 좀 할 수 있을까요?"

22 Mom: "물론이지."

23 이제 마지막 동영상을 봅시다.

24 Anna와 Julie는 가장 친한 친구 사이이지만, Anna가 종종 Julie의 마음을 상하게 합니다.

25 Anna: "네 가방을 내 책상에 놓지 마!"

26 Anna가 don't라는 단어를 써서 요구했기 때문에 Julie는 아마 불편하게 느꼈을 거예요.

27 사람들은 명령 받는 것을 전혀 좋아하지 않아요.

28 Anna는 can, could 또는 please와 같은 말을 사용하도록 노력해야 해요.

29 그러면 그녀가 하는 말이 요구보다는 요청처럼 들릴 거예요.

30 Anna: "네 가방은 네 책상에 놔두겠니?"

31 우리가 동영상에서 본 것처럼, 우리 자신을 표현하는 방식을 조금만 바꾸어도 의사소통의 문제를 해결하거나 심지어 막을 수도 있답니다.

32 이 조언들을 명심합시다!

※ 다음 우리말과 일치하도록 빈칸에 알맞은 말을 쓰시오.

1 Speak Your _____ _____

2 _____ _____ "All about _____."

3 _____ Dr. Carter.

4 Today, we're going to talk about _____ _____ _____ _____ to express _____ more _____.

5 _____ start with _____ _____ _____ about Brian.

6 When he _____ _____ talk to his brother, he always _____ _____ _____ with his brother.

7 Let's _____ _____ _____ _____ _____ he has this problem.

8 **Brian:** *You _____ my earphones again. Why are you so _____?*

9 Brian is starting a _____ _____ "you" _____ _____ _____ _____.

10 _____, he should use the "_____."

11 Starting with "I" can help him _____ _____ what he feels or thinks _____ _____ _____ _____ _____ _____ his brother.

12 **Brian:** _____ *really _____ because my favorite earphones _____ _____.*

13 _____ is Calli.

14 She is trying to talk to her mother, but she _____ _____ _____ to go to work.

15 Let's _____ _____ _____.

1 당신의 마음을 효과적으로 말하라

2 '십 대들의 모든 것'에 오신 걸 환영합니다.

3 저는 Carter 박사입니다.

4 오늘 우리는 자신을 더 효과적으로 표현하기 위해 적절한 의사소통 기술을 사용하는 것에 대해 이야기해 보겠습니다.

5 Brian에 대한 첫 번째 동영상으로 시작해 보죠.

6 Brian이 남동생과 이야기하려고 할 때, 그는 결국 동생과 항상 말다툼을 하게 돼요.

7 그에게 이런 문제가 있는 이유를 알아봅시다.

8 Brian: "너 또 내 이어폰 잃어버렸지. 너는 왜 그렇게 조심성이 없니?"

9 Brian은 그의 감정을 표현하기 위해 '너'로 문장을 시작하고 있군요.

10 대신에 그는 '나 메시지'를 써야 해요.

11 '나'로 시작하는 것은 그가 남동생을 비난하기보다는 자신이 느끼거나 생각하는 것에 집중하도록 도울 수 있답니다.

12 Brian: "내가 가장 좋아하는 이어폰이 없어져서 난 정말 속상해."

13 다음은 Calli입니다.

14 그녀는 어머니와 이야기하려고 하지만, 어머니는 출근 준비로 바쁘시군요.

15 한번 보시죠.

16 **Calli:** *Hey, Mom.* _____ _____ *talk to you about something?*

17 Calli _____ _____ find _____ _____ _____ to talk to her mom.

18 Maybe Calli's mom wanted to listen to _____ Calli was _____ _____ _____.

19 But she didn't have _____ _____ _____ _____ with her daughter.

20 Calli should _____ _____ _____ when her mom _____ _____ _____ _____.

21 **Calli:** *Hey, Mom.* _____ _____ *talk to you about something?*

22 **Mom:** _____.

23 Now, let's _____ _____ _____ _____ our last clip.

24 Anna and Julie are best friends, but Anna often _____ Julie's _____.

25 **Anna:** _____ _____ *your bag on my desk!*

26 Julie probably _____ _____ because Anna _____ _____ _____ using the word "don't."

27 People _____ don't like _____ _____.

28 Anna _____ _____ to use words _____ _____ "can," "could," or "please."

29 Then, _____ she says will _____ _____ a _____ rather than a _____.

30 **Anna:** _____ _____ *put your bag on your desk?*

31 As we saw in the video clips, _____ _____ _____ in the way we _____ _____ can solve or even _____ _____ _____.

32 Let's _____ these tips _____ _____!

---

16 Calli: "저기, 엄마. 엄마랑 뭔가에 대해 이야기 좀 할 수 있을까요?"

16 Calli는 어머니와 이야기를 나눌 적절한 때를 찾아야 해요.

16 Calli의 어머니도 아마 Calli가 말하려고 했던 것을 듣고 싶어 하셨을 거예요.

16 그러나 어머니에게는 딸과 이야기할 시간이 충분하지 않았어요.

20 Calli는 어머니가 들으실 준비가 된 때를 골라야 해요.

21 Calli: "저기, 엄마. 엄마랑 뭔가에 대해 이야기 좀 할 수 있을까요?"

22 Mom: "물론이지."

23 이제 마지막 동영상을 봅시다.

24 Anna와 Julie는 가장 친한 친구 사이이지만, Anna가 종종 Julie의 마음을 상하게 합니다.

25 Anna: "네 가방을 내 책상에 놓지 마!"

26 Anna가 don't라는 단어를 써서 요구했기 때문에 Julie는 아마 불편하게 느꼈을 거예요.

27 사람들은 명령 받는 것을 전혀 좋아하지 않아요.

28 Anna는 can, could 또는 please와 같은 말을 사용하도록 노력해야 해요.

29 그러면 그녀가 하는 말이 요구보다는 요청처럼 들릴 거예요.

30 Anna: "네 가방은 네 책상에 놔두겠니?"

31 우리가 동영상에서 본 것처럼, 우리 자신을 표현하는 방식을 조금만 바꾸어도 의사소통의 문제를 해결하거나 심지어 막을 수도 있답니다.

32 이 조언들을 명심합시다!

※ 다음 문장을 우리말로 쓰시오.

1 ▶ Speak Your Mind Effectively

➡ _____

2 ▶ Welcome to "All about Teens."

➡ _____

3 ▶ I'm Dr. Carter.

➡ _____

4 ▶ Today, we're going to talk about using good communication skills to express ourselves more effectively.

➡ _____

5 ▶ Let's start with our first clip about Brian.

➡ _____

6 ▶ When he tries to talk to his brother, he always ends up arguing with his brother.

➡ _____

7 ▶ Let's find out the reason why he has this problem.

➡ _____

8 ▶ Brian: You lost my earphones again. Why are you so careless?

➡ _____

9 ▶ Brian is starting a sentence with "you" to express his feelings.

➡ _____

10 ▶ Instead, he should use the "I-message."

➡ _____

11 ▶ Starting with "I" can help him focus on what he feels or thinks rather than point the finger at his brother.

➡ _____

12 ▶ Brian: I'm really upset because my favorite earphones are lost.

➡ _____

13 ▶ Next is Calli.

➡ _____

14 ▶ She is trying to talk to her mother, but she is busy preparing to go to work.

➡ _____

15 ▶ Let's have a look.

➡ _____

16 Calli: Hey, Mom. Could I talk to you about something?
➡ _____

17 Calli needs to find the right time to talk to her mom.
➡ _____

18 Maybe Calli's mom wanted to listen to what Calli was going to say.
➡ _____

19 But she didn't have enough time to talk with her daughter.
➡ _____

20 Calli should pick a time when her mom is ready to listen.
➡ _____

21 Calli: Hey, Mom. Could I talk to you about something?
➡ _____

22 Mom: Sure.
➡ _____

23 Now, let's take a look at our last clip.
➡ _____

24 Anna and Julie are best friends, but Anna often hurts Julie's feelings.
➡ _____

25 Anna: Don't put your bag on my desk!
➡ _____

26 Julie probably felt uncomfortable because Anna made a demand using the word "don't."
➡ _____

27 People simply don't like taking orders.
➡ _____

28 Anna should try to use words such as "can," "could," or "please."
➡ _____

29 Then, what she says will sound like a request rather than a demand.
➡ _____

30 Anna: Could you put your bag on your desk?
➡ _____

31 As we saw in the video clips, a small change in the way we express ourselves can solve or even prevent communication problems.
➡ _____
_____

32 Let's keep these tips in mind!
➡ _____

※ 다음 괄호 안의 단어들을 우리말에 맞도록 바르게 배열하시오.

1 (Your / Speak / Effectively / Mind)
➡ _____

2 (to / Welcome / about / "All / Teens.")
➡ _____

3 (Carter. / Dr. / I'm)
➡ _____

4 (we're / today, / to / going / about / talk / using / communication / good / to / skills / express / more / ourselves / effectively.)
➡ _____
_____

5 (start / let's / our / with / clip / first / Brian. / about)
➡ _____

6 (he / when / to / tries / talk / his / to / brother, / always / he / up / ends / with / arguing / brother. / his)
➡ _____
_____

7 (find / let's / out / reason / the / he / why / this / problem. / has)
➡ _____

8 (Brian: / lost / you / earphones / my / again. // are / why / so / you / careless?)
➡ _____

9 (is / Brian / a / starting / with / sentence / to / "you" / his / express / feelings.)
➡ _____
_____

10 (he / instead, / use / should / "I-message." / the)
➡ _____

11 (with / starting / can / "I" / help / him / help / focus / what / on / feels / he / thinks / or / than / rather / the / point / at / finger / his / brother.)
➡ _____
_____

12 (Brian: / really / I'm / because / upset / favorite / my / earphones / lost. / are)
➡ _____
_____

13 (Calli. / is / next)
➡ _____

14 (is / she / to / trying / talk / her / to / mother, / she / but / is / preparing / busy / go / to / work. / to)
➡ _____
_____

15 (have / let's / look. / a)
➡ _____

1 당신의 마음을 효과적으로 말하라

2 '십 대들의 모든 것'에 오신 걸 환영합니다.

3 저는 Carter 박사입니다.

4 오늘 우리는 자신을 더 효과적으로 표현하기 위해 적절한 의사소통 기술을 사용하는 것에 대해 이야기해 보겠습니다.

5 Brian에 대한 첫 번째 동영상으로 시작해 보죠.

6 Brian이 남동생과 이야기하려고 할 때, 그는 결국 동생과 항상 말다툼을 하게 돼요.

7 그에게 이런 문제가 있는 이유를 알아봅시다.

8 Brian: "너 또 내 이어폰 잃어버렸지. 너는 왜 그렇게 조심성이 없니?"

9 Brian은 그의 감정을 표현하기 위해 '너'로 문장을 시작하고 있군요.

10 대신에 그는 '나 메시지'를 써야 해요.

11 '나'로 시작하는 것이 그가 남동생을 비난하기보다는 자신이 느끼거나 생각하는 것에 집중하도록 도울 수 있답니다.

12 Brian: "내가 가장 좋아하는 이어폰이 없어서 난 정말 속상해."

13 다음은 Calli입니다.

14 그녀는 어머니와 이야기하려고 하지만, 어머니는 출근 준비로 바쁘시군요.

15 한번 보시죠.

16 (Calli: / Mom. / hey, // I / could / to / talk / about / you / something?)
➡ _____

17 (needs / Calli / find / to / right / the / to / time / to / talk / mom. / her)
➡ _____

18 (Calli's / maybe / wanted / mom / listen / to / what / to / was / Calli / going / say. / to)
➡ _____

19 (she / but / have / didn't / time / enough / talk / to / her / with / daughter.)
➡ _____

20 (should / Calli / pick / time / a / her / when / is / mom / to / ready / listen.)
➡ _____

21 (Calli: / Mom. / hey, // I / could / talk / you / to / something? / about)
➡ _____

22 (sure. / Mom:)
➡ _____

23 (let's / now, / a / take / at / look / clip. / last)
➡ _____

24 (Julie / and / Anna / best / are / friends, / Anna / but / hurts / often / feelings. / Julie's)
➡ _____

25 (Anna: / put / don't / bag / your / on / desk! / my)
➡ _____

26 (Julie / felt / probably / because / uncomfortable / made / Anna / demand / a / using / word / "don't." / the)
➡ _____
_____

27 (simply / people / like / don't / orders. / taking)
➡ _____

28 (should / Anna / to / try / words / use / as / such /. "could," / or / "can," / "please.")
➡ _____

29 (what / then, / says / she / sound / will / a / like / rather / request / than / demand. / a)
➡ _____

30 (Anna: / you / could / your / put / bag / your / on / desk?)
➡ _____

31 (we / as / in / saw / video / the / clips, / small / a / change / the / in / way / express / we / can / ourselves / solve / or / prevent / even / problems. / communication)
➡ _____
_____

32 (keep / let's / tips / these / mind! / in)
➡ _____

---

16 Calli: "저기, 엄마. 엄마랑 뭔가에 대해 이야기 좀 할 수 있을까요?"

16 Calli는 어머니와 이야기를 나눌 적절한 때를 찾아야 해요.

16 Calli의 어머니도 아마 Calli가 말하려고 했던 것을 듣고 싶어 하셨을 거예요.

16 그러나 어머니에게는 딸과 이야기할 시간이 충분하지 않았어요.

20 Calli는 어머니가 들으실 준비가 된 때를 골라야 해요.

21 Calli: "저기, 엄마. 엄마랑 뭔가에 대해 이야기 좀 할 수 있을까요?"

22 Mom: "물론이지."

23 이제 마지막 동영상을 봅시다.

24 Anna와 Julie는 가장 친한 친구 사이이지만, Anna가 종종 Julie의 마음을 상하게 합니다.

25 Anna: "네 가방을 내 책상에 놓지 마!"

26 Anna가 don't라는 단어를 써서 요구했기 때문에 Julie는 아마 불편하게 느꼈을 거예요.

27 사람들은 명령 받는 것을 전혀 좋아하지 않아요.

28 Anna는 can, could 또는 please와 같은 말을 사용하도록 노력해야 해요.

29 그러면 그녀가 하는 말이 요구보다는 요청처럼 들릴 거예요.

30 Anna: "네 가방은 네 책상에 놔두겠니?"

31 우리가 동영상에서 본 것처럼, 우리 자신을 표현하는 방식을 조금만 바꾸어도 의사소통의 문제를 해결하거나 심지어 막을 수도 있답니다.

32 이 조언들을 명심합시다!

※ **다음 우리말을 영어로 쓰시오.**

1 당신의 마음을 효과적으로 말하라

➡ _____

2 '십 대들의 모든 것'에 오신 걸 환영합니다.

➡ _____

3 저는 Carter 박사입니다.

➡ _____

4 오늘 우리는 자신을 더 효과적으로 표현하기 위해 적절한 의사소통 기술을 사용하는 것에 대해 이야기해 보겠습니다.

➡ _____

5 Brian에 대한 첫 번째 동영상으로 시작해 보죠.

➡ _____

6 Brian이 남동생과 이야기하려고 할 때, 그는 결국 동생과 항상 말다툼을 하게 돼요.

➡ _____

7 그에게 이런 문제가 있는 이유를 알아봅시다.

➡ _____

8 Brian: "너 또 내 이어폰 잃어버렸지. 너는 왜 그렇게 조심성이 없니?"

➡ _____

9 Brian은 그의 감정을 표현하기 위해 '너'로 문장을 시작하고 있군요.

➡ _____

10 대신에 그는 '나 메시지'를 써야 해요.

➡ _____

11 '나'로 시작하는 것은 그가 남동생을 비난하기보다는 자신이 느끼거나 생각하는 것에 집중하도록 도울 수 있답니다.

➡ _____

12 Brian: "내가 가장 좋아하는 이어폰이 없어져서 난 정말 속상해."

➡ _____

13 다음은 Calli입니다.

➡ _____

14 그녀는 어머니와 이야기하려고 하지만, 어머니는 출근 준비로 바쁘시군요.

➡ _____

15 한번 보시죠.

➡ _____

16 Calli: "저기, 엄마. 엄마랑 뭔가에 대해 이야기 좀 할 수 있을까요?"

➡ _____

17 Calli는 어머니와 이야기를 나눌 적절한 때를 찾아야 해요.

➡ _____

18 Calli의 어머니도 아마 Calli가 말하려고 했던 것을 듣고 싶어 하셨을 거예요.

➡ _____

19 그러나 어머니에게는 딸과 이야기할 시간이 충분하지 않았어요.

➡ _____

20 Calli는 어머니가 들으실 준비가 된 때를 골라야 해요.

➡ _____

21 Calli: "저기, 엄마. 엄마랑 뭔가에 대해 이야기 좀 할 수 있을까요?"

➡ _____

22 Mom: "물론이지."

➡ _____

23 이제 마지막 동영상을 봅시다.

➡ _____

24 Anna와 Julie는 가장 친한 친구 사이이지만, Anna가 종종 Julie의 마음을 상하게 합니다.

➡ _____

25 Anna: "네 가방을 내 책상에 놓지 마!"

➡ _____

26 Anna가 don't라는 단어를 써서 요구했기 때문에 Julie는 아마 불편하게 느꼈을 거예요.

➡ _____

27 사람들은 명령 받는 것을 전혀 좋아하지 않아요.

➡ _____

28 Anna는 can, could 또는 please와 같은 말을 사용하도록 노력해야 해요.

➡ _____

29 그러면 그녀가 하는 말이 요구보다는 요청처럼 들릴 거예요.

➡ _____

30 Anna: "네 가방은 네 책상에 놔두겠니?"

➡ _____

31 우리가 동영상에서 본 것처럼, 우리 자신을 표현하는 방식을 조금만 바꾸어도 의사소통의 문제를 해결하거나 심지어 막을 수도 있답니다.

➡ _____

➡ _____

32 이 조언들을 명심합시다!

➡ _____

※ 다음 우리말과 일치하도록 빈칸에 알맞은 말을 쓰시오.

Wrap Up 1

1. M: You _____ _____, Anna. What's _____?

2. W: Well, I'm _____ _____ my sister, Elsa.

3. M: _____ are you _____ _____ her?

4. W: She _____ _____ me _____.

5. M: Oh, maybe you should _____ _____ _____ _____ _____.

Wrap Up 2

1. W: Hey, Mike! _____ _____ you _____ _____ to my birthday party yesterday?

2. M: Sorry. I really _____ _____ _____ _____ _____ yesterday.

3. W: _____ did you hit your books? _____ you _____ _____ something?

4. M: Oh no, that's _____ _____ I _____. I _____ _____ _____ yesterday _____ I had an exam this morning.

Read and Think B

1. _____ _____ was _____ _____ _____ to you, and why?

2. _____ the "I-message" was _____ _____ _____.

3. I often _____ _____ _____ _____ my sister, and now I understand _____ _____.

After You Read A. Read and Write

1. _____ _____ good communication skills, we can _____ _____ more _____.

2. ⓐ _____ the "I-message."

3. You can _____ _____ _____ you feel or think _____ _____ point the finger at others.

4. ⓑ _____ the _____ _____.

5. Others will listen to you when they have _____ _____ _____ _____ you.

6. ⓒ _____ a _____.

7. Use words _____ _____ "can," "could," or "please."

※ 다음 우리말을 영어로 쓰시오.

Wrap Up 1

1. M: 너 화나 보여, Anna. 무슨 일 있니?
➡ _____

2. W: 음, 난 내 여동생 Elsa에 대해 화가
➡ _____

3. M: 왜 Elsa 때문에 화가 났니?
➡ _____

4. W: 그녀는 계속 나한테 이래라저래라 해.
➡ _____

5. M: 오, 어쩌면 네가 어떻게 느끼는지 그녀에게 말해야 할지도 몰라.
➡ _____

Wrap Up 2

1. W: 안녕, Mike! 너는 왜 어제 내 생일 파티에 안 왔니?
➡ _____

2. M: 미안해. 나는 어제 정말 'hit the books(공부하다)' 해야 했어.
➡ _____

3. W: 왜 책을 쳤니? 너 뭔가에 화가 났니?
➡ _____

4. M: 아 아니, 그런 뜻이 아니야. 나는 오늘 아침에 시험이 있어서 어제 공부를 해야 했어.
➡ _____

Read and Think B

1. 어떤 조언이 너에게 가장 도움이 되었니, 그리고 이유는?
➡ _____

2. "나 메세지"를 사용하는 것이 가장 도움이 되었어.
➡ _____

3. 나는 자주 내 여동생과 논쟁을 벌이곤 했는데, 이제 그 이유를 이해해.
➡ _____

After You Read A. Read and Write

1. 좋은 대화 기술을 사용함으로써, 우리는 스스로를 더 효과적으로 표현할 수 있다.
➡ _____

2. ⓐ "나 메세지"를 사용하라.
➡ _____

3. 남을 비난하기보다 당신이 느끼거나 생각하는 것에 초점을 맞출 수 있다.
➡ _____

4. ⓑ 올바른 시간을 선택하라.
➡ _____

5. 다른 사람들은 그들이 당신과 이야기할 충분한 시간이 있을 때 당신의 말을 들을 것이다.
➡ _____

6. ⓒ 요청을 하라.
➡ _____

7. "can," "could," 또는 "please"와 같은 말을 사용하라.
➡ _____

※ 다음 영어를 우리말로 쓰시오.

01 shape _____

02 unique _____

03 spiky _____

04 unusual _____

05 yellow dust _____

06 investigate _____

07 view _____

08 sticky _____

09 combination _____

10 peak _____

11 shoot _____

12 shooting star _____

13 location _____

14 period _____

15 survive _____

16 rainfall _____

17 glacier _____

18 competition _____

19 countless _____

20 develop _____

21 alive _____

22 ecologist _____

23 cliff _____

24 improve _____

25 insight _____

26 personal _____

27 miracle _____

28 research _____

29 glow _____

30 harsh _____

31 honor _____

32 inspire _____

33 clothing _____

34 colorist _____

35 stand in for _____

36 be[get] inspired by _____

37 come true _____

38 be filled with _____

39 get in shape _____

40 keep ~ on one's toes _____

41 due to 명사 _____

42 be made by ~ _____

43 walk along _____

※ 다음 우리말을 영어로 쓰시오.

01 통찰력 _____

02 절벽 _____

03 많은, 셀 수 없는 _____

04 절정[최대한도]에 이르다 _____

05 의류, 옷 _____

06 개선하다, 향상시키다 _____

07 색채화가 _____

08 위치, 장소 _____

09 조합 _____

10 놀라운 일, 기적 _____

11 모양, 형태 _____

12 만들다, 발전하다 _____

13 생태학자 _____

14 빛나다 _____

15 암초 _____

16 (날씨, 생활환경이) 혹독한 _____

17 촬영하다 _____

18 영감을 주다, 고무하다 _____

19 빙하 _____

20 조사하다 _____

21 끝이 뾰족한 _____

22 살아남다, 생존하다 _____

23 조사하다, 연구하다 _____

24 영광으로 생각하다 _____

25 강우 _____

26 끈적거리는, 달라붙는 _____

27 생기 넘치는, 살아 있는 _____

28 특이한, 흔치 않은 _____

29 풍경, 전망 _____

30 모험 _____

31 개인적인 _____

32 황사 _____

33 실제로 _____

34 최근의 _____

35 수백만의 _____

36 발견하다, 알아보다 _____

37 ～에 기인하다 _____

38 ～을 대신하다 _____

39 ～에 의해 영감을 받다 _____

40 ～로 가득차다 _____

41 좋은 몸 상태를 유지하다 _____

42 ～ 때문에 _____

43 자르다 _____

※ 다음 영영풀이에 알맞은 단어를 <보기>에서 골라 쓴 후, 우리말 뜻을 쓰시오.

1 _____ : to shine with a soft light: _____

2 _____ : the steep side of an area of high land: _____

3 _____ : very special, unusual, or good: _____

4 _____ : to reach the highest point or level: _____

5 _____ : a large hole in the side of a hill or under the ground: _____

6 _____ : difficult to live in and very uncomfortabl: _____

7 _____ : something that combines several things: _____

8 _____ : a particular length of time with a beginning and an end: _____

9 _____ : a very large mass of ice that moves very slowly: _____

10 _____ : consisting of several different types of things or people: _____

11 _____ : an exciting experience in which dangerous or unusual things happen:
  _____

12 _____ : very many, especially more than you think is reasonable: _____

13 _____ : a scientist who studies the environment and the way that plants, animals,
  and humans live together and affect each other: _____

14 _____ : to encourage someone by making them feel confident and eager to do
  something: _____

15 _____ : to study a subject in detail, especially in order to discover new facts or test
  new ideas: _____

16 _____ : a piece of rock or metal from space that burns brightly as it falls towards
  the Earth: _____

harsh	shooting star	cave	adventure
period	ecologist	combination	research
cliff	glacier	glow	inspire
peak	countless	unique	mixed

※ 다음 우리말과 일치하도록 빈칸에 알맞은 말을 쓰시오.

Listen & Talk 1 Get Ready

A: The _____ of the _____ of the mountain is going to be _____.

B: Yeah, I _____ _____ _____ see the view. Let's _____ _____ there!

A: 산꼭대기의 경치는 멋질 거야.
B: 그래, 빨리 경치가 보고 싶어. 저곳으로 뛰어 올라가자!

Listen & Talk 1 A-1

W: David, _____ your summer _____?

M: My family is _____ _____ China. I can't _____ _____ _____ the Rainbow Mountains.

W: The Rainbow Mountains?

M: They _____ some mountains _____ _____ _____ in rainbow colors.

W: That _____ amazing! _____ _____ _____ pictures!

W: David, 여름 계획은 뭐야?
M: 우리 가족은 중국에 갈 거야. 나는 레인보우 산맥을 빨리 방문하고 싶어.
W: 레인보우 산맥?
M: 그것은 무지개 색깔의 화폭처럼 보이는 산들이야.
W: 정말 멋지구나! 사진 많이 찍어!

Listen & Talk 1 A-2

M: Do you _____ _____ _____ the new 3D movie?

W: _____ one?

M: The one _____ _____ _____ the sea. It _____ _____ near Australia's Great Barrier Reef.

W: Oh, I've _____ _____ it. It _____ the most beautiful _____ _____.

M: Right. I _____ _____ _____ _____ the movie. Let's _____ _____ _____ the ticket.

M: 너 새로 나온 3D 영화 보고 싶니?
W: 어느 영화?
M: 바다 밑의 모험에 관한 거야. 그것은 오스트레일리아의 Great Barrier Reef 근처에서 촬영되었어.
W: 오, 난 그것에 대해 들어본 적이 있어. 거기에는 가장 아름다운 해양 생물이 있어.
M: 맞아. 난 그 영화를 빨리 보고 싶어. 가서 표를 사자.

Listen & Talk 1 B

W: Dad, my science club _____ _____ _____ _____ to Dokdo _____ July.

M: Oh, really? _____ do you _____ _____ do there?

W: We are _____ _____ _____ the _____ on the island and _____ bird _____.

W: 아빠, 제 과학 동아리는 7월에 독도에 갈 거예요.
M: 오, 정말? 그곳에서 무엇을 할 계획이니?
W: 우리는 섬에 있는 동굴을 연구하고 새를 관찰하러 갈 거예요.

M: Sounds _____ it will be an _____ _____.

W: Yeah. _____ _____ _____ _____ Dokdo in books. I can't _____ _____ _____ _____ there.

M: I _____ you _____ your _____!

Listen & Talk 2 Get Ready

A: The level of yellow dust _____ really _____ today.

B: Yeah. _____ _____ _____ the yellow dust _____ _____ the deserts of Mongolia _____ Korea.

Listen & Talk 2 A-1

M: Mom, did you watch the _____ _____ today? We will be _____ to see _____ _____ _____ _____ tonight!

W: Wow, fantastic! _____ is the best time _____ _____ _____?

M: I've _____ _____ the _____ _____ will peak _____ 12 a.m. _____ 2 a.m.

W: Wow, it will be a _____ _____!

Listen & Talk 2 A-2

M: Erica, what _____ the white things in the picture?

W: _____ _____ snow rollers. _____ _____ _____ they are _____ _____ strong wind and _____ snow.

M: Interesting! They _____ _____ snow rings.

W: Yeah, I'd _____ to _____ see them _____.

Listen & Talk 2 B

M: Jisu, did you know _____ the sun never _____ in Norway _____ _____?

W: No, I didn't know _____. _____ _____!

M: Yeah, and I've _____ _____ people go hiking and _____ _____ at night _____ it isn't dark.

W: I'd _____ to go hiking and cycling _____ _____ _____ _____ the night!

M: Me, _____. I hope we _____ the _____ _____ _____ it _____.

Communication

M: Let's welcome Ms. Scarlett Lee, the _____ of this year's photo _____.

W: Hello, thank you _____ _____ me. I've _____ _____ _____ the award.

M: Let's _____ about your photo. I've _____ _____ this photo _____ _____ in the Maldives. Is that _____?

W: Yes, this _____ _____ is _____ _____ plankton.

M: Wow, it truly is _____!

W: Yes, it is. I _____ _____ _____ _____ more pictures of _____ _____.

M: I _____ you the _____ of luck!

M: 지수야, 여름 동안 노르웨이에서는 해가 지지 않는다는 걸 알고 있니?

W: 아니, 그건 몰랐어. 정말 흥미롭구나!

M: 그래, 그리고 난 사람들이 밤에 어둡지 않아서 하이킹 가고 심지어 자전거를 타러 간다고 들었어.

W: 나는 한밤중에 하이킹과 자전거를 타러 가고 싶어!

M: 나도. 언젠가 그것을 해볼 기회가 있으면 좋겠어.

M: 올해 사진 대회 우승자인 Scarlett Lee 양을 환영합시다.

W: 안녕하세요, 초대해 주셔서 감사합니다. 상을 받게 되어 영광으로 생각합니다.

M: 사진에 대해 얘기해 봅시다. 저는 이 사진이 몰디브에서 찍힌 거라고 들었어요. 그게 사실인가요?

W: 네, 이 빛나는 해변은 플랑크톤 때문에 생긴 거예요.

M: 와, 정말 놀랍네요!

W: 네, 그래요. 저는 빨리 멋진 해변의 사진을 더 많이 찍고 싶어요.

M: 행운을 빌어요!

※ 다음 우리말에 맞도록 대화를 영어로 쓰시오.

Listen & Talk 1 Get Ready

A: _____

B: _____

Listen & Talk 1 A-1

W: _____

M: _____

W: _____

M: _____

W: _____

Listen & Talk 1 A-2

M: _____

W: _____

M: _____

_____

W: _____

M: _____

Listen & Talk 1 B

W: _____

M: _____

W: _____

M: _____

W: _____

M: _____

M: 흥미로운 여행이 될 것 같구나.

W: 네. 저는 책에서만 독도에 대해서 읽었어요. 빨리 그곳을 실제로 방문하고 싶어요.

M: 즐거운 여행이 되길 바라!

Listen & Talk 2 Get Ready

A: _____

B: _____

_____

A: 오늘 황사의 정도가 정말 심해.

B: 그래. 황사는 몽골의 사막에서 한국으로 이동한다고 들었어.

Listen & Talk 2 A-1

M: _____

_____

W: _____

M: _____

W: _____

M: 엄마, 오늘 일기예보 보셨어요? 우리는 오늘 밤 수많은 유성을 볼 수 있을 거예요!

W: 와, 환상적이야! 그것을 보기에 가장 좋은 시간은 언제니?

M: 저는 유성이 오전 12시에서 2시 사이에 절정에 이를 거라고 들었어요.

W: 와, 특별한 밤이 되겠구나!

Listen & Talk 2 A-2

M: _____

W: _____

_____

M: _____

W: _____

M: Erica, 사진 속의 흰 것들은 뭐니?

W: 그것들은 두루마리 눈이야. 나는 그것이 강한 바람과 끈적끈적한 눈으로 만들어진다고 들었어.

M: 흥미롭구나! 그것들은 눈 반지처럼 보여.

W: 그래, 나도 언젠가 그것들을 실제로 보고 싶어.

Listen & Talk 2 B

M: _____

W: _____

M: _____
_____

W: _____

M: _____

Communication

M: _____

W: _____

M: _____
_____

W: _____

M: _____

W: _____

M: _____

M: 지수야, 여름 동안 노르웨이에서는 해가 지지 않는다는 걸 알고 있니?

W: 아니, 그건 몰랐어. 정말 흥미롭구나!

M: 그래, 그리고 난 사람들이 밤에 어둡지 않아서 하이킹 가고 심지어 자전거를 타러 간다고 들었어.

W: 나는 한밤중에 하이킹과 자전거를 타러 가고 싶어!

M: 나도. 언젠가 그것을 해볼 기회가 있으면 좋겠어.

M: 올해 사진 대회 우승자인 Scarlett Lee 양을 환영합시다.

W: 안녕하세요, 초대해 주셔서 감사합니다. 상을 받게 되어 영광으로 생각합니다.

M: 사진에 대해 얘기해 봅시다. 저는 이 사진이 몰디브에서 찍힌 거라고 들었어요. 그게 사실인가요?

W: 네, 이 빛나는 해변은 플랑크톤 때문에 생긴 거예요.

M: 와, 정말 놀랍네요!

W: 네, 그래요. 저는 빨리 멋진 해변의 사진을 더 많이 찍고 싶어요.

M: 행운을 빌어요!

※ 다음 우리말과 일치하도록 빈칸에 알맞은 것을 골라 쓰시오.

1 The _____ _____ My _____
A. Eyes　　　　B. Through　　　C. World

2 "The _____ of _____ _____ us all.
A. nature　　　B. beauty　　　C. inspires

3 Let's _____ _____ how people from different _____ of work get _____ by nature."
A. out　　　B. inspired　　　C. fields　　　D. find

4 _____ Wang, _____
A. Ecologist　　　B. Lin

5 **Tsingy, the _____ _____ of Madagascar**
A. Forest　　　B. Stone

6 I've _____ _____ the stone forest of Madagascar to study plants and animals _____ _____ 20 years.
A. for　　　B. been　　　C. over　　　D. visiting

7 The _____ stones of this place are _____ _____ of nature.
A. true　　　B. spiky　　　C. miracles

8 This _____ shape _____ _____ _____ by rainfall.
A. created　　　B. has　　　C. amazing　　　D. been

9 Rain has cut _____ the stones and made them _____ and _____ _____ a long period of time.
A. over　　　B. down　　　C. spiky　　　D. sharp

10 The _____ is _____ for _____ to live in, but they have found ways to _____.
A. harsh　　　B. survive　　　C. animals　　　D. environment

11 For example, lemurs, _____ only live in Madagascar, have _____ legs _____ help them jump from one stone tower to _____.
A. frog-like　　　B. which　　　C. another　　　D. that

12 _____ me, the stone forest _____ _____ a jack-in-the-box.
A. like　　　B. is　　　C. for

13 It always _____ me and _____ me _____ my _____!
A. keeps　　　B. surprises　　　C. toes　　　D. on

14 **Amber Smith, _____ _____**
A. Colorist　　　B. Fashion

15 **Caño Cristales, the _____ _____ _____ of Colombia**
A. Colors　　　B. River　　　C. Five　　　D. of

16 The world is _____ _____ millions of _____ colors.
A. with　　　B. different　　　C. filled

1　내 눈에 비친 세계

2　"자연의 아름다움은 우리 모두에게 영감을 준다.

3　서로 다른 직업 분야의 사람들이 자연에 의해 어떻게 영감을 받는지 알아보자."

4　Lin Wang, 생태학자

5　Tsingy, 마다가스카르의 석림

6　나는 20년 이상 동안 식물과 동물을 연구하기 위해서 마다가스카르의 석림을 방문하고 있다.

7　이 지역의 뾰족한 돌들은 진정한 자연의 놀라움이다.

8　이 놀라운 모양은 비에 의해서 만들어졌다.

9　비가 오랜 기간 동안 돌을 침식해서 날카롭고 뾰족하게 만들었다.

10　이런 환경은 동물들이 살기에 험난하지만, 동물들은 생존할 방법들을 찾아냈다.

11　예를 들어, 마다가스카르에서만 사는 여우원숭이는 한 개의 돌탑에서 다른 돌탑으로 뛸 수 있도록 도와주는 개구리와 같은 다리를 가지고 있다.

12　나에게 석림은 '잭인더박스(열면 인형이 튀어나오는 상자)'와 같다.

13　그것은 늘 나를 놀라게 하고 정신을 바짝 차리게 한다!

14　Amber Smith, 패션 색채 전문가

15　Caño Cristales, 콜롬비아의 다섯 색깔의 강

16　세계는 수백만의 다양한 색깔로 가득 차 있다.

17 It is my job to _____, _____, and _____ colors for _____.

    A. clothing   B. mix   C. create   D. develop

18 _____ the years, I've _____ _____ _____ from the beautiful colors of Caño Cristales.

    A. insights   B. over   C. gaining   D. been

19 You cannot see the wonderful _____ colors of this river _____ _____ in the _____.

    A. else   B. mixed   C. anywhere   D. world

20 The _____ of _____ plants under the water and sunlight makes the colors more _____ and _____.

    A. alive   B. combination   C. bright   D. colorful

21 _____ I visit the Caño Cristales, it makes me think that maybe there are still _____ colors that are _____ to be _____.

    A. countless   B. waiting   C. whenever   D. created

22 Danny Mehta, _____ _____

    A. Scout   B. Location

23 Vatnajökull _____ Park, _____ _____ of Iceland

    A. Beauty   B. National   C. Frozen

24 I'm a _____ scout and my job is finding _____ places to _____ movies.

    A. shoot   B. location   C. perfect

25 Iceland is the best place _____ many location scouts to visit _____ _____ its unusual _____.

    A. due   B. beauty   C. to   D. for

26 _____ _____ _____ is the Vatnajökull National Park.

    A. favorite   B. personal   C. my

27 The sharp cliffs, blue _____ caves, and long mountain _____ can _____ in for any _____ in the world or the universe.

    A. glacier   B. stand   C. ranges   D. place

28 In fact, the _____ sci-fi movie we _____ here was produced _____ _____ computer graphics!

    A. using   B. shot   C. without   D. recent

29 Iceland can _____ _____ our wildest dreams _____ _____ on the movie screen.

    A. come   B. make   C. true   D. help

---

17 의류를 위해서 색을 섞고, 발전시키고, 만들어 내는 것이 나의 일이다.

18 수년 동안, 나는 카뇨 크리스탈레스의 아름다운 색으로부터 영감을 얻어 오고 있다.

19 이 강의 아름답게 혼합된 색깔은 세상 어느 다른 곳에서도 볼 수 없다.

20 물속의 화려한 식물들과 햇빛의 결합은 그 색깔을 더 생생하고 밝게 만든다.

21 내가 카뇨 크리스탈레스를 방문할 때마다 그 강은 나로 하여금 아마도 여전히 만들어지기를 기다리고 있는 셀 수 없이 많은 색깔이 있음을 생각하게 한다.

22 Danny Mehta, 장소 섭외가

23 Vatnajökull 국립 공원, 아이슬란드의 얼음으로 덮인 아름다움

24 나는 장소 섭외가이고 나의 일은 영화를 찍기에 완벽한 장소를 찾는 것이다.

25 아이슬란드는 비범한 아름다움 때문에 많은 장소 섭외가들이 방문하기에 최고의 장소이다.

26 내가 개인적으로 가장 선호하는 곳은 바트나이외쿠틀 국립 공원이다.

27 가파른 절벽, 푸른 빙하 동굴, 그리고 긴 산맥들은 세계나 혹은 우주의 어느 장소도 대신할 수 있다.

28 사실상, 우리가 여기서 찍은 최근의 공상 과학 영화는 컴퓨터 그래픽 없이 만들어졌다!

29 아이슬란드는 우리의 가장 무모한 꿈을 영화 스크린에서 실현할 수 있게 해 준다.

※ 다음 우리말과 일치하도록 빈칸에 알맞은 말을 쓰시오.

1 The _____ _____ My Eyes

2 "The _____ of nature _____ _____ _____.

3 _____ _____ _____ how people from different _____ _____ _____ _____ _____ by nature."

4 Lin Wang, _____

5 Tsingy, the _____ _____ of Madagascar

6 _____ _____ _____ the _____ _____ of Madagascar to study plants and animals _____ _____ 20 years.

7 The _____ _____ of this place are _____ _____ of nature.

8 This _____ shape _____ _____ _____ _____ _____.

9 Rain has _____ _____ the stones and made them _____ and _____ _____ a long period of time.

10 The environment is _____ _____ _____ _____ _____ _____, but they have found ways _____ _____.

11 For example, lemurs, _____ only live in Madagascar, have _____ legs _____ _____ them _____ _____ one stone tower _____ _____.

12 For me, the stone forest _____ _____ a _____.

13 It always _____ me and _____ _____ _____ _____!

14 Amber Smith, _____ _____

15 Caño Cristales, the _____ _____ _____ _____ of Colombia

16 The world _____ _____ _____ _____ _____ different colors.

---

1 내 눈에 비친 세계

2 "자연의 아름다움은 우리 모두에게 영감을 준다.

3 서로 다른 직업 분야의 사람들이 자연에 의해 어떻게 영감을 받는지 알아보자."

4 Lin Wang, 생태학자

5 Tsingy, 마다가스카르의 석림

6 나는 20년 이상 동안 식물과 동물을 연구하기 위해서 마다가스카르의 석림을 방문하고 있다.

7 이 지역의 뾰족한 돌들은 진정한 자연의 놀라움이다.

8 이 놀라운 모양은 비에 의해서 만들어졌다.

9 비가 오랜 기간 동안 돌을 침식해서 날카롭고 뾰족하게 만들었다.

10 이런 환경은 동물들이 살기에 험난하지만, 동물들은 생존할 방법들을 찾아냈다.

11 예를 들어, 마다가스카르에서만 사는 여우원숭이는 한 개의 돌탑에서 다른 돌탑으로 뛸 수 있도록 도와주는 개구리와 같은 다리를 가지고 있다.

12 나에게 석림은 '잭인더박스(열면 인형이 튀어나오는 상자)'와 같다.

13 그것은 늘 나를 놀라게 하고 정신을 바짝 차리게 한다!

14 Amber Smith, 패션 색채 전문가

15 Caño Cristales, 콜롬비아의 다섯 색깔의 강

16 세계는 수백만의 다양한 색깔로 가득 차 있다.

17 It is my job to _____, _____, and _____ _____ for clothing.

18 Over the years, _____ _____ _____ insights from the _____ _____ of Caño Cristales.

19 You cannot see the _____ _____ _____ of this river _____ _____ in the world.

20 The _____ of _____ _____ under the water and sunlight _____ the colors _____ _____ and _____ .

21 _____ I visit the Caño Cristales, it _____ me _____ that maybe there are still _____ colors that are _____ _____ _____ _____ .

22 Danny Mehta, _____ _____

23 Vatnajökull National Park, _____ _____ of Iceland

24 I'm a location scout and my job is finding _____ _____ _____ _____ _____ .

25 Iceland is the best place _____ _____ _____ to visit _____ _____ its _____ _____ .

26 _____ _____ _____ is the Vatnajökull National Park.

27 The sharp _____, blue _____ _____, and long mountain ranges can _____ _____ _____ _____ _____ in the world or the universe.

28 _____ _____, the recent sci-fi movie _____ _____ was _____ _____ _____ computer graphics!

29 Iceland can _____ _____ our wildest dreams _____ _____ on the movie screen.

본문 Test **35**

---

17 의류를 위해서 색을 섞고, 발전시키고, 만들어 내는 것이 나의 일이다.

18 수년 동안, 나는 카뇨 크리스탈레스의 아름다운 색으로부터 영감을 얻어 오고 있다.

19 이 강의 아름답게 혼합된 색깔은 세상 어느 다른 곳에서도 볼 수 없다.

20 물속의 화려한 식물들과 햇빛의 결합은 그 색깔을 더 생생하고 밝게 만든다.

21 내가 카뇨 크리스탈레스를 방문할 때마다 그 강은 나로 하여금 아마도 여전히 만들어지기를 기다리고 있는 셀 수 없이 많은 색깔이 있음을 생각하게 한다.

22 Danny Mehta, 장소 섭외가

23 Vatnajökull 국립 공원, 아이슬란드의 얼음으로 덮인 아름다움

24 나는 장소 섭외가이고 나의 일은 영화를 찍기에 완벽한 장소를 찾는 것이다.

25 아이슬란드는 비범한 아름다움 때문에 많은 장소 섭외가들이 방문하기에 최고의 장소이다.

26 내가 개인적으로 가장 선호하는 곳은 바트나이외쿠틀 국립 공원이다.

27 가파른 절벽, 푸른 빙하 동굴, 그리고 긴 산맥들은 세계나 혹은 우주의 어느 장소도 대신할 수 있다.

28 사실상, 우리가 여기서 찍은 최근의 공상 과학 영화는 컴퓨터 그래픽 없이 만들어졌다!

29 아이슬란드는 우리의 가장 무모한 꿈을 영화 스크린에서 실현할 수 있게 해 준다.

※ 다음 문장을 우리말로 쓰시오.

1 The World Through My Eyes

➡ _____

2 "The beauty of nature inspires us all.

➡ _____

3 Let's find out how people from different fields of work get inspired by nature."

➡ _____

4 Lin Wang, Ecologist

➡ _____

5 Tsingy, the Stone Forest of Madagascar

➡ _____

6 I've been visiting the stone forest of Madagascar to study plants and animals for over 20 years.

➡ _____

7 The spiky stones of this place are true miracles of nature.

➡ _____

8 This amazing shape has been created by rainfall.

➡ _____

9 Rain has cut down the stones and made them sharp and spiky over a long period of time.

➡ _____

10 The environment is harsh for animals to live in, but they have found ways to survive.

➡ _____

11 For example, lemurs, which only live in Madagascar, have frog-like legs that help them jump from one stone tower to another.

➡ _____

_____

12 For me, the stone forest is like a jack-in-the-box.

➡ _____

13 It always surprises me and keeps me on my toes!

➡ _____

14 Amber Smith, Fashion Colorist

➡ _____

15 Caño Cristales, the River of Five Colors of Colombia

➡ _____

16 The world is filled with millions of different colors.

➡ _____

17 It is my job to mix, develop, and create colors for clothing.

➡ _____

18 Over the years, I've been gaining insights from the beautiful colors of Caño Cristales.

➡ _____

19 You cannot see the wonderful mixed colors of this river anywhere else in the world.

➡ _____

20 The combination of colorful plants under the water and sunlight makes the colors more alive and bright.

➡ _____

21 Whenever I visit the Caño Cristales, it makes me think that maybe there are still countless colors that are waiting to be created.

➡ _____

_____

22 Danny Mehta, Location Scout

➡ _____

23 Vatnajökull National Park, Frozen Beauty of Iceland

➡ _____

24 I'm a location scout and my job is finding perfect places to shoot movies.

➡ _____

25 Iceland is the best place for many location scouts to visit due to its unusual beauty.

➡ _____

26 My personal favorite is the Vatnajökull National Park.

➡ _____

27 The sharp cliffs, blue glacier caves, and long mountain ranges can stand in for any place in the world or the universe.

➡ _____

28 In fact, the recent sci-fi movie we shot here was produced without using computer graphics!

➡ _____

29 Iceland can help make our wildest dreams come true on the movie screen.

➡ _____

※ 다음 괄호 안의 단어들을 우리말에 맞도록 바르게 배열하시오.

1 (World / The / My / Eyes / Through)
➡ _____

2 (beauty / "the / nature / of / us / all. / inspires)
➡ _____

3 (find / let's / out / people / how / different / from / of / fields / work / by / get / inspired / nature.")
➡ _____
_____

4 (Wang, / Lin / Ecologist)
➡ _____

5 (the / Tsingy, / Stone / of / Forest / Madagascar)
➡ _____

6 (been / I've / the / visiting / stone / of / forest / Madagascar / study / to / and / plants / for / animals / 20 / over / years.)
➡ _____
_____

7 (spiky / the / of / stones / this / are / place / true / of / miracles / nature.)
➡ _____

8 (amazing / this / has / shape / been / by / rainfall. / created)
➡ _____

9 (has / rain / down / cut / stones / the / and / them / made / sharp / over / and / spiky / long / a / of / period / time.)
➡ _____
_____

10 (environment / the / is / for / harsh / to / animals / in, / live / but / have / they / found / ways / survive. / to)
➡ _____
_____

11 (example, / for / which / lemurs, / only / in / live / Madagascar, / frog-like / have / that / legs / them / help / from / jump / stone / one / to / another. / tower)
➡ _____
_____

12 (me, / for / stone / the / is / forest / a / like / jack-in-the-box.)
➡ _____

13 (always / it / me / surprises / and / me / keeps / my / on / toes!)
➡ _____

14 (Smith, / Amber / Colorist / Fashion)
➡ _____

15 (Cristales, / Caño / River / the / Five / of / Colors / Colombia / of)
➡ _____

16 (world / the / filled / is / with / of / millions / of / colors. / different)
➡ _____

1 내 눈에 비친 세계

2 "자연의 아름다움은 우리 모두에게 영감을 준다.

3 서로 다른 직업 분야의 사람들이 자연에 의해 어떻게 영감을 받는지 알아보자."

4 Lin Wang, 생태학자

5 Tsingy, 마다가스카르의 석림

6 나는 20년 이상 동안 식물과 동물을 연구하기 위해서 마다가스카르의 석림을 방문하고 있다.

7 이 지역의 뾰족한 돌들은 진정한 자연의 놀라움이다.

8 이 놀라운 모양은 비에 의해서 만들어졌다.

9 비가 오랜 기간 동안 돌을 침식해서 날카롭고 뾰족하게 만들었다.

10 이런 환경은 동물들이 살기에 험난하지만, 동물들은 생존할 방법들을 찾아냈다.

11 예를 들어, 마다가스카르에서만 사는 여우원숭이는 한 개의 돌탑에서 다른 돌탑으로 뛸 수 있도록 도와주는 개구리와 같은 다리를 가지고 있다.

12 나에게 석림은 '잭인더박스(열면 인형이 튀어나오는 상자)'와 같다.

13 그것은 늘 나를 놀라게 하고 정신을 바짝 차리게 한다!

14 Amber Smith, 패션 색채 전문가

15 Caño Cristales, 콜롬비아의 다섯 색깔의 강

16 세계는 수백만의 다양한 색깔로 가득 차 있다.

17 (is / it / job / my / mix, / to / and / develop, / colors / create / clothing. / for)

➡ _____

18 (over / years, / the / been / I've / insights / gaining / the / from / colors / beautiful / of / Cristales. / Caño)

➡ _____

19 (cannot / you / see / wonderful / the / mixed / of / colors / this / river / else / anywhere / the / in / world.)

➡ _____

20 (combination / the / colorful / of / under / plants / water / the / and / makes / sunlight / colors / the / alive / more / bright. / and)

➡ _____

21 (I / whenever / vist / Caño / the / Cristales, / makes / it / think / me / maybe / that / are / there / countless / still / that / colors / are / to / waiting / created. / be)

➡ _____

22 (Mehta, / Danny / Scout / Location)

➡ _____

23 (Vatnajökull / Park, / National / Beauty / Frozen / Iceland / of)

➡ _____

24 (a / I'm / scout / location / and / job / my / finding / is / places / perfect / shoot / to / movies.)

➡ _____

25 (is / Iceland / the / place / best / many / for / scouts / location / to / due / visit / to / unusual / its / beauty.)

➡ _____

26 (personal / my / is / favorite / the / National / Vatnajökull / Park.)

➡ _____

27 (sharp / the / cliffs, / glacier / blue / caves, / long / and / ranges / mountain / can / in / stand / for / place / any / the / in / world / the / or / universe.)

➡ _____

28 (fact, / in / recent / the / sci-fi / we / movie / shot / was / here / without / produced / computer / using / graphics!)

➡ _____

29 (can / Iceland / make / help / wildest / our / dreams / true / come / the / on / screen. / movie)

➡ _____

17 의류를 위해서 색을 섞고, 발전시키고, 만들어 내는 것이 나의 일이다.

18 수년 동안, 나는 카뇨 크리스탈레스의 아름다운 색으로부터 영감을 얻어 오고 있다.

19 이 강의 아름답게 혼합된 색깔은 세상 어느 다른 곳에서도 볼 수 없다.

20 물속의 화려한 식물들과 햇빛의 결합은 그 색깔을 더 생생하고 밝게 만든다.

21 내가 카뇨 크리스탈레스를 방문할 때마다 그 강은 나로 하여금 아마도 여전히 만들어지기를 기다리고 있는 셀 수 없이 많은 색깔이 있음을 생각하게 한다.

22 **Danny Mehta, 장소 섭외가**

23 **Vatnajökull 국립 공원, 아이슬란드의 얼음으로 덮인 아름다움**

24 나는 장소 섭외가이고 나의 일은 영화를 찍기에 완벽한 장소를 찾는 것이다.

25 아이슬란드는 비범한 아름다움 때문에 많은 장소 섭외가들이 방문하기에 최고의 장소이다.

26 내가 개인적으로 가장 선호하는 곳은 바트나이외쿠틀 국립 공원이다.

27 가파른 절벽, 푸른 빙하 동굴, 그리고 긴 산맥들은 세계나 혹은 우주의 어느 장소도 대신할 수 있다.

28 사실상, 우리가 여기서 찍은 최근의 공상 과학 영화는 컴퓨터 그래픽 없이 만들어졌다!

29 아이슬란드는 우리의 가장 무모한 꿈을 영화 스크린에서 실현할 수 있게 해 준다.

※ 다음 우리말을 영어로 쓰시오.

1 내 눈에 비친 세계

➡ _____

2 "자연의 아름다움은 우리 모두에게 영감을 준다.

➡ _____

3 서로 다른 직업 분야의 사람들이 자연에 의해 어떻게 영감을 받는지 알아보자."

➡ _____

4 Lin Wang, 생태학자

➡ _____

5 Tsingy, 마다가스카르의 석림

➡ _____

6 나는 20년 이상 동안 식물과 동물을 연구하기 위해서 마다가스카르의 석림을 방문하고 있다.

➡ _____

7 이 지역의 뾰족한 돌들은 진정한 자연의 놀라움이다.

➡ _____

8 이 놀라운 모양은 비에 의해서 만들어졌다.

➡ _____

9 비가 오랜 기간 동안 돌을 침식해서 날카롭고 뾰족하게 만들었다.

➡ _____

10 이런 환경은 동물들이 살기에 험난하지만, 동물들은 생존할 방법들을 찾아냈다.

➡ _____

11 예를 들어, 마다가스카르에서만 사는 여우원숭이는 한 개의 돌탑에서 다른 돌탑으로 뛸 수 있도록 도와주는 개구리와 같은 다리를 가지고 있다.

➡ _____

_____

12 나에게 석림은 '잭인더박스(열면 인형이 튀어나오는 상자!)'와 같다.

➡ _____

13 그것은 늘 나를 놀라게 하고 정신을 바짝 차리게 한다!

➡ _____

14 Amber Smith, 패션 색채 전문가

➡ _____

15 Caño Cristales, 콜롬비아의 다섯 색깔의 강

➡ _____

16 세계는 수백만의 다양한 색깔로 가득 차 있다.

➡ _____

17 의류를 위해서 색을 섞고, 발전시키고, 만들어 내는 것이 나의 일이다.

➡ _____

18 수년 동안, 나는 카뇨 크리스탈레스의 아름다운 색으로부터 영감을 얻어 오고 있다.

➡ _____

19 이 강의 아름답게 혼합된 색깔은 세상 어느 다른 곳에서도 볼 수 없다.

➡ _____

20 물속의 화려한 식물들과 햇빛의 결합은 그 색깔을 더 생생하고 밝게 만든다.

➡ _____

21 내가 카뇨 크리스탈레스를 방문할 때마다 그 강은 나로 하여금 아마도 여전히 만들어지기를 기다리고 있는 셀 수 없이 많은 색깔이 있음을 생각하게 한다.

➡ _____

_____

22 Danny Mehta, 장소 섭외가

➡ _____

23 Vatnajökull 국립 공원, 아이슬란드의 얼음으로 덮인 아름다움

➡ _____

24 나는 장소 섭외가이고 나의 일은 영화를 찍기에 완벽한 장소를 찾는 것이다.

➡ _____

25 아이슬란드는 비범한 아름다움 때문에 많은 장소 섭외가들이 방문하기에 최고의 장소이다.

➡ _____

26 내가 개인적으로 가장 선호하는 곳은 바트나이외쿠틀 국립 공원이다.

➡ _____

27 가파른 절벽, 푸른 빙하 동굴, 그리고 긴 산맥들은 세계나 혹은 우주의 어느 장소도 대신할 수 있다.

➡ _____

_____

28 사실상, 우리가 여기서 찍은 최근의 공상 과학 영화는 컴퓨터 그래픽 없이 만들어졌다!

➡ _____

29 아이슬란드는 우리의 가장 무모한 꿈을 영화 스크린에서 실현할 수 있게 해 준다.

➡ _____

※ 다음 우리말과 일치하도록 빈칸에 알맞은 말을 쓰시오.

Communication Step B

1. A: Congratulations _____ _____ the award. _____ _____ that this photo _____ _____ in India. Is that _____?

2. B: Yes, this rainbow cloud _____ _____ _____ thin clouds and water _____.

3. A: Wow, it _____ _____ _____!

4. B: Yes, it is. I _____ _____ _____ _____ more photos of _____ _____.

5. A: I _____ you _____ _____ _____ _____!

1. A: 상 받은 것을 축하해. 이 사진이 인도에서 찍힌 것이라고 들었어. 맞니?
2. B: 응, 이 무지개 구름은 얇은 구름과 물방울에 의해 생긴 거야.
3. A: 와, 정말 멋지다!
4. B: 응, 그래. 어서 더 많은 멋진 구름 사진을 찍고 싶어.
5. A: 행운을 빌어!

Wrap Up 1

1. W: Your uncle, John, is _____ _____ _____ South America this weekend.

2. M: That's great. He _____ _____ _____ for almost 2 years, _____?

3. W: Yeah, he's been in the jungle _____ _____ _____ _____ _____ _____.

4. M: Wow, that's amazing. I _____ _____ _____ _____ him and _____ _____ his stories.

5. W: Me, too. We're _____ _____ with him this Saturday, so _____ _____ _____ _____.

6. M: Okay, I _____, Mom.

1. W: 네 삼촌, John이 이번 주말에 남아메리카에서 돌아올 거야.
2. M: 잘됐네요. 그는 거의 2년 동안 떨어져 있었죠, 그렇죠?
3. W: 그래, 그는 연구를 위해 대부분의 시간을 정글에 있었어.
4. M: 와, 정말 놀랍네요. 빨리 그를 보고 그의 이야기를 듣고 싶어요.
5. W: 나도. 이번 토요일에 그와 저녁 식사를 할 거니까 다른 계획은 세우지 마.
6. M: 알았어요, 안 그럴게요. 엄마.

Think & Write Step A

1. _____ Jiri and Mt. Seorak
2. _____ for _____ Fans
3. • _____ _____ beautiful hiking _____
4. • learn how to get _____ _____ and _____
5. _____ for _____ Fans
6. Madrid and _____
7. • meet _____ _____
8. • learn _____ _____ _____ your soccer skills
9. _____ and London
10. _____ _____ _____ Fans
11. • visit _____ _____ _____
12. • learn _____ _____ _____ pictures _____

1. 지리산과 설악산
2. 하이킹 팬들을 위한 여행
3. • 아름다운 하이킹 길을 따라 걷는다
4. • 좋은 몸매를 유지하고 건강을 유지하는 법을 배운다
5. 축구 팬들을 위한 여행
6. 마드리드와 맨체스터
7. • 유명한 선수들을 만난다
8. • 여러분의 축구 기술을 향상시키는 법을 배운다
9. 파리와 런던
10. 예술 팬들을 위한 여행
11. • 유명한 미술관을 방문한다
12. • 창조적으로 그림을 그리는 법을 배운다

※ 다음 우리말을 영어로 쓰시오.

Communication Step B

1. A: 상 받은 것을 축하해. 이 사진이 인도에서 찍힌 것이라고 들었어. 맞니?
➡
2. B: 응, 이 무지개 구름은 얇은 구름과 물방울에 의해 생긴 거야.
➡
3. A: 와, 정말 멋지다!
➡
4. B: 응, 그래. 어서 더 많은 멋진 구름 사진을 찍고 싶어.
➡
5. A: 행운을 빌어!
➡

Wrap Up 1

1. W: 네 삼촌, John이 이번 주말에 남아메리카에서 돌아올 거야.
➡
2. M: 잘됐네요. 그는 거의 2년 동안 떨어져 있었죠, 그렇죠?
➡
3. W: 그래, 그는 연구를 위해 대부분의 시간을 정글에 있었어.
➡
4. M: 와, 정말 놀랍네요. 빨리 그를 보고 그의 이야기를 듣고 싶어요.
➡
5. W: 나도. 이번 토요일에 그와 저녁 식사를 할 거니까 다른 계획은 세우지 마.
➡
6. M: 알았어요, 안 그럴게요. 엄마.
➡

Think & Write Step A

1. 지리산과 설악산
➡
2. 하이킹 팬들을 위한 여행
➡
3. • 아름다운 하이킹 길을 따라 걷는다
➡
4. • 좋은 몸매를 유지하고 건강을 유지하는 법을 배운다
➡
5. 축구 팬들을 위한 여행
➡
6. 마드리드와 맨체스터
➡
7. • 유명한 선수들을 만난다
➡
8. • 여러분의 축구 기술을 향상시키는 법을 배운다
➡
9. 파리와 런던
➡
10. 예술 팬들을 위한 여행
➡
11. • 유명한 미술관을 방문한다
➡
12. • 창조적으로 그림을 그리는 법을 배운다
➡

※ 다음 영어를 우리말로 쓰시오.

01	horrible	22	invention
02	article	23	embarrassing
03	biography	24	strange
04	ruin	25	female
05	husband	26	whisper
06	detective	27	marriage
07	fortress	28	chest
08	gamble	29	since
09	disappointing	30	merchant
10	afterwards	31	clinic
11	fortune	32	solve
12	general	33	truth
13	include	34	scholar
14	locker	35	instead of
15	whenever	36	yell at
16	independence	37	be used to (동)명사
17	movement	38	devote one's life to 명사
18	wooden	39	at that moment
19	odd	40	make an arrangement
20	officer	41	keep a secret
21	realistic	42	behind one's back
		43	It is said that 주어+동사 ~

※ 다음 우리말을 영어로 쓰시오.

01 나중에, 그 뒤에

02 상인

03 자서전, 전기

04 서랍장, 큰 상자, 장롱

05 (정치적 · 사회적) 운동

06 망치다, 파산시키다

07 실망시키는

08 부끄러운, 당황스러운

09 독립, 광복

10 이상한

11 재산, 행운

12 도박하다, ～을 도박으로 잃다

13 사회

14 장군

15 소곤소곤 이야기하다

16 ～을 포함하다

17 기계, 기구

18 학자

19 발명품, 발명

20 끔찍한

21 기사

22 결혼, 혼인

23 여자; 여자의, 여성의

24 궁금하다

25 물건

26 요새

27 병원, 진료소

28 진짜 같은, 사실적인

29 형사, 탐정

30 구하다

31 남편

32 나무로 된, 목재의

33 사물함

34 낯선, 모르는

35 비밀을 지키다

36 ～에게 고함치다

37 ～을 보다

38 청구하다, 청하다

39 그 순간에

40 ～ 대신에

41 입어 보다, 신어 보다

42 ～을 결정하다

43 ～하는 데 익숙하다

※ 다음 영영풀이에 알맞은 단어를 <보기>에서 골라 쓴 후, 우리말 뜻을 쓰시오.

1 _____ : relating to women or girls: _____

2 _____ : a very large amount of money: _____

3 _____ : the man that somebody is married to: _____

4 _____ : a large strong heavy box used for storing things: _____

5 _____ : to make someone lose all their money or power: _____

6 _____ : an officer of very high rank in the army or air force: _____

7 _____ : to contain someone or something as a part: _____

8 _____ : a book that someone writes about someone else's life: _____

9 _____ : someone who buys and sells goods in large quantities: _____

10 _____ : to make someone or something safe from danger, harm, or destruction: _____

11 _____ : a large strong building used for defending an important place: _____

12 _____ : freedom from control by another country or organization: _____

13 _____ : a piece of writing about a particular subject that is published in a newspaper or magazine: _____

14 _____ : a gradual development or change of an attitude, opinion, or policy: _____

15 _____ : a small cabinet that can be locked, where you can leave your clothes, bags, etc. while you play a sport or go somewhered: _____

16 _____ : someone who studies a particular subject and knows a lot about it, especially a subject that is not scientific: _____

article	husband	save	fortress
locker	ruin	include	chest
movement	female	merchant	fortune
scholar	independence	biography	general

※ 다음 우리말과 일치하도록 빈칸에 알맞은 말을 쓰시오.

Listen & Talk 1 Get Ready

A: Kim Deuksin _____ _____ _____.

B: No! I _____ a book and _____ _____ _____ that he was a

_____.

C: Don't _____. You are _____ _____.

A: 김득신은 화가였어.
B: 아니야! 내가 책을 읽었는데 그는 학자였다고 해.
C: 싸우지 마. 너희 둘 다 옳아.

Listen & Talk 1 A-1

M: Lisa, _____ are you _____?

W: I'm _____ a _____ of Gwon Giok.

M: I _____ _____ about her. Who is she?

W: She was _____ _____ _____ pilot in Korea. _____ _____

_____ _____ she had _____ 7,000 hours of _____ _____.

M: Wow, I didn't know that.

M: Lisa, 너 뭐 읽고 있니?
W: 권기옥의 전기를 읽고 있어.
M: 그녀에 대해 들어본 적이 없어. 그녀는 누구니?
W: 그녀는 한국의 첫 번째 여성 조종사야. 그녀는 비행시간이 7,000시간이 넘는다고 해.
M: 와, 난 몰랐어.

Listen & Talk 1 A-2

M: I watched an _____ movie yesterday. Jeong Yakyong was a

_____ in it.

W: Jeong Yakyong? Wasn't he a _____ in the Joseon Dynasty?

M: Yeah, _____ _____ _____ _____ _____ _____ _____

_____ _____ a detective. He _____ about 90 _____.

W: Oh, I _____ _____ _____ he was also a _____.

M: 난 어제 흥미 있는 영화를 보았어. 그 영화에서 정약용이 탐정이었어.
W: 정약용? 그는 조선 왕조의 학자 아니었니?
M: 응, 하지만 그는 탐정이기도 했다고 해. 그는 약 90개의 사건을 해결했어.
W: 아, 그가 또한 탐정이었다는 건 몰랐어.

Listen & Talk 1 B

W: Hey, Mark, do you _____ _____ Father Lee Taeseok?

M: Yeah, I've _____ of him. Why?

W: _____ _____ _____ _____ this article. He is going

_____ _____ _____ in the _____ _____ textbook in

South Sudan.

M: Wow, that's great.

W: Yeah, he _____ the children _____ _____ _____ _____

and a school. It is said _____ _____ will _____

_____ the textbook.

M: _____ is good _____ hear _____ students will learn about

_____ a great person.

W: 어이, Mark, 너 이태석 신부에 대해 아니?
M: 응, 그에 대해 들어본 적이 있어. 왜?
W: 이 기사를 봐. 그는 남수단의 사회 교과서에 실릴 거야.
M: 와, 그거 대단하구나.
W: 그래, 그는 병원과 학교를 지어 아이들을 도와주었어. 그런 이야기들이 교과서에 실릴 거라고 해.
M: 학생들이 그토록 훌륭한 사람에 대해 배울 거라는 말을 들으니 좋군.

Listen & Talk 2 A-1

W: Excuse me, you _____ _____ your backpack inside the _____.

M: Oh, I didn't know that. _____ _____ _____ if I bring in my _____ _____?

W: Yes, that's fine. You can _____ your bag _____ the locker.

M: Okay, thank you.

W: 죄송합니다만, 박물관에 가방을 가지고 들어갈 수 없어요.

M: 아, 몰랐어요. 물병은 가지고 들어가도 괜찮나요?

W: 네, 그건 괜찮아요. 가방은 라커에 두시면 돼요.

M: 알았어요. 감사합니다.

Listen & Talk 2 A-2

W: Hi, _____ _____ the National Museum. _____ can I help you?

M: Hi, _____ _____ _____ _____ _____ _____ _____ _____ the museum?

W: Yes, but please _____ _____ a flash.

M: Oh, I see. Thank you.

W: 안녕하세요, 국립박물관에 오신 걸 환영합니다. 무엇을 도와드릴까요?

M: 안녕하세요, 박물관에서 사진을 찍어도 괜찮나요?

W: 네, 하지만 플래시는 사용하지 마세요.

M: 아, 알겠습니다. 감사합니다.

Listen & Talk 2 B

M: Hello, Ms. Jackson. _____ _____ your tour of the *Hanok Village*?

W: It was wonderful. The houses _____ really beautiful.

M: That's great.

W: Actually, I didn't _____ _____ _____ _____ _____ have dinner. Is it _____ _____ _____ cook in the kitchen at this hour?

M: Yes, but please _____ _____ the kitchen _____ _____ 10 p.m.

W: Okay. The kitchen is _____ the _____ _____, right?

M: Yes, it is. _____ _____ _____ _____ you need anything.

M: 안녕하세요, Jackson 씨. 한옥 마을 관광은 어땠어요?

W: 굉장했어요. 집들이 정말 아름다웠습니다.

M: 대단하네요.

W: 사실 전 저녁식사를 할 기회가 없었어요. 이 시간에 부엌에서 요리해도 괜찮나요?

M: 네, 하지만 부엌이 오후 10시에 문을 닫는 걸 기억하세요.

W: 알겠습니다. 부엌은 5층에 있죠, 맞나요?

M: 네, 그래요. 무언가 필요하시면 제게 말씀해 주세요.

Communication Step A

M: All right, everyone! This way, please. Now, we _____ _____ _____ the Joseon Dynasty. _____ _____ _____ _____, there were _____ interesting _____. This one _____ _____ the *Jagyeongnu*.

W: Is it a _____ _____?

M: Actually, this is a _____ _____. _____ _____ _____ _____ _____ _____ the _____ and _____ _____ water clock in Korea.

W: _____ amazing! _____ _____ _____ _____ I take a _____ _____ it?

M: Sure.

M: 좋아요, 여러분! 이쪽으로 오세요. 이제, 우리는 조선 왕조로 옮겨갑니다. 보시다시피, 많은 흥미 있는 발명품들이 있습니다. 이것은 자격루라고 불립니다.

W: 그것은 악기인가요?

M: 사실은 이것은 물시계입니다. 그것은 한국에서 가장 오래되고, 가장 큰 물시계라고 합니다.

W: 정말 놀랍군요. 그것을 사진 찍어도 괜찮나요?

M: 물론입니다.

Wrap Up 1

W: James, _____ are you _____?

M: Oh, I'm _____ a video about Yi Sunsin.

W: _____ _____ the one that _____ Joseon from Japan?

M: Right. _____ _____ _____ _____ _____ _____ the war only with twelve _____ _____.

W: Wow, _____ can that be _____?

M: He was a _____ _____ _____ _____ _____ plans.

W: James, 뭘 보고 있니?

M: 아, 이순신에 관한 비디오를 보고 있어.

W: 그는 일본으로부터 조선을 구한 사람 아니니?

M: 맞아. 그는 겨우 12척의 목선으로 전쟁에 이겼다고 해.

W: 와, 그게 어떻게 가능할 수 있지?

M: 그는 창의적인 계획을 세운 현명한 장군이었어.

Wrap Up 2

W: Excuse me, sir. _____ _____ _____ _____ have curry or *bibimbap*?

M: _____ _____ _____ have *bibimbap*, please.

W: _____ you are.

M: Thank you. Oh, _____ _____ _____ _____ I use the _____ now?

W: Sure, but _____ the seat light is _____, you should _____ in _____ _____.

M: Okay, thank you.

W: 실례합니다, 선생님. 카레를 드시겠어요 아니면 비빔밥을 드시겠어요?

M: 비빔밥을 먹고 싶습니다.

W: 여기 있습니다.

M: 고마워요. 아, 지금 화장실을 이용해도 괜찮나요?

W: 그럼요, 하지만 좌석 불이 켜져 있으면 선생님 좌석에 있으셔야 합니다.

M: 알았어요, 감사합니다.

대화문 Test

※ 다음 우리말에 맞도록 대화를 영어로 쓰시오.

Listen & Talk 1 Get Ready

A: _____

B: _____

C: _____

A: 김득신은 화가였어.
B: 아니야! 내가 책을 읽었는데 그는 학자였다고 해.
C: 싸우지 마. 너희 둘 다 옳아.

Listen & Talk 1 A-1

M: _____

W: _____

M: _____

W: _____

_____

M: _____

M: Lisa, 너 뭐 읽고 있니?
W: 권기옥의 전기를 읽고 있어.
M: 그녀에 대해 들어본 적이 없어. 그녀는 누구니?
W: 그녀는 한국의 첫 번째 여성 조종사야. 그녀는 비행시간이 7,000 시간이 넘는다고 해.
M: 와, 난 몰랐어.

Listen & Talk 1 A-2

M: _____

W: _____

M: _____

W: _____

M: 난 어제 흥미 있는 영화를 보았어. 그 영화에서 정약용이 탐정이었어.
W: 정약용? 그는 조선 왕조의 학자 아니었니?
M: 응, 하지만 그는 탐정이기도 했다고 해. 그는 약 90개의 사건을 해결했어.
W: 아, 그가 또한 탐정이었다는 건 몰랐어.

Listen & Talk 1 B

W: _____

M: _____

W: _____

_____

M: _____

W: _____

_____

M: _____

W: 어이, Mark, 너 이태석 신부에 대해 아니?
M: 응, 그에 대해 들어본 적이 있어. 왜?
W: 이 기사를 봐. 그는 남수단의 사회 교과서에 실릴 거야.
M: 와, 그거 대단하구나.
W: 그래, 그는 병원과 학교를 지어 아이들을 도와주었어. 그런 이야기들이 교과서에 실릴 거라고 해.
M: 학생들이 그토록 훌륭한 사람에 대해 배울 거라는 말을 들으니 좋군.

Listen & Talk 2 A-1

W: _____

M: _____

W: _____

M: _____

W: 죄송합니다만, 박물관에 가방을 가지고 들어갈 수 없어요.

M: 아, 몰랐어요. 물병은 가지고 들어가도 괜찮나요?

W: 네, 그건 괜찮아요. 가방은 라커에 두시면 돼요.

M: 알았어요. 감사합니다.

Listen & Talk 2 A-2

W: _____

M: _____

W: _____

M: _____

W: 안녕하세요, 국립박물관에 오신 걸 환영합니다. 무엇을 도와드릴까요?

M: 안녕하세요, 박물관에서 사진을 찍어도 괜찮나요?

W: 네, 하지만 플래시는 사용하지 마세요.

M: 아, 알겠습니다. 감사합니다.

Listen & Talk 2 B

M: _____

W: _____

M: _____

W: _____

_____

M: _____

W: _____

M: _____

M: 안녕하세요. Jackson 씨. 한옥 마을 관광은 어땠어요?

W: 굉장했어요. 집들이 정말 아름다웠습니다.

M: 대단하네요.

W: 사실 전 저녁식사를 할 기회가 없었어요. 이 시간에 부엌에서 요리해도 괜찮나요?

M: 네, 하지만 부엌이 오후 10시에 문을 닫는 걸 기억하세요.

W: 알겠습니다. 부엌은 5층에 있죠, 맞나요?

M: 네, 그래요. 무언가 필요하시면 제게 말씀해 주세요.

Communication Step A

M: _____
_____
_____
W: _____
M: _____
_____
W: _____
M: _____

M: 좋아요, 여러분! 이쪽으로 오세요. 이제, 우리는 조선 왕조로 옮겨갑니다. 보시다시피, 많은 흥미 있는 발명품들이 있습니다. 이것은 자격루라고 불립니다.
W: 그것은 악기인가요?
M: 사실은 이것은 물시계입니다. 그것은 한국에서 가장 오래되고, 가장 큰 물시계라고 합니다.
W: 정말 놀랍군요. 그것을 사진 찍어도 괜찮나요?
M: 물론입니다.

Wrap Up 1

W: _____
M: _____
W: _____
M: _____
W: _____
M: _____

W: James, 뭘 보고 있니?
M: 아, 이순신에 관한 비디오를 보고 있어.
W: 그는 일본으로부터 조선을 구한 사람 아니니?
M: 맞아. 그는 겨우 12척의 목선으로 전쟁에 이겼다고 해.
W: 와, 그게 어떻게 가능할 수 있지?
M: 그는 창의적인 계획을 세운 현명한 장군이었어.

Wrap Up 2

W: _____
M: _____
W: _____
M: _____
W: _____
M: _____

W: 실례합니다, 선생님. 카레를 드시겠어요 아니면 비빔밥을 드시겠어요?
M: 비빔밥을 먹고 싶습니다.
W: 여기 있습니다.
M: 고마워요. 아, 지금 화장실을 이용해도 괜찮나요?
W: 그럼요, 하지만 좌석 불이 켜져 있으면 선생님 좌석에 있으셔야 합니다.
M: 알았어요, 감사합니다.

※ 다음 우리말과 일치하도록 빈칸에 알맞은 것을 골라 쓰시오.

1 The _____ of _____ _____
A. Father   B. Secret   C. My

2 In 1946, a _____ man _____ me and _____, "Are you Mr. Kim Yonghwan's _____?"
A. visited   B. daughter   C. asked   D. strange

3 For me, this was am _____ question because I was more _____ _____ _____ called the daughter of a *parakho*.
A. used   B. odd   C. to   D. being

4 "I'm _____ _____ _____.
A. father's   B. your   C. friend

5 You may _____ _____ it is _____, but your father...," the man said.
A. if   B. wonder   C. true

6 At that _____, I was _____ _____ news since I did not have good _____ of my father.
A. disappointing   B. memories   C. moment   D. expecting

7 _____ in the 1920's, _____ people saw me in the village, they would say, "_____ _____ the parakho's daughter."
A. goes   B. back   C. there   D. whenever

8 My father was a son _____ a very _____ _____.
A. rich   B. from   C. family

9 _____ of _____ the life of a *seonbi*, he was _____ at the _____ house.
A. gambling   B. living   C. instead   D. always

10 That is _____ he was called a *parakho*, _____ means someone who _____ his family's _____.
A. which   B. why   C. fortune   D. ruins

11 "Your father has _____ _____ all of the money, and now he's _____ _____ more.
A. away   B. asking   C. gambled   D. for

12 Go and tell him that we _____ no more money _____," my mother_____ tell me _____ she sent me to the gambling house.
A. left   B. whenever   C. would   D. have

13 Then, my father would _____ _____ me _____, "Why did you come _____?
A. angrily   B. empty-handed   C. at   D. yell

14 _____ me _____ money!"
A. more   B. bring

1 아버지의 비밀

2 1946년에, 낯선 남자가 나를 찾아와 물었다. "당신이 김용환 씨의 딸입니까?"

3 나는 파락호의 딸이라고 불리는 것이 더 익숙했으므로 나에게 이것은 이상한 질문이었다.

4 "나는 당신 아버지의 친구입니다.

5 당신은 이것이 사실인지 의아하겠지만, 당신의 아버지는…,"이라고 그 남자는 말했다.

6 나는 내 아버지에 대해 좋은 기억을 가지고 있지 않았으므로 그 순간에 실망스러운 소식을 예상하고 있었다.

7 1920년대에 마을에서 사람들이 나를 볼 때마다 그들은 "저기에 파락호의 딸이 가네."라고 말하곤 했다.

8 나의 아버지는 매우 부유한 집안의 아들이었다.

9 선비의 삶을 사는 대신, 아버지는 항상 도박장에 계셨다.

10 그것이 그가 집안의 재산을 탕진하는 사람이라는 뜻의 파락호로 불린 이유이다.

11 "네 아버지는 도박으로 모든 돈을 써 버리고 지금 더 요구하고 계신다.

12 가서 더 이상 남아 있는 돈이 없다고 말씀드려라."라고 나의 어머니는 나를 도박장으로 보낼 때마다 말씀하시곤 했다.

13 그러면, 아버지는 나에게 화를 내시며 소리치셨다. "왜 빈손으로 왔니?

14 돈을 더 가져와!"

15 When I was sixteen years old, my family _____ _____ _____ an _____ for me to marry Mr. Seo.

    A. arrangement   B. already   C. made   D. had

16 As _____ of the wedding _____ , Mr. Seo's family sent my family some money to buy a new _____ for _____ .

    A. part   B. chest   C. tradition   D. clothes

17 _____ _____ the wedding day, my mother came into my room and said, "Your father has _____ the _____ for the chest."

    A. before   B. taken   C. right   D. money

18 I asked _____ , "How could he do _____ a _____ ?

    A. thing   B. such   C. horrible   D. angrily

19 _____ _____ we _____ now?"

    A. do   B. should   C. what

20 "We _____ _____ _____ .

    A. choice   B. no   C. have

21 You'll _____ _____ _____ your aunt's old _____ ," my mother said.

    A. chest   B. to   C. have   D. take

22 "_____ _____ for the family," people would whisper _____ my _____ .

    A. embarrassing   B. back   C. how   D. behind

23 _____ the first day of _____ , life at my husband's house had _____ _____ for me.

    A. marriage   B. difficult   C. since   D. been

24 "Your father, my _____ friend...," my father's friend _____ his _____ .

    A. continued   B. dear   C. story

25 "He _____ _____ a _____ .

    A. not   B. was   C. gambler

26 Your father sent the _____ _____ to the _____ _____ in Manchuria.

    A. money   B. fighters   C. family   D. independence

27 He _____ _____ look like a gambler to _____ this a _____ from the Japanese officers."

    A. secret   B. himself   C. keep   D. made

28 At first, I was not _____ he was _____ the _____ .

    A. telling   B. if   C. truth   D. sure

29 But _____ , I found _____ the truth about my father and I _____ that I had been _____ about him.

    A. wrong   B. afterwards   C. out   D. realized

30 Ever _____ that moment, I have been _____ to be the daughter of a *parakho* who had _____ his life to the independence _____ .

    A. proud   B. devoted   C. since   D. movement

15 내가 16살이 되었을 때, 나의 가족은 나를 서 씨와 결혼시키기로 이미 결정을 했었다.

16 결혼 풍습의 일부로, 서 씨네 가족은 새 장롱을 사라고 우리 가족에게 돈을 보냈다.

17 결혼식 바로 전날, 나의 어머니는 내 방에 들어오셔서 말씀하셨다. "네 아버지가 장롱을 살 돈을 가져가 버렸다."

18 나는 화가 나서 물었다 "어떻게 그리 끔찍한 일을 하실 수 있나요?

19 우린 이제 어떡해요?"

20 "우리에게 선택권은 없구나.

21 큰어머니의 옛 장롱을 가져가야겠구나."라고 어머니가 말씀하셨다.

22 "가문에 부끄러운 일이야."라고 사람들이 내 뒤에서 속삭이곤 했다.

23 결혼 첫날부터, 남편의 집에서의 생활은 나에게 힘겨웠다.

24 "당신의 아버지, 나의 친애하는 친구…," 나의 아버지의 친구분은 그의 이야기를 이어가셨다.

25 "그는 도박꾼이 아니었어요.

26 당신의 아버지는 가족의 돈을 만주에 있는 독립운동가들에게 보냈답니다.

27 그는 이것을 일본 순사들에게 비밀로 하기 위해 그 자신을 도박꾼처럼 보이게 했어요."

28 처음엔, 나는 그분이 사실을 얘기하시는 건지 확신할 수 없었다.

29 그러나 나중에, 나는 나의 아버지에 대한 진실을 알게 되었고 내가 아버지에 관해 오해하고 있었다는 것을 깨달았다.

30 그 순간부터, 나는 독립운동에 그의 인생을 헌신하신 파락호의 딸인 것이 자랑스러웠다.

Step2

※ 다음 우리말과 일치하도록 빈칸에 알맞은 말을 쓰시오.

1 The _____ of My _____

2 In 1946, _____ _____ _____ me and _____, "Are you Mr. Kim Yonghwan's daughter?"

3 For me, this was _____ _____ _____ because I _____ _____ _____ _____ _____ the daughter of a *parakho*.

4 "I'm _____ _____ _____.

5 You may _____ _____ it is _____, but your father...," the man said.

6 At that moment, I was _____ _____ news _____ I did not have _____ _____ of my father.

7 _____ in the 1920's, _____ people saw me in the village, they would say, "_____ _____ the parakho's daughter."

8 My father was a son _____ a very _____ _____.

9 _____ _____ _____ the life of a *seonbi*, he was always at the _____ _____.

10 _____ _____ _____ he _____ _____ a *parakho*, _____ means someone who _____ his family's fortune.

11 "Your father _____ _____ _____ all of the money, and now he's _____ _____ more.

12 Go and tell him that we _____ _____ _____ _____ _____," my mother _____ tell me _____ she _____ me to the gambling house.

13 Then, my father _____ _____ _____ me _____, "Why did you come _____?

14 _____ _____ more _____!"

1 아버지의 비밀

2 1946년에, 낯선 남자가 나를 찾아와 물었다. "당신이 김용환 씨의 딸입니까?"

3 나는 파락호의 딸이라고 불리는 것이 더 익숙했으므로 나에게 이것은 이상한 질문이었다.

4 "나는 당신 아버지의 친구입니다.

5 당신은 이것이 사실인지 의아하겠지만, 당신의 아버지⋯,"이라고 그 남자는 말했다.

6 나는 내 아버지에 대해 좋은 기억을 가지고 있지 않았으므로 그 순간에 실망스러운 소식을 예상하고 있었다.

7 1920년대에 마을에서 사람들이 나를 볼 때마다 그들은 "저기에 파락호의 딸이 가네."라고 말하곤 했다.

8 나의 아버지는 매우 부유한 집안의 아들이었다.

9 선비의 삶을 사는 대신, 아버지는 항상 도박장에 계셨다.

10 그것이 그가 집안의 재산을 탕진하는 사람이라는 뜻의 파락호로 불린 이유이다.

11 "네 아버지는 도박으로 모든 돈을 써 버리고 지금 더 요구하고 계신다.

12 가서 더 이상 남아 있는 돈이 없다고 말씀드려라."라고 나의 어머니는 나를 도박장으로 보낼 때마다 말씀하시곤 했다.

13 그러면, 아버지는 나에게 화를 내시며 소리치셨다. "왜 빈손으로 왔니?

14 돈을 더 가져와!"

15 When I was sixteen years old, my family _____ _____ _____ _____ _____ for me to _____ Mr. Seo.

16 _____ _____ _____ the wedding tradition, Mr. Seo's family sent my family some money to buy _____ _____ _____ _____ _____.

17 _____ _____ the wedding day, my mother _____ _____ my room and said, "Your father _____ _____ _____ for the chest."

18 I asked _____, "How could he do _____ _____ _____ _____?

19 _____ should we do now?"

20 "We have _____ _____.

21 _____ _____ _____ _____ _____ your aunt's old chest," my mother said.

22 "_____ _____ for the family," people would _____ _____ _____ _____.

23 Since the first day of _____, life at my husband's house _____ _____ _____ _____ _____.

24 "Your father, my dear friend...," my father's friend _____ _____ _____.

25 "He was not _____ _____.

26 Your father sent the family money to the _____ _____ in Manchuria.

27 He _____ _____ look like a gambler to _____ _____ _____ _____ _____ the _____ _____."

28 At first, I was not sure _____ he was _____ the _____.

29 But _____, I found out the truth about my father and I realized that I _____ _____ _____ about him.

30 Ever since that moment, I have been proud to be the daughter of a *parakho* who _____ _____ _____ _____ the _____ _____.

15 내가 16살이 되었을 때, 나의 가족은 나를 서 씨와 결혼시키 기로 이미 결정을 했었다.

16 결혼 풍습의 일부로, 서 씨네 가족은 새 장롱을 사라고 우리 가족에게 돈을 보냈다.

17 결혼식 바로 전날, 나의 어머니는 내 방에 들어오셔서 말씀하셨다. "네 아버지가 장롱을 살 돈을 가져가 버렸다."

18 나는 화가 나서 물었다 "어떻게 그리 끔찍한 일을 하실 수 있나요?

19 우린 이제 어떡해요?"

20 "우리에게 선택권은 없구나.

21 큰어머니의 옛 장롱을 가져가야겠구나."라고 어머니가 말씀하셨다.

22 "가문에 부끄러운 일이야."라고 사람들이 내 뒤에서 속삭이곤 했다.

23 결혼 첫날부터, 남편의 집에서의 생활은 나에게 힘겨웠다.

24 "당신의 아버지, 나의 친애하는 친구…," 나의 아버지의 친구분은 그의 이야기를 이어가셨다.

25 "그는 도박꾼이 아니었어요.

26 당신의 아버지는 가족의 돈을 만주에 있는 독립운동가들에게 보냈답니다.

27 그는 이것을 일본 순사들에게 비밀로 하기 위해 그 자신을 도박꾼처럼 보이게 했어요."

28 처음엔, 나는 그분이 사실을 얘기하시는 건지 확신할 수 없었다.

29 그러나 나중에, 나는 나의 아버지에 대한 진실을 알게 되었고 내가 아버지에 관해 오해하고 있었다는 것을 깨달았다.

30 그 순간부터, 나는 독립운동에 그의 인생을 헌신하신 파락호의 딸인 것이 자랑스러웠다.

※ 다음 문장을 우리말로 쓰시오.

1 The Secret of My Father

➡ _____

2 In 1946, a strange man visited me and asked, "Are you Mr. Kim Yonghwan's daughter?

➡ _____

3 For me, this was an odd question because I was more used to being called the daughter of a *parakho*.

➡ _____

4 "I'm your father's friend.

➡ _____

5 You may wonder if it is true, but your father...," the man said.

➡ _____

6 At that moment, I was expecting disappointing news since I did not have good memories of my father.

➡ _____

7 Back in the 1920's, whenever people saw me in the village, they would say, "There goes the *parakho's* daughter."

➡ _____

8 My father was a son from a very rich family.

➡ _____

9 Instead of living the life of a seonbi, he was always at the gambling house.

➡ _____

10 That is why he was called a parakho, which means someone who ruins his family's fortune.

➡ _____

11 "Your father has gambled away all of the money, and now he's asking for more.

➡ _____

12 Go and tell him that we have no more money left," my mother would tell me whenever she sent me to the gambling house.

➡ _____

13 Then, my father would yell at me angrily, "Why did you come empty-handed?

➡ _____

14 Bring me more money!"

➡ _____

15 When I was sixteen years old, my family had already made an arrangement for me to marry Mr. Seo.

➡ _____

16 As part of the wedding tradition, Mr. Seo's family sent my family some money to buy a new chest for clothes.

➡ _____

17 Right before the wedding day, my mother came into my room and said, "Your father has taken the money for the chest."

➡ _____

18 I asked angrily, "How could he do such a horrible thing?

➡ _____

19 What should we do now?"

➡ _____

20 "We have no choice.

➡ _____

21 You'll have to take your aunt's old chest," my mother said.

➡ _____

22 "How embarrassing for the family," people would whisper behind my back.

➡ _____

23 Since the first day of marriage, life at my husband's house had been difficult for me.

➡ _____

24 "Your father, my dear friend...," my father's friend continued his story.

➡ _____

25 "He was not a gambler.

➡ _____

26 Your father sent the family money to the independence fighters in Manchuria.

➡ _____

27 He made himself look like a gambler to keep this a secret from the Japanese officers."

➡ _____

28 At first, I was not sure if he was telling the truth.

➡ _____

29 But afterwards, I found out the truth about my father and I realized that I had been wrong about him.

➡ _____

30 Ever since that moment, I have been proud to be the daughter of a parakho who had devoted his life to the independence movemen

➡ _____

Step4

※ 다음 괄호 안의 단어들을 우리말에 맞도록 바르게 배열하시오.

1 (Secret / The / My / of / Father)
➡ _____

2 (1946, / in / strange / a / visited / man / me / asked, / and / "are / Mr. / you / Kim / daughter?" / Yonghwan's)
➡ _____

3 (me, / for / was / this / odd / an / question / I / because / was / used / more / to / called / being / daughter / the / a / of / *parakho*.)
➡ _____

4 (your / "I'm / friend. / father's)
➡ _____

5 (may / you / wonder / it / if / true, / is / but / father...," / your / man / the / said.)
➡ _____

6 (that / at / moment, / was / I / expecting / news / disappointing / since / did / I / have / not / good / of / memories / father. / my)
➡ _____

7 (in / back / 1920's, / the / whenever / saw / people / me / the / in / village, / would / they / say, / goes / "there / *parakho*'s / the / daughter.")
➡ _____

8 (father / my / a / was / son / a / from / rich / very / family.)
➡ _____

9 (of / instead / living / life / the / a / of / *seonbi*, / was / he / at / always / the / house. / gambling)
➡ _____

10 (is / that / why / was / he / called / *parakho*, / a / means / which / who / someone / ruins / family's / his / fortune.)
➡ _____

11 (father / your / has / away / gambled / all / the / of / money, / now / and / he's / for / asking / more.)
➡ _____

12 (tell / and / go / him / we / that / no / have / money / more / left," / mother / my / tell / would / whenever / me / she / me / sent / to / gambling / the / house.)
➡ _____

13 (my / then, / father / yell / would / me / at / angrily, / did / "why / come / you / empty-handed?)
➡ _____

14 (me / bring / money!" / more)
➡ _____

1 아버지의 비밀

2 1946년에, 낯선 남자가 나를 찾아와 물었다. "당신이 김용환 씨의 딸입니까?"

3 나는 파락호의 딸이라고 불리는 것이 더 익숙했으므로 나에게 이것은 이상한 질문이었다.

4 "나는 당신 아버지의 친구입니다.

5 당신은 이것이 사실인지 의아하겠지만, 당신의 아버지는…,"이라고 그 남자는 말했다.

6 나는 내 아버지에 대해 좋은 기억을 가지고 있지 않았으므로 그 순간에 실망스러운 소식을 예상하고 있었다.

7 1920년대에 마을에서 사람들이 나를 볼 때마다 그들은 "저기에 파락호의 딸이 가네."라고 말하곤 했다.

8 나의 아버지는 매우 부유한 집안의 아들이었다.

9 선비의 삶을 사는 대신, 아버지는 항상 도박장에 계셨다.

10 그것이 그가 집안의 재산을 탕진하는 사람이라는 뜻의 파락호로 불린 이유이다.

11 "네 아버지는 도박으로 모든 돈을 써 버리고 지금 더 요구하고 계신다.

12 가서 더 이상 남아 있는 돈이 없다고 말씀드려라."라고 나의 어머니는 나를 도박장으로 보낼 때마다 말씀하시곤 했다.

13 그러면, 아버지는 나에게 화를 내시며 소리치셨다. "왜 빈손으로 왔니?

14 돈을 더 가져와!"

15 (I / when / was / years / sixteen / old, / family / my / already / had / an / made / arrangement / me / for / marry / to / Seo. / Mr.)
➡ _____

16 (part / as / the / of / tradition, / wedding / Seo's / Mr. / sent / family / my / some / family / money / buy / to / a / chest / new / clothes. / for)
➡ _____

17 (before / right / the / day, / wedding / mother / my / into / came / room / my / and / said, / father / "your / taken / has / the / for / money / chest." / the)
➡ _____

18 (asked / I / angrily, / could / "how / do / he / a / such / thing? / horrible)
➡ _____

19 (should / what / do / we / now?")
➡ _____

20 (have / "we / choice. / no)
➡ _____

21 (have / you'll / take / to / aunt's / your / chest," / old / mother / my / said.)
➡ _____

22 (embarrassing / "how / the / for / family," / would / people / whisper / my / behind / back.)
➡ _____

23 (the / since / day / first / marriage, / of / life / my / at / husband's / had / house / been / for / difficult / me.)
➡ _____

24 (father / "your / dear / my / friend...," / father's / my / continued / friend / story. / his)
➡ _____

25 (was / "he / a / not / gambler.)
➡ _____

26 (father / your / sent / family / the / to / money / the / fighters / independence / Manchuria. / in)
➡ _____

27 (made / he / look / himself / like / gambler / a / keep / to / this / secret / a / from / Japanese / the / officers.")
➡ _____

28 (first, / at / was / I / sure / not / he / if / telling / was / truth. / the)
➡ _____

29 (afterwards, / but / found / I / the / out / truth / about / father / my / and / realized / I / that / been / had / about / him. / wrong)
➡ _____

30 (since / ever / moment, / that / have / I / been / to / proud / be / daughter / the / a / of / *parakho* / who / devoted / had / life / his / the / to / movement. / independence)
➡ _____
_____

---

15 내가 16살이 되었을 때, 나의 가족은 나를 서 씨와 결혼시키기로 이미 결정을 했었다.

16 결혼 풍습의 일부로, 서 씨네 가족은 새 장롱을 사라고 우리 가족에게 돈을 보냈다.

17 결혼식 바로 전날, 나의 어머니는 내 방에 들어오셔서 말씀하셨다. "네 아버지가 장롱을 살 돈을 가져가 버렸다."

18 나는 화가 나서 물었다 "어떻게 그리 끔찍한 일을 하실 수 있나요?

19 우린 이제 어떡해요?"

20 "우리에게 선택권은 없구나.

21 큰어머니의 옛 장롱을 가져가야 겠구나."라고 어머니가 말씀하셨다.

22 "가문에 부끄러운 일이야."라고 사람들이 내 뒤에서 속삭이곤 했다.

23 결혼 첫날부터, 남편의 집에서의 생활은 나에게 힘겨웠다.

24 "당신의 아버지, 나의 친애하는 친구…" 나의 아버지의 친구분은 그의 이야기를 이어가셨다.

25 "그는 도박꾼이 아니었어요.

26 당신의 아버지는 가족의 돈을 만주에 있는 독립운동가들에게 보냈답니다.

27 그는 이것을 일본 순사들에게 비밀로 하기 위해 그 자신을 도박꾼처럼 보이게 했어요."

28 처음엔, 나는 그분이 사실을 얘기하시는 건지 확신할 수 없었다.

29 그러나 나중에, 나는 나의 아버지에 대한 진실을 알게 되었고 내가 아버지에 관해 오해하고 있었다는 것을 깨달았다.

30 그 순간부터, 나는 독립운동에 그의 인생을 헌신하신 파락호의 딸인 것이 자랑스러웠다.

※ 다음 우리말을 영어로 쓰시오.

1 아버지의 비밀

➡ _____

2 1946년에, 낯선 남자가 나를 찾아와 물었다. "당신이 김용환 씨의 딸입니까?"

➡ _____

3 나는 파락호의 딸이라고 불리는 것이 더 익숙했으므로 나에게 이것은 이상한 질문이었다.

➡ _____

4 "나는 당신 아버지의 친구입니다.

➡ _____

5 당신은 이것이 사실인지 의아하겠지만, 당신의 아버지는…,"이라고 그 남자는 말했다.

➡ _____

6 나는 내 아버지에 대해 좋은 기억을 가지고 있지 않았으므로 그 순간에 실망스러운 소식을 예상하고 있었다.

➡ _____

7 1920년대에 마을에서 사람들이 나를 볼 때마다 그들은 "저기에 파락호의 딸이 가네."라고 말하곤 했다.

➡ _____
_____

8 나의 아버지는 매우 부유한 집안의 아들이었다.

➡ _____

9 선비의 삶을 사는 대신, 아버지는 항상 도박장에 계셨다.

➡ _____

10 그것이 그가 집안의 재산을 탕진하는 사람이라는 뜻의 파락호로 불린 이유이다.

➡ _____

11 "네 아버지는 도박으로 모든 돈을 써 버리고 지금 더 요구하고 계신다.

➡ _____

12 가서 더 이상 남아 있는 돈이 없다고 말씀드려라."라고 나의 어머니는 나를 도박장으로 보낼 때마다 말씀하시곤 했다.

➡ _____
_____

13 그러면, 아버지는 나에게 화를 내시며 소리치셨다. "왜 빈손으로 왔니?

➡ _____

14 돈을 더 가져와!"

➡ _____

15 내가 16살이 되었을 때, 나의 가족은 나를 서 씨와 결혼시키기로 이미 결정을 했었다.

➡ _____

16 결혼 풍습의 일부로, 서 씨네 가족은 새 장롱을 사라고 우리 가족에게 돈을 보냈다.

➡ _____

17 결혼식 바로 전날, 나의 어머니는 내 방에 들어오셔서 말씀하셨다. "네 아버지가 장롱을 살 돈을 가져가 버렸다."

➡ _____

➡ _____

18 나는 화가 나서 물었다 "어떻게 그리 끔찍한 일을 하실 수 있나요?

➡ _____

19 우린 이제 어떡해요?"

➡ _____

20 "우리에게 선택권은 없구나.

➡ _____

21 큰어머니의 옛 장롱을 가져가야겠구나."라고 어머니가 말씀하셨다.

➡ _____

22 "가문에 부끄러운 일이야."라고 사람들이 내 뒤에서 속삭이곤 했다.

➡ _____

23 결혼 첫날부터, 남편의 집에서의 생활은 나에게 힘겨웠다.

➡ _____

24 "당신의 아버지, 나의 친애하는 친구…," 나의 아버지의 친구분은 그의 이야기를 이어가셨다.

➡ _____

25 "그는 도박꾼이 아니었어요.

➡ _____

26 당신의 아버지는 가족의 돈을 만주에 있는 독립운동가들에게 보냈답니다.

➡ _____

27 그는 이것을 일본 순사들에게 비밀로 하기 위해 그 자신을 도박꾼처럼 보이게 했어요."

➡ _____

28 처음엔, 나는 그분이 사실을 얘기하시는 건지 확신할 수 없었다.

➡ _____

29 그러나 나중에, 나는 나의 아버지에 대한 진실을 알게 되었고 내가 아버지에 관해 오해하고 있었다는 것을 깨달았다.

➡ _____

30 그 순간부터, 나는 독립운동에 그의 인생을 헌신하신 파락호의 딸인 것이 자랑스러웠다.

➡ _____

➡ _____

※ 다음 우리말과 일치하도록 빈칸에 알맞은 말을 쓰시오.

Grammar in Real Life A

1. Mary Jane, your fans _____ _____ _____ about _____ _____.
2. 1. _____ you _____ _____ _____ a new song this month?
3. 2. Are you _____ _____ _____ music _____?
4. 3. Do you have any _____ _____ _____ _____ _____?
5. 4. Are you _____ _____ _____ _____ a _____ _____ this year?

1. Mary Jane, 너의 팬들은 너의 계획에 대해 많은 질문들을 가지고 있어.
2. 1. 넌 이 달에 새 노래를 발표할 거니?
3. 2. 넌 다양한 음악 장르에 관심이 있니?
4. 3. 넌 다른 아티스트들과 일할 계획을 가지고 있니?
5. 4. 넌 금년에 월드 투어를 떠날 거니?

Grammar in Real Life B

1. When I _____ _____ _____, my parents _____ _____ out for a walk.
2. The house was dark and quiet, but it _____ _____ _____ _____.
3. I _____ that I _____ _____ the door in my room open.
4. I _____ that someone _____ _____ the lamp.
5. I _____ _____ that someone _____ _____ my cookies on the table.
6. _____ _____ I knew _____ _____ _____!
7. I _____ _____ _____ _____ of my dog, Lucy, and the cat next door

1. 내가 집에 돌아왔을 때 나의 부모님은 산보를 나가셨다.
2. 집은 어둡고 조용했지만, 조금 이상해 보였다.
3. 나는 내 방문을 열어둔 것이 기억났다.
4. 나는 누군가가 램프를 깨뜨린 것을 알았다.
5. 나는 누군가가 식탁 위에 있던 내 쿠키를 먹은 것을 알아냈다.
6. 마침내 나는 누가 그런 일을 했는지 알았다!
7. 나는 내 개 Lucy와 옆집 고양이의 작은 발자국들을 발견했다.

After You Read: Read and Write A

1. The _____ of My Father
2. I _____ my father was ...
3. My father _____ _____ _____ a *parakho*.
4. He _____ _____ _____ a rich family but he _____ _____ all of the money.
5. He _____ _____ the money for _____ _____ _____ _____ _____.
6. _____ my father was ...
7. My father was not a gambler.
8. He _____ the family money to the _____ _____ in Manchuria.
9. He _____ _____ _____ _____ a gambler to _____ _____ _____ _____ from the Japanese officers.

1. 나의 아버지의 비밀
2. 나는 아버지가 …라고 생각했다.
3. 나의 아버지는 '파락호'라고 알려져 있었다.
4. 그는 부잣집에 태어났지만, 모든 돈을 노름으로 날렸다.
5. 그는 심지어 새 장롱을 살 돈도 가져갔다.
6. 사실 나의 아버지는 …이었다.
7. 나의 아버지는 노름꾼이 아니었다.
8. 그는 가족의 돈을 만주에 있는 독립 운동가들에게 보냈다.
9. 그는 일본 경찰들로부터 이것을 비밀로 지키려고 스스로를 노름꾼처럼 보이게 했다.

※ **다음 우리말을 영어로 쓰시오.**

Grammar in Real Life A

1. Mary Jane, 너의 팬들은 너의 계획에 대해 많은 질문들을 가지고 있어.
➡ _____

2. 1. 넌 이 달에 새 노래를 발표할 거니?
➡ _____

3. 2. 넌 다양한 음악 장르에 관심이 있니?
➡ _____

4. 3. 넌 다른 아티스트들과 일할 계획을 가지고 있니?
➡ _____

5. 4. 넌 금년에 월드 투어를 떠날 거니?
➡ _____

Grammar in Real Life B

1. 내가 집에 돌아왔을 때 나의 부모님은 산보를 나가셨다.
➡ _____

2. 집은 어둡고 조용했지만, 조금 이상해 보였다.
➡ _____

3. 나는 내 방문을 열어둔 것이 기억났다.
➡ _____

4. 나는 누군가가 램프를 깨뜨린 것을 알았다.
➡ _____

5. 나는 누군가가 식탁 위에 있던 내 쿠키를 먹은 것을 알아냈다.
➡ _____

6. 마침내 나는 누가 그런 일을 했는지 알았다!
➡ _____

7. 나는 내 개 Lucy와 옆집 고양이의 작은 발자국들을 발견했다.
➡ _____

After You Read: Read and Write A

1. 나의 아버지의 비밀
➡ _____

2. 나는 아버지가 …라고 생각했다.
➡ _____

3. 나의 아버지는 '파락호'라고 알려져 있었다.
➡ _____

4. 그는 부잣집에 태어났지만, 모든 돈을 노름으로 날렸다.
➡ _____

5. 그는 심지어 새 장롱을 살 돈도 가져갔다.
➡ _____

6. 사실 나의 아버지는 …이었다.
➡ _____

7. 나의 아버지는 노름꾼이 아니었다.
➡ _____

8. 그는 가족의 돈을 만주에 있는 독립 운동가들에게 보냈다.
➡ _____

9. 그는 일본 경찰들로부터 이것을 비밀로 지키려고 스스로를 노름꾼처럼 보이게 했다.
➡ _____

MEMO

영어 기출 문제집

1학기

정답 및 해설

비상 | 김진완

중 **3**

적중100

영어 기출 문제집

정답 및 해설

1학기

비상 | 김진완

중 3

적중100

The Art of Communication

01 ③   02 ④   03 ②   04 ③

05 ②   06 ③   07 ①, ⑤

01 upset: 화난, 기분 나쁜

02 focus on: ~에 집중하다 concentrate on: ~에 집중하다

03 ①, ④번은 (2)의 뜻으로, ③, ⑤번은 (1)의 뜻으로 사용되었
다. ②번의 mean은 '잔인한 또는 친절하지 않은'의 의미로 사용
되어 '그것은 친구에게 하는 못된 장난이다.'로 해석된다.

04 stressed out: 스트레스로 지친, 스트레스가 쌓인 / 학기 말에
나는 스트레스로 완전히 지쳐 있었다. work out: 해결하다 / 모
든 일이 잘 해결돼서 다행이다.

05 get cold feet: 긴장하다, 겁을 먹다 have one's head in the
clouds: 공상에 잠겨 있다(to be out of touch with reality
and have impractical ideas about achieving success)
hit the books: 공부하다 let one's hair down: 느긋하게 쉬
다 let the cat out of the bag: 비밀을 누설하다

06 (A) free from: ~이 없는 (B) find out: 발견하다, 알아내다 (C)
first of all: 먼저, 무엇보다도

07 take[have] a look at: ~을 보다

01 ⓑ ready leaving → ready to leave

    ⓒ end up to spend → end up spending

02 (c)old (f)eet

03 (K)eep, in mind

04 (1) effectively (2) (d)isappointed (3) hid

    (4) (r)eason

05 long

06 (1) Many trees can help to prevent landslides from
flood.

    (2) She can help you solve your problem.

    (3) This coat is uncomfortable to wear.

    (4) Instead, your effort is important.

01 ⓐ be busy 동사ing: ~하느라 바쁘다 / 나는 중간고사 준비하느
라고 바쁘다. ⓑ be ready to 동사원형: ~할 준비가 되다 / 우린
아직 떠날 준비가 안 되었어! ⓒ end up 동사ing: 결국 ~하게
되다 / 고객들은 결국 써야 할 돈보다 더 많은 돈을 써 버리고 맙

니다.

02 get cold feet: 긴장하다, 겁을 먹다

03 keep ~ in mind: ~을 명심하다

04 (1) effectively: 효과적으로 (2) disappointed: 실망한, 낙담
한 (3) hide: 숨다, 감추다 bush: 덤불 (4) reason: 이유

05 long: 긴 / 올해는 춥고 긴 겨울이 계속되네요. long face: 우울
한 얼굴 / 그는 시험에 떨어진 후 침울한 얼굴을 하고 있다.

06 (1) prevent: 막다, 예방하다 (2) solve: 해결하다 (3)
uncomfortable: 불편한 (4) instead: 그 대신에

Conversation

1 I am upset with my friend.   2 (C) → (B) → (A)

3 I'm very angry at[with] my sisters.

4 That's not what I meant. I meant

5 (B) → (C) → (A)

교과서 대화문 익히기

1 T   2 F   3 F   4 T   5 F   6 T   7 T   8 F

교과서 확인학습

Listen & Talk 1 Get Ready

Why, unhappy / about / take it

Listen & Talk 1 A-1

come, with, these days / upset about an argument /
Why / cutting me off in / mad, talking to

Listen & Talk 1 A-2

How, going / I'm upset about / I don't think that, on

Listen & Talk 1 B

Why, long / angry at, said some mean / to sleep,
But, talking loudly on the phone / upset / haven't
worked it / that, but I don't know how / Why, send

Listen & Talk 2 Get Ready

let the cat out of the bag / That's not what, a secret

get, in, should / concentrate, first of all, have your head in the clouds / see the sky / That's not what I meant, meant, focus

Listen & Talk 2 A-2

go diving / got cold feet / get a cold / I meant that, scared

Listen & Talk 2 B

stressed out about / two more to go / finishing, go on a, hair down / hair style / what I meant, feel free from

Communication

seem / keep telling me that, direct, upset / what they're talking about / tend to say what's on, strongly / Should / That's not what I meant, try to consider / try

---

시험대비 기본평가 　　　　　　　　　　p.18

01 ③　　　　02 ③　　　　03 ④
04 That's not what I meant.

01 That's not what I meant.는 '그런 뜻이 아니야.'라는 의미이며, 상대방이 자신의 말의 의도를 오해할 때 정정하기 위해 쓰는 표현이다. 'That's not what I meant to say.', 'I'm afraid you don't understand what I'm saying.', 'I didn't mean to say that.', 'I hope there is no misunderstanding.' 등도 비슷한 표현이다.

02 (B) 동생에게 화가 났다는 말에 (C) 무슨 일인지 질문하자 (A) 여동생이 물어보지 않고, 옷을 입는다고 화난 이유에 관해 설명한다. upset: 화난, 기분 나쁜 without: ~ 없이

03 'I got cold feet.'에 대해 여자가 감기 걸린 것으로 이해해서 남자가 'I meant that I got scared.(내가 무서웠다는 말이야.)'로 말하며 자신이 의도하고 싶었던 내용을 말한다.

04 That's not what I meant.: 내가 의미한 것은 그게 아니야.

시험대비 실력평가 　　　　　　　　　p.19~20

01 ③　　　02 ⑤　　　03 ①　　　04 ③
05 unhappy　06 ⑤　　　07 ①　　　08 ②
09 ④　　　10 ③

01 (C) 좋은 영어 성적을 얻기 위한 조언을 부탁하자 (A) Brown 선생님은 무엇보다도 수업 시간에 집중하라고 말하며 수진이가 종종 공상에 잠겨 있다고(have your head in the clouds) 말

하자 (B) 교실에서 하늘을 볼 수 없다고 말하고 (D) 선생님은 그 뜻이 아니라 수업 시간에 집중을 안 한다는 의미로 말했다고 설명한다.

02 'That's not what I meant.(내가 의미한 것은 그게 아니야.)'는 상대방이 자신의 말의 의도를 오해할 때 정정하기 위해 쓰는 표현이다. 자신의 말의 의도를 정정해 주는 'You can try to consider others' feelings.(다른 사람들의 감정을 이해하려고 노력해 봐.)'란 말 앞에 오는 것이 적절하다.

03 여자가 사람들이 Jason에 대해 말한 것을 어느 정도 이해한다고 말하고, 남자의 질문에 이에 대한 자세한 설명을 하고 있으므로 'What do you mean?(무슨 의미야?)'이 어울린다.

04 사람들은 Jason이 단도직입적이라고 말했고 이에 대해 Jason이 화가 났다.

05 'I'm upset about Roy.(Roy에게 화가 났어.)'라고 말하고 있으므로 happy(행복한)는 어울리지 않는다. unhappy: 불만스러운, 불행한

06 'I am upset about ~.(나는 ~에 화가 나.)', 'I can't stand ~.(나는 ~을 참을 수 없어.)' 둘 다 화가 난 감정을 나타낼 때 사용하는 표현이다.

07 왜 우울한 얼굴을 하고 있는지(무슨 일이 있는지) 질문하자 (B) 여동생에게 화가 나서 그녀에게 심술궂은 말을 했다고 대답한다. (A) 왜 화가 났는지 이유를 물어보자 (C) 피곤해서 자려고 했는데 동생이 전화로 시끄럽게 통화해서 화가 났다고 대답한다. (D) 아직 화해를 했는지 남자가 여자에게 물어보고 여자는 아직 못 했다고 대답하며 어떻게 화해할지 모르겠다고 말한다.

08 'let the cat out of the bag(비밀을 누설하다)'을 고양이를 가방에서 꺼내는 것으로 받아들이고 있는 상대방에게 자신이 말한 의도는 그것이 아니었다고 말하며, 말하고 싶어하는 내용을 다시 말하고 있다.

09 A는 B가 Clara의 생일 파티를 비밀로 유지하기를 원하고 있다.

10 남동생에게 화가 났다는 말에, 그가 시험을 잘못 봤다는 말은 어울리지 않는다.

서술형 시험대비 　　　　　　　　　　p.21

01 I am upset about an argument we had.
02 off
03 Why are you upset about her?
04 ordering
05 out
06 go
07 I didn't mean to say that.
08 ⓔ that → what

01 upset: 화난, 기분 나쁜 'be upset about ~'은 '~에 대해서 화가 나다'라는 의미로 화가 난 감정을 나타낼 때 사용하는 표현이다. an argument와 we had 사이에 목적격 관계대명사가 생략되어 있다.

02 cut ~ off: ~을 중단시키다, 잘라내다

03 be upset about ~: ~에게 화가 나다

04 keep 동사ing: ~을 계속하다 order 사람 around: ~에게 자꾸 이래라저래라 하다

05 stressed out: 스트레스로 지친, 스트레스가 쌓인

06 go: (일의 진행이 어떻게) 되어가다, 진전되다 go on a trip: 여행가다

07 mean: 의미하다 say: 말하다

08 That's not what I meant.는 '그런 뜻이 아니야.'라는 의미이며, 상대방이 자신의 말의 의도를 오해할 때 정정하기 위해 쓰는 표현이다. meant의 목적어가 없고 not 뒤에 보어가 없기 때문에 선행사를 포함한 관계대명사 what을 사용해야 한다.

교과서 Grammar

핵심 Check
p.22~23

1 (1) what　(2) what　(3) What

2 (1) when　(2) where　(3) why

시험대비 기본평가
p.24

01 ②　　02 ④　　03 ⑤

04 (1) Spring is a beautiful time when the flowers bloom.
　(2) Is there any reason why you are here?
　(3) Don't live in a town where there are no doctors.

01 선행사가 the house이므로 where가 적절하다.

02 know의 목적어와 think의 목적어 역할을 할 수 있는 것으로 선행사를 포함하는 관계대명사 what이 나와야 한다.

03 선행사 the way와 관계부사 how는 함께 쓸 수 없으며 the way나 how만 써야 하며, 선행사가 the way일 때 how 대신에 that을 쓸 수 있다.

04 (1) 선행사가 time이므로 when이 적절하다. (2) 선행사가 reason이므로 why가 적절하다. (3) 선행사가 a town이므로 where가 적절하다.

01 ②　　02 ③　　03 ④

04 (1) why　(2) that　(3) when　(4) what　(5) that

05 ⑤　　06 ①　　07 ③　　08 ②, ④

09 Christmas is a time when we share with families.

10 that → what　　11 ⑤　　12 ①

13 ②　　14 ⑤

15 I found the reality quite different from what I had imagined.　16 ①, ④

17 (1) He didn't let us know the way(또는 how, the way that) he solved the problem.
　(2) Judy went to the restaurant in[at] which(또는 where) she had dinner with her friends.
　(3) Yuna remembers the day when she won the Olympic gold medal.
　(4) I can't believe what you're saying.
　(5) I like the bag that[which] I bought yesterday.
　(6) I would like to do what I want when I want.

18 1950 is the year when the Korean War broke out.

01 ① This is the house where Anne was born. ③ This is the park where I met Sophie. ④ Tell me how[the way] you solved the problem. ⑤ I remember the day when I met her first.

02 두 개의 동사 believe의 목적어 역할을 할 수 있도록 that을 what으로 고쳐야 한다.

03 첫 번째 문장에서 was doing의 목적어와 would be의 주어 역할을 할 수 있는 것은 What이다. 두 번째 문장에서 the hotel이 선행사이므로 관계부사 where가 적절하다.

04 (1) the reason이 선행사이므로 관계부사 why가 적절하다. (2) the way가 있으므로 how를 쓸 수 없으며 that을 쓸 수 있다. (3) times가 선행사이므로 관계부사 when이 적절하다. (4) for의 목적어가 없으므로 what이 이끄는 절이 sell의 목적어가 되도록 해야 한다. (5) 선행사로 all이 있으므로 관계대명사 that이 적절하다. all을 없애고 what만 써도 어법상 바른 문장이다.

05 had의 목적어와 was의 주어 역할을 할 수 있는 what이 적절하다.

06 the place가 선행사이므로 관계부사 where가 적절하다.

07 관계부사 how는 선행사 the way와 함께 쓸 수 없고 반드시 둘 중 하나는 생략해야 한다.

08 what이 관계대명사인지 의문대명사인지 구분하는 문제로 보통 의문사 what은 '무엇이 ~인(한)지'로, 관계대명사 what은 '~하는 것'으로 해석한다. ① 의문대명사 ② 관계대명사 ③ 의문대명사 ④ 관계대명사 ⑤ 의문대명사

09 a time이 선행사이므로 관계부사 when을 쓴다.

10 what is called: 소위, 이른바

11 the thing which[that]의 역할을 하는 what을 이용하여 나타내도록 한다.

12 ①번은 선행사가 the house로 where가 들어가야 하고, 나머지는 선행사가 시간이므로 when이 적절하다.

13 ②번은 the bank라는 선행사가 있으므로 which나 that이 들어가야 하고 나머지는 선행사가 없으므로 what[What]이 적절하다.

14 관계부사 where는 '전치사 in+which'로 바꿔 쓸 수 있다.

15 선행사를 포함하는 관계대명사 what을 추가하여 쓴다.

16 ① for와 did의 목적어 역할을 해야 하므로 that을 what으로 고쳐야 한다. ④ 선행사가 the day이므로 how를 when으로 고쳐야 한다.

17 (1) 관계부사 how는 선행사 the way와 함께 쓸 수 없고 반드시 둘 중 하나는 생략해야 한다. 또는 the way that을 쓴다. (2) the restaurant이 선행사이지만 뒤에 이어지는 절이 완전하므로 in which나 관계부사 where를 써야 한다. (3) 선행사가 the day이므로 관계부사 when을 써야 한다. (4) that을 believe와 saying의 목적어 역할을 할 수 있는 what으로 고쳐야 한다. (5) the bag이 선행사로 나왔으므로 what이 아니라 which나 that을 써야 한다. (6) that을 do와 want의 목적어 역할을 할 수 있는 what으로 고쳐야 한다.

18 the year가 선행사이므로 when을 이용한다.

서술형 시험대비
p.28~29

01 (1) Do you know the reason why he came here?
   Do you know the reason for which he came here?
   Do you know the reason which he came here for?

   (2) Natural disasters damage the place where people live.
   Natural disasters damage the place in which people live.
   Natural disasters damage the place which people live in.

02 (1) She has the right to do what she wants to do in her life.

   (2) What I want to do is to adopt a dog.

   (3) May I ask you the reason why you made that decision?

03 (1) where we stayed

   (2) what I want

04 (1) where[at which]

   (2) how[the way]

(3) why[for which]

05 (1) He politely denied what I suggested.

   (2) He did not listen to what I said.

   (3) What was proposed by him was not allowed.

   (4) Love is what helps mend a broken heart.

06 (1) I don't know the reason why he hides it.

   (2) Bill didn't know the time when she would arrive.

   (3) Avoid the area where the accident took place.

   (4) We studied how computers store information.

   (5) Cambridge Park is a nice park where you can sit on the grass.

07 (1) that은 앞에 있는 선행사를 수식하는 주격 관계대명사이며 형용사절을 이끈다.

   (2) what은 선행사를 포함하는 관계대명사로 명사절을 이끌어 does의 목적어 역할을 한다.

08 (1) where → which[that]

   (2) the way how → the way(또는 how 또는 the way that 또는 the way in which)

   (3) which → when(또는 at which), 또는 which he is least busy → which he is least busy at

   (4) what → that, 또는 the things 삭제

   (5) That → What   (6) that → what

01 (1) why는 'for+which'로 바꿔 쓸 수 있으며, 이때 for는 which의 바로 앞이나 관계사절의 마지막에 쓸 수 있다. (2) where는 'in+which'로 바꿔 쓸 수 있으며, 이때 in은 which의 바로 앞이나 관계사절의 마지막에 쓸 수 있다.

02 (1)~(2) 선행사를 포함하는 관계대명사 what을 이용한다. what이 선행사를 포함하므로 문장에서 두 가지의 역할을 함에 유의한다. (3) the reason이 선행사로 나올 때는 관계부사 why를 쓴다.

03 (1) 선행사가 the hotel이므로 관계부사 where를 이용한다. (2) 선행사를 포함하는 관계대명사 what을 이용한다.

04 (1) where는 'at which'로, (3) why는 'for which'로 바꿔 쓸 수 있다. (2) 완전한 절이 이어지므로 내용상 관계부사how가 적절하다. how 대신 the way를 써도 좋다.

05 the things which[that]의 역할을 하는 what을 이용하여 하나의 문장으로 쓴다.

06 관계부사는 두 문장을 연결하는 접속사의 역할과 부사의 역할을 동시에 하며 선행사에 따라 관계부사 when(시간), where(장소), why(이유), how(방법)를 쓴다.

07 what = the thing[something] that

08 (1) 이어지는 절에서 built의 목적어가 없으므로 where를 관계대명사 that이나 which로 고쳐야 한다. (2) 관계부사 how는 선행사 the way와 함께 쓰지 않고 반드시 둘 중의 하나만 써야

하며 the way that이나 the way in which를 쓸 수 있다. (3) 이어지는 절이 완전하고 선행사로 the time이 나왔으므로 관계대명사 which를 when이나 at which로 고쳐야 한다. at을 관계사절의 끝에 써도 된다. (4) the things라는 선행사가 있으므로 what을 that으로 고쳐 쓴다. 또는 the things를 삭제한다. (5) That을 do의 목적어와 is의 주어 역할을 할 수 있는 What으로 고쳐야 한다. (6) understand와 said의 목적어 역할을 할 수 있도록 that을 what으로 고쳐야 한다.

Reading

확인문제 p.30

1 T 2 F 3 T 4 F 5 T 6 F

확인문제 p.31

1 T 2 F 3 T 4 F 5 T 6 F

교과서 확인학습 A p.32~33

01 Effectively 02 Welcome to 03 I'm
04 using good communication skills
05 our first clip 06 ends up arguing
07 the reason why 08 *careless*
09 to express his feelings
10 Instead, I-message
11 focus on, rather than
12 *I'm, upset, are lost* 13 Next
14 is busy preparing
15 have a look
16 *Could I*
17 the right time
18 what 19 enough time
20 pick a time, is ready to listen
21 *Could I* 22 *Sure*
23 take a look at 24 hurts 25 *Don't put*
26 felt uncomfortable
27 taking orders 28 such as
29 what, request, demand
30 *Could you*
31 a small change, prevent communication problems
32 keep, in mind

교과서 확인학습 B p.34~35

1 Speak Your Mind Effectively
2 Welcome to "All about Teens."
3 I'm Dr. Carter.
4 Today, we're going to talk about using good communication skills to express ourselves more effectively.
5 Let's start with our first clip about Brian.
6 When he tries to talk to his brother, he always ends up arguing with his brother.
7 Let's find out the reason why he has this problem.
8 Brian: You lost my earphones again. Why are you so careless?
9 Brian is starting a sentence with "you" to express his feelings..
10 Instead, he should use the "I-message."
11 Starting with "I" can help him focus on what he feels or thinks rather than point the finger at his brother.
12 Brian: I'm really upset because my favorite earphones are lost.
13 Next is Calli.
14 She is trying to talk to her mother, but she is busy preparing to go to work.
15 Let's have a look.
16 Calli: Hey, Mom. Could I talk to you about something?
17 Calli needs to find the right time to talk to her mom.
18 Maybe Calli's mom wanted to listen to what Calli was going to say.
19 But she didn't have enough time to talk with her daughter.
20 Calli should pick a time when her mom is ready to listen.
21 Calli: Hey, Mom. Could I talk to you about something?
22 Mom: Sure.
23 Now, let's take a look at our last clip.
24 Anna and Julie are best friends, but Anna often hurts Julie's feelings.
25 Anna: Don't put your bag on my desk!
26 Julie probably felt uncomfortable because Anna made a demand using the word "don't."
27 People simply don't like taking orders.
28 Anna should try to use words such as "can," "could," or "please."
29 Then, what she says will sound like a request

rather than a demand.

30 Anna: Could you put your bag on your desk?

31 As we saw in the video clips, a small change in the way we express ourselves can solve or even prevent communication problems.

32 Let's keep these tips in mind!

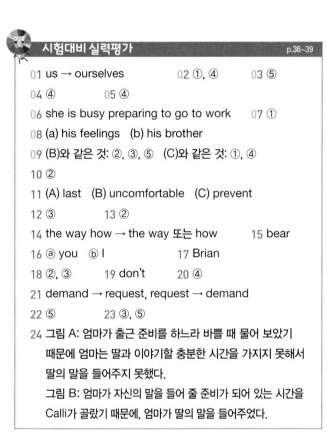

시험대비 실력평가
p.36~39

01 us → ourselves　　02 ①, ④　　03 ⑤

04 ④　　　　05 ④

06 she is busy preparing to go to work　07 ①

08 (a) his feelings　(b) his brother

09 (B)와 같은 것: ②, ③, ⑤　(C)와 같은 것: ①, ④

10 ②

11 (A) last　(B) uncomfortable　(C) prevent

12 ③　　　　　13 ②

14 the way how → the way 또는 how　　15 bear

16 ⓐ you　ⓑ I　　　　17 Brian

18 ②, ③　　19 don't　　20 ④

21 demand → request, request → demand

22 ⑤　　　　23 ③, ⑤

24 그림 A: 엄마가 출근 준비를 하느라 바쁠 때 물어 보았기 때문에 엄마는 딸과 이야기할 충분한 시간을 가지지 못해서 딸의 말을 들어주지 못했다.

　그림 B: 엄마가 자신의 말을 들어 줄 준비가 되어 있는 시간을 Calli가 골랐기 때문에, 엄마가 딸의 말을 들어주었다.

01 주어와 목적어가 같으므로 재귀대명사로 고치는 것이 적절하다.

02 ⓐ와 ①, ④: 명사적 용법, ②, ⑤: 부사적 용법, talk over a cup of coffee: 커피를 마시면서 이야기하다, ③: 형용사적 용법

03 ⑤ '브라이언과 남동생 사이의 말다툼을 하게 된 이유에 대해 알아보자'고 했으므로, 위 글에서는 그 이유를 알 수 없다. ① All about Teens. ② Dr. Carter. ③ Using good communication skills to express ourselves more effectively(자신을 더 효과적으로 표현하기 위해 좋은 의사소통 기술을 사용하는 것). ④ The reason of the argument between Brian and his brother. subject: (논의 등의) 주제, 대상, 화제

04 ④ '아마' Calli의 엄마는 Calli가 말하려고 하는 것을 듣고 싶었을 것이라고 하는 것이 적절하다. Maybe: 아마, ① 그 결과, 따라서, ② 정확히, ③, ⑤: 특히

05 ④는 Calli가 아니라 'Calli의 엄마'를 지칭한다.

06 be busy ~ing: ~하느라 바쁘다

07 ⓐ focus on: (관심, 노력 등을) 집중하다, 초점을 맞추다, ⓑ

point the finger at: …을 비난[책망]하다

08 Brian은 '그의 감정'을 표현하기 위해 "너"로 문장을 시작하면서 그의 남동생을 비난하기 때문에, 그는 결국 언제나 '남동생'과 말다툼을 하게 된다.

09 (B)와 ②, ③, ⑤: 현재분사, (C)와 ①, ④: 동명사

10 앞 문장에서 Julie는 Anna가 "don't"라는 단어를 사용하며 요구했기 때문에 아마 불편하게 느꼈을 것이라고 했기 때문에, 사람들은 단순히 '명령을 받는 것'을 좋아하지 않는다고 하는 것이 적절하다. take orders: 명령을 받다, ① ask advice: 충고를 구하다, ③ give advice: 충고를 하다, ④ take turns: 교대로 하다, ⑤ give orders: 지시하다

11 (A) 몇 개의 동영상 중에서 '마지막' 동영상을 말하는 것이므로 last가 적절하다. last: 마지막의, latest: 최근의, (B) 'feel+형용사 보어'를 써야 하므로 uncomfortable이 적절하다. (C) 의사소통의 문제를 '막을 수 있다'고 해야 하므로 prevent가 적절하다. prevent: 막다[예방/방지하다], protect: 보호하다

12 이 글은 '사람들은 단순히 명령을 받는 것을 좋아하지 않으므로 "can," "could," 또는 "please"와 같은 단어들을 사용하려고 노력해야 한다.'는 내용의 글이므로, 어울리는 속담으로는 ③번 '가는 말이 고우면 오는 말도 곱다.'가 적절하다. ① 늦더라도 않는 것보다 낫다. ② 어려울 때 친구가 진정한 친구이다. ④ 깃털이 같은 새들이 함께 모인다.(유유상종) ⑤ 손 안에 든 새 한 마리가 숲 속에 있는 두 마리보다 낫다.

13 ⓐ와 ②: …처럼, …하는 대로, ① [비례] …함에 따라, …할수록, ③ …일 때, ④ (자격·기능 등이) …로(서)(전치사), ⑤ [이유·원인] …이므로, …이기 때문에

14 the way와 how는 같이 쓸 수 없다.

15 keep ~ in mind = bear ~ in mind: 명심하다

16 ⓐ Brian은 그의 감정을 표현하기 위해 "너"로 문장을 시작하고 있다. ⓑ "나"로 시작하는 것은 그의 남동생을 비난하기보다 자신이 느끼거나 생각하는 것에 집중하도록 도울 수 있다.

17 Brian을 가리킨다.

18 ② 비판[비난]하다, ③ …을 탓하다, ① (…해야 한다고) 고집하다[주장하다/우기다], ④ (~이 어떠한지를) 말하다[서술하다], ⑤ (아이디어·계획을) 제안[제의]하다

19 Julie는 Anna가 "don't"라는 단어를 사용하며 요구했기 때문에 아마 불편하게 느꼈을 것이라고 하는 것이 적절하다.

20 ⓑ와 ④: 명령, take orders: 명령을 받다, ① 순서, ② 정돈, ③ (사회적) 질서, ⑤ (상품의) 주문 restore: 복구하다

21 Anna가 "can," "could" 또는 "please"와 같은 말을 사용하려고 노력하면, 그녀가 하는 말이 '요구'라기보다는 '요청'처럼 들릴 것이라고 하는 것이 적절하다.

22 ⓐ와 ⑤: 알맞은, ① 오른쪽의, ② 옳은, ③ 정확히, 바로(부사), ④ 권리[권한](명사)

23 ⓑ와 ③, ⑤: 형용사적 용법, ①, ②: 부사적 용법, ④: 명사적

용법

24 Calli가 엄마에게 말을 걸 적절한 때를 찾아내어 물어보았는지 아닌지를 구별해서 대답하면 정답이다.

서술형 시험대비 p.40~41

01 why

02 (1) in order (2) so as (3) in order that
   (4) so that, can[may]

03 he always ends up arguing with his brother

04 preparing

05 the thing which[that]

06 (A) find the right time (B) is ready to listen

07 starting a sentence

08 자신이 느끼거나 생각하는 것에 집중하도록 "나"로 문장을 시작하는 것이다.

09 point the finger at his brother → focus on what he feels or thinks, focus on what he feels or thinks → point the finger at his brother

10 have, look at

11 Could[Can] you put your bag on your desk? 또는 Please put your bag on your desk.

12 request, demand / demand, request / demand, request

13 to use words such as "can," "could," or "please"

14 "don't" / "can", "could", "please"

01 선행사가 the reason이므로, 관계부사 why가 적절하다.

02 부사적 용법(목적)을 나타내는 to부정사는 in order to = so as to = in order that ~ can[may] = so that ~ can[may] 으로 바꿔 쓸 수 있다.

03 end up ~ing: 결국 ~하게 되다

04 be busy ~ing: ~하느라 바쁘다

05 관계대명사 what은 선행사를 포함한 관계대명사이다. 지금은 동사가 was이므로 선행사를 단수 형태인 the thing으로 쓰는 것이 적절하다.

06 문제점: Calli는 엄마에게 말을 걸 적절한 때를 찾아내지 못했다. 효과적인 의사소통 방법: Calli는 엄마가 들어 줄 준비가 되어 있는 시간을 골라야 한다.

07 그의 감정을 표현하기 위해 "너"로 '문장을 시작하는' 대신에

08 뒤에 이어지는 내용을 쓰면 된다.

09 rather than 앞과 뒤의 말들을 서로 바꿔 쓰는 것이 적절하다.
   B rather than A: A라기보다는 B

10 take a look at = have a look at = look at

11 "can," "could," 또는 "please"와 같은 말을 사용하면 요구라

12 A라기보다는 B: B rather than A = rather[more] B than A = not so much A as B = less A than B

13 "can," "could" 또는 "please"와 같은 말을 사용하는 것이다.

14 사용하지 말아야 할 단어: '요구'하는 것처럼 들리는 단어, 사용하려고 노력해야 하는 단어들: '요청'하는 것처럼 들리는 단어들

영역별 핵심문제 p.43~47

01 ④   02 Keep(keep)
03 (1) off (2) on (3) in   04 ②   05 ④
06 argument 07 ②, ③   08 ①   09 ⑤
10 ④   11 ①, ⑤   12 ④
13 I'm so stressed out about my exams
14 ①   15 ②   16 ③   17 ⑤
18 (1) What she said (2) what I've missed (3) what I ate
19 (1) My parents got married on the day.
   (2) I make gimchi in the way.
20 (1) The house where Anne lives has a small garden.
   (2) The house in which Anne lives has a small garden.
   (3) The house which Anne lives in has a small garden.
21 ⓐ, ⓒ, ⓔ, ⓕ   22 ③, ④
23 Whenever 24 for which 25 ③   26 ④
27 maybe 또는 perhaps
28 what she says will sound like a request rather than a demand
29 (A) made a demand (B) can, could, please
30 ②   31 Calli's mother   32 ⑤

01 pre-는 '미리, 먼저(before, beforehand)'의 의미가 있는 접두어이다. precaution: 조심, 예방책 preview: 미리 보기 prepare: 준비하다 prevent: 막다, 예방하다 premium: 고급의

02 keep ~ in mind: ~을 명심하다 / 이 교훈을 명심해라. keep 동사ing: ~을 계속하다, 반복하다 / 그녀가 그에게 설거지하라고 말해서 그는 계속해서 TV를 볼 수 없었다.

03 (1) cut ~ off: ~을 중단시키다, 잘라내다 / 내가 말할 때 내 말을 자르지 마. (2) focus on: ~에 집중하다 / 그는 사진 찍는 데 집중했다. (3) in the middle of: ~ 도중에, ~ 중간에 / 나는 지금 꽤 중요한 일을 하는 중이다.

04 mean: 못된, 심술궂은 / 잔인한 또는 친절하지 않은

05 how come: 어찌하여, 왜

07 ① Anna가 Sally의 말을 중간에 끊었다. ④ 남자가 Sally에게 왜 그녀가 Anna와 말을 안 하는지 물은 것을 보아 왜 사이가 안

좋았는지에 대해 모르고 있었다. ⑤ Sally는 Anna의 행동에 화가 났다.

08 'What should I do?'는 '어떻게 해야 하지?'의 의미로 충고를 구할 때 쓰는 표현으로 Brown씨가 수업에 집중하라고 충고해 주고 있는 대답의 질문으로 적절하다.

09 first of all: 먼저, 무엇보다도 / 좋은 영어 성적을 얻기 위해 무엇을 해야 하는지 충고를 구하는 말에 무엇보다도 수업 시간에 집중하라는 충고를 해 주고 있다.

10 ④번은 상대방이 내가 한 말을 정확히 이해했다는 의미이며, 이외의 나머지 보기들은 상대방이 자신의 말을 이해하지 못했을 때 쓸 수 있는 표현들이다.

11 자신이 화났음을 표현할 때 upset을 사용해서 'I am upset about[with, because of] ~. (나는 ~에 대해[~에게, ~ 때문에] 화가 나)'라고 말할 수 있다.

12 언니가 Anna에게 이래라저래라 하는 것에 화가 난다고 말하고 있으므로 남자아이는 Anna가 느끼는 감정을 언니인 Elsa에게 말해야 한다고 충고하고 있다.

13 stressed out: 스트레스로 지친, 스트레스가 쌓인

14 let one's hair down: 느긋하게 쉬다

15 관계부사 where는 의미에 맞게 '전치사(in, at, on 등)+관계대명사 which'로 바꿔 쓸 수 있다. 여기서 where는 in which나 at which로 바꿔 쓸 수 있다.

16 I like what she bought for me. 선행사가 없으므로 선행사를 포함하는 관계대명사 what을 이용하여 '~하는 것'을 나타낸다.

17 <보기>와 ⑤번은 관계부사이다. ① 의문사, ② 의문사, ③ 접속사, ④ 명사

18 선행사를 포함한 관계대명사 what(= the thing(s) which[that])을 이용한다.

19 관계부사는 '전치사+관계대명사(which)'로 바꿔 쓸 수 있다. when = in/on/at which, how = in which

20 관계부사는 '전치사+관계대명사(which)'로 바꿔 쓸 수 있는데, which를 쓸 때는 전치사를 which 바로 앞에 쓰거나 관계부사절의 끝에 쓴다. where = in which

21 ⓑ that → what ⓓ which → where ⓖ the way how → the way 또는 how 또는 the way that 또는 the way in which

22 ⓐ와 ③, ④: 동명사, ①, ②, ⑤: 현재분사, ② 빈 수레가 요란하다(실속은 없는데 허세를 부릴 때 자주 쓰는 속담).

23 When ~, always = Whenever: ~할 때마다

24 관계부사 why는 for which로 고칠 수 있다.

25 ③번 다음 문장의 But에 주목한다. 주어진 문장의 내용과 상반되는 내용을 이끌고 있으므로 ③번이 적절하다.

26 'Calli's mom' didn't have enough time to talk with 'her daughter.'

27 probably = maybe = perhaps: 아마

28 'what'을 보충하면 된다.

29 문제점: Anna는 "don't"라는 단어를 사용하며 '요구했다.' 효과적인 의사소통 방법: Anna는 "can," "could," 또는 "please"와 같은 말을 사용함으로써 그녀가 말하는 것이 요구라기보다는 요청처럼 들리게 만들어야 한다.

30 선행사가 시간이므로 관계부사 when이 적절하다.

31 'Calli의 엄마'를 가리킨다.

32 Calli가 얼마나 자주 그녀의 엄마와 이야기할 수 있는지는 대답할 수 없다. ① No. ② When her mom is busy preparing to go to work. ③ She needs to find the right time to talk to her mom. ④ Yes.

단원별 예상문제
p.48~51

01 uncomfortable　　02 ②　　03 got
04 ⑤　　05 ①　　06 ③
07 I'm upset about my science group.　　08 ③
09 ③　　10 ②　　11 What　　12 ③
13 ④　　14 ②
15 (1) The report showed what I wanted to know.
(2) He was proud of what he did.
(3) This telescope can do what others cannot.
(4) July is the month when the summer heat actually begins.
(5) We stayed in a village where time has stood still.
(6) The Internet is changing the way people shop.
16 ⓐ relationship ⓑ I will keep my promises. Also I will try to be honest with her.
17 (1) 엄마와의 약속을 지키지 않은 것
(2) 엄마에게 거짓말을 한 것　　18 better
19 They will listen to you when they have enough time to talk with you.
20 (1) 1) Use the "I-message."
(2) Pick the right time.
(3) Make a request.　　21 ①
22 focus on what he feels or thinks rather than point the finger at his brother　　23 ⑤

01 comfortable: 편안한 uncomfortable: 불편한 'What's the problem?(무엇이 문제입니까?)'의 문장으로 보아 음식에 대해 편안한 것이 아니라 불편한 것을 나타내는 말이 나와야 어울린다.

02 express: 표현하다, 나타내다 ④ 그것에 관해 말하거나 써서 감정, 의견 또는 목표를 말하다 / 사람들은 울음으로써 슬픔을 표현한다. solve: 해결하다 ① 어려움을 유발하는 어떤 것에 대

9

한 해결책을 찾다 / 너는 문제를 해결하기에 충분히 똑똑하다. disappointed: 실망한, 낙담한 ⑤ 바라거나 예상했던 것이 일어나지 않았거나, 예상했던 누군가나 어떤 것이 예상만큼 좋지 않아 행복하지 않은 / 경기에서 져서 실망스럽니? helpful: 도움이 되는, 유용한 ③ 유용한, 도움을 제공하는 / 그 책은 그 시험을 준비하는 데 정말 도움이 되었다. ② reason: 이유 / 왜 어떤 일이 발생했는지, 왜 누군가가 그것을 행했는지, 또는 왜 그것이 진짜인지 등에 대해 설명하는 사실이나 상황 또는 의도

03 get cold feet: 긴장하다, 겁을 먹다 / Sally는 마지막 순간에 겁을 먹고 결혼을 취소했다. get a good grade: 좋은 성적을 얻다 / 나는 지난 토요일에 피아노 축제에서 좋은 점수를 얻었다.

04 make a demand: 요구하다 / 너는 지금 요구할 위치에 있지 않다.

05 빈칸에 이어 'Not good.(좋지 않아.)'이란 대답이 온 것과 다음의 질문에 그룹 구성원들이 말만 하고 듣지 않아서 제시간에 과제를 끝낼 수 없다는 말로 보아 과학 숙제가 어떻게 되어 가고 있는지 묻는 것이 어울린다.

06 남자는 그룹 구성원들이 말만 하고 전혀 듣지 않아 주어진 시간에 끝낼 수 있을 것이라고 생각하고 있지 않다.

07 be upset about ~: ~에 대해서 화나다

08 주어진 문장은 '너희 둘 아직 화해 못 했니?'라는 의미의 질문으로 여자가 'No, not yet.'이라고 대답하고 있으므로 ③에 들어가는 것이 적절하다.

09 대화에서 mean은 '못된, 심술궂은'의 의미로 사용했다. ① 수단 ②, ④, ⑤ 의미하다 ③ 못된, 심술궂은 / 너의 여동생에게 못되게 굴지 마라.

10 ② Julie가 화가 나서 동생한테 큰 소리로 얘기한 것이 아니라, Julie의 동생이 크게 전화 통화를 해서 화가 났다. ① Julie는 피곤해서 자기를 원했다. ③ Julie는 그녀의 동생에게 한 일 때문에 우울하다. ④ Julie는 그녀의 여동생에게 문자 메시지를 보낼 것 같다. ⑤ Julie는 그녀의 여동생에게 미안하다고 얘기하고 싶어 한다.

11 관계대명사 what은 선행사를 포함한 관계대명사로 the thing(s) which[that]를 나타낸다.

12 첫 번째 문장에서는 선행사가 없으므로 선행사를 포함하는 관계대명사 What이 적절하다. 두 번째 문장에서는 the reason이 선행사로 나와 있으므로 관계부사 why가 적절하다.

13 ① Calli's mom wanted to listen to what Calli was going to say. ② What I want for breakfast is just a glass of juice. ③ The painting is what you saw in the house. ⑤ I'd rather talk about the things that are happening. 또는 I'd rather talk about what are happening.

14 뒤에 나오는 절이 완전하며 선행사가 the TV station이므로

which를 where로 바꾸는 것이 적절하다.

15 (1)~(3) 선행사를 포함한 관계대명사 what을 이용한다. (4)~(6) 이어지는 절이 완전한 경우 관계부사를 이용한다. 선행사가 시간을 나타내는 경우 when을 쓰고, 장소를 나타내는 경우 where를 쓰고, 방법을 나타내는 경우 how나 the way를 쓴다.

16 ⓐ '관계', ⓑ '엄마와의 약속을 지킬 것이다. 또한, 엄마에게 정직하려고 노력할 것이다.'를 가리킨다.

17 글쓴이는 '엄마와의 약속을 지키지 않아서' 엄마를 화나게 했고, '엄마에게 거짓말을 해서' 엄마를 실망시켰다.

18 글쓴이는 엄마와의 관계를 '더 좋게' 만들기를 원한다.

19 그들이 당신과 이야기할 충분한 시간을 가질 때 그들은 당신의 말을 들을 것이다.

20 (1) "나 메세지"를 사용하라. (2) 적절한 때를 골라라. (3) 요청을 하라.

21 ⓐ와 ①, ③, ④, ⑤: 부사적 용법, ②: 명사적 용법

22 B rather than A: A라기보다는 B.

23 "나"로 시작하는 것은 '그의 남동생을 비난하기보다' 자신이 느끼고 생각하는 것에 집중하도록 도울 수 있다고 했다.

🦉 서술형 실전문제 p.52~53

01 That's not what I meant.
I didn't mean to say that.
You misunderstood me.

02 She kept cutting me off in the middle of my sentences, so I got mad.

03 ⓓ stopped to talk → stopped talking

04 (1) What he remembers
(2) what you want to wear
(3) what she wanted to explain

05 (1) I don't know the reason why Jane is crying. / I don't know the reason for which Jane is crying.
(2) Smart phones have changed the way people live. / Smart phones have changed how people live. / Smart phones have changed the way that people live.

06 (1) Do you remember the library where we studied together?
(2) Do you know the date when Jake will get married?

07 (1) the place   (2) the reason   08 what

09 pointing

10 (A) you   (B) what he feels or thinks

11 arguing

12 (a) the reason   (b) his brother

13 Brian이 남동생과 이야기를 하려고 할 때, 결국 언제나 동생과 말다툼을 하게 되는 것.

01 빈칸 다음에 의미를 다시 이야기하고 있는 것으로 보아 빈칸에는 오해를 지적하는 말이 들어가야 한다. 오해를 지적하는 말에 'That's not what I meant.(내가 의미한 것은 그게 아니야.)', 'I didn't mean to say that.(그 말을 하려던 것이 아니었어.)', 'You misunderstood me.(너는 나를 오해했어.)' 등이 올 수 있다.

02 keep 동사ing: ~을 계속하다, 반복하다 cut ~ off: ~을 중단시키다, 잘라내다 in the middle of: ~ 도중에, ~ 중간에 get+감정형용사: ~하게 되다

03 싸워서 말하는 것을 멈췄다는 말이 어울리므로 stopped to talk를 stopped talking으로 바꾸는 것이 적절하다. stop to 동사원형: ~하기 위해서 멈추다 stop 동사ing: ~을 그만두다, ~하지 않게 되다

04 what은 선행사를 포함한 관계대명사로 '~하는 것'으로 해석하며, the thing(s) which[that]를 나타낸다.

05 (1) 선행사가 '이유'를 나타낼 때 관계부사는 why를 쓰며 이때의 why는 'for which'로 바꿔 쓸 수 있다. (2) 선행사가 '방법'을 나타낼 때 관계부사는 how를 쓰며 이때 how와 함께 the way를 쓰지 않는다는 것을 주의한다. the way나 how 또는 the way that이나 the way in which를 쓴다.

06 (1) 선행사가 the library이므로 관계부사 where를 쓴다. (2) 선행사가 the date이므로 관계부사 when을 쓴다.

07 관계부사의 선행사가 the place, the reason, the time 등일 경우에는 생략할 수 있다.

08 how는 think의 목적어가 될 수 없으므로 what이 적절하다.

09 instead of 뒤에 동명사를 쓰는 것이 적절하다.

10 문제점: Brian은 그의 감정을 표현하기 위해 "너"로 문장을 시작하고 있다. 효과적인 의사소통 방법: 그는 "나 메세지"를 사용해야 한다. 그러면, 그는 그의 남동생을 비난하기보다 '자신이 느끼고 생각하는 것'에 집중할 수 있다.

11 end up ~ing: 결국 ~하게 되다

12 이 동영상은 동생과 이야기를 하려는 Brian의 시도가 결국 항상 동생과 그 사이의 말다툼으로 끝나게 되는 이유를 보여준다. end up ~ing (with+명사): 결국 ~하게 되다

13 앞 문장의 내용을 쓰면 된다.

창의사고력 서술형 문제   p.54

|모범답안|

01 That's not what I meant. I mean our project is postponed.

02 (1) This is my grandparents' house where my first birthday party was held.

(2) Can you show me the way this copy machine works?

(3) Saturday is the day when I don't go to school.

(4) Do you know the reason why she left early?

03 (A) |모범답안| worst (B) |모범답안| got angry

(C)|모범답안| disappointed

(D)|모범답안| keep my promises

(E)|모범답안| to be honest with her

01 That's not what I meant.는 '그런 뜻이 아니야.'라는 의미이며, 상대방이 자신의 말의 의도를 오해할 때 정정하기 위해 쓰는 표현이다. postpone: 미루다, 연기하다 mean: 의미하다

단원별 모의고사   p.55~58

01 (p)oint the finger

02 ⓑ keep to work → keep working   03 ⑤

04 uncertain   05 got   06 ③, ⑤   07 ②

08 ⑤   09 ④   10 ⑤

11 It means to study.   12 ①

13 (A) to talk   (B) many   (C) quiet   (D) to talk

14 detail   15 ②   16 why

17 (1) that → what

(2) what → that[which], 또는 the thing what → what

(3) the way how → the way 또는 how 또는 the way that

(4) which → when 또는 in which   18 ⑤

19 (1) I know a restaurant where we can have delicious *samgyupsal*.

(2) Winter is the season when leaves fall.

20 ①, ④   21 clip   22 ③   23 ②

24 Calli should pick a time when her mom is ready to listen.

25 Calli → Calli's mom, mom → daughter, school→ work

01 point the finger at: ~을 비난하다

02 ⓐ stop 동사ing: ~을 그만두다, ~하지 않게 되다 / 의사가 그에게 담배 피는 것을 그만 둘 것을 충고했다. ⓑ keep 동사ing: ~을 계속하다, 반복하다 / 계속 노력하면 너는 그 시험에 통과할 것이다. ⓒ tend to 동사원형: ~하는 경향이 있다 / 그 체육관은 6시 정도에 매우 바빠지는 경향이 있다. ⓓ try to 동사원형: ~을 노력하다 / 나는 불필요한 말싸움을 피하려고 한다.

03 (A) order+사람+around: ~에게 자꾸 이래라저래라 하다 / 그녀가 이래라저래라 명령하도록 내버려 두지 마. (B) concentrate on: ~에 집중하다 / 그들은 공부에 집중하지 못했다. (C) work out: 해결하다 / 우리는 어려움을 해결했다.

04 주어진 단어의 관계는 반의어이다. honest 정직한 dishonest 부정직한 certain: 확실한 uncertain: 불확실한

05 get cold feet: 긴장하다, 겁을 먹다 get+감정형용사: ~하게 되

다 scared: 두려워하는, 겁먹은

06 ① Nick은 어제 다이빙을 했는가?(아니오) ② "get cold feet"은 무슨 의미인가?(겁을 먹다) ③ 왜 Nick은 다이빙을 하는 것이 겁이 났는가? ④ 왜 Nick은 다이빙을 안 했는가?(무서워져서) ⑤ 어디로 Nick은 다이빙을 하러 갔는가?

07 ② go: (일의 진행이 어떻게) 되어가다, 진전되다 / 프로그램이 진행될 때, 연출자는 조정실에 앉아 있다. 나머지 보기들은 '가다'의 의미로 사용되었다.

08 individual: 개인의 / 과학 숙제는 개인 과제가 아니라 그룹 과제였다.

09 어제 왜 생일 파티에 안 왔느냐는 질문에, 남자는 "hit the books"를 해야 했기 때문에 못 갔다고 말했는데, 이것을 이해하지 못한 여자가 왜 책을 쳤는지 물어보며, 무언가에 대해 화났는지 물어보는 것이 어울리므로 ④가 적절하다.

10 '오늘 아침에 시험이 있었다.'와 '나는 어제 공부를 해야 했다.'의 두 문장은 원인과 결과로 이어질 수 있다.

11 hit the books: 공부하다

12 주어진 문장에서 that은 사람들이 자신이 너무 많이 말한다고 계속 말하는 것을 의미한다. 그러므로 사람들이 말한 내용에 이어서 그것에 대해 화가 난다고 말하는 것이 어울린다.

13 (A) tend to 동사원형: ~하는 경향이 있다 (B) details는 셀 수 있는 명사로 s가 붙어 있으므로 셀 수 있는 명사를 수식할 수 있는 many(많은)가 어울린다. (C) A는 자신이 계속 말하고, 세부 사항에 대해 말하는 자신의 경향에 대해 듣고 그러면 자신이 계속 조용히 있어야 하는지를 질문하고 있다. (D) try to 동사원형: ~을 노력하다

14 detail: 구체적 내용, 자세한 내용 / 어떤 상황에 관계된 많은 사소한 사실들이나 정보 중의 하나

15 선행사가 '이유'를 나타낼 때 관계부사는 why를 쓴다. 관계부사 why는 'for+which'로 바꿔 쓸 수 있는데, 전치사를 which 바로 앞에 쓰거나 관계부사절의 끝에 쓴다.

16 선행사로 the reason이 있으므로 why가 적절하며 the reason은 생략 가능하다.

17 (1) that을 wear와 want의 목적어 역할을 할 수 있는 what으로 고치는 것이 적절하다. (2) what = the thing that[which] (3) 선행사 the way와 관계부사 how는 함께 쓸 수 없으며 the way나 how만 써야 하며, 선행사가 the way일 때 how 대신에 that을 쓸 수 있다. (4) 선행사가 시간을 나타내는 the year이므로 which를 when으로 고치는 것이 적절하다. when은 'in which'와 바꿔 쓸 수 있으므로 in which로 고쳐도 좋다.

18 ⑤번은 이어지는 절이 완전하므로 접속사 that이 들어가야 하지만 나머지는 이어지는 절이 불완전하므로 선행사를 포함하는 관계대명사 what이 들어가는 것이 적절하다.

19 (1) a restaurant을 선행사로 하는 관계부사 where를 이용한다. (2) the season을 선행사로 하는 관계부사 when을 이용한

20 ⓐ와 ①, ④: 부사적 용법, ②, ⑤: 명사적 용법, ③: 형용사적 용법

21 동영상 / 인터넷 웹사이트에서 볼 수 있는 짧은 비디오 녹화

22 ⓐ와 ②, ④: 현재분사, ①, ③, ⑤: 동명사

23 ② 'Anna'가 자주 'Julie'의 감정을 상하게 한다.

24 be ready to: ~할 준비가 되어 있다

25 'Calli의 엄마'가 '출근' 준비를 하느라고 바빠서 '그녀의 딸'과 이야기할 시간이 없었다.

Lesson 2

Wonderful Nature

시험대비 실력평가

p.62

01 ①	02 ①	03 ③	04 ④
05 ⑤	06 ②		

01 harsh: (날씨·생활 환경이) 혹독한 / 혹독한 날씨 때문에, 마라톤이 2주 동안 연기되었다.

02 peak: 절정[최대한도]에 이르다 / 석유 생산은 1980년대 초에 최고조에 달했다.

03 ① in fact: 사실상, 실제로 / 나는 그 시장을 매우 잘 안다. 사실 나는 지난주에 그녀와 저녁을 먹었다. ② in the middle of the night: 한밤중에 / 한밤중에 전화가 울렸다. ③ be[get] inspired by: ~에 의해 영감을 받다 / 그 영화는 실제 사건에 의해 영감을 받았다. ④ stand in for: ~을 대신하다 / 위험한 장면에서는 한 여성 스턴트가 Goldie Hawn을 대신했다. ⑤ get in shape: 좋은 몸 상태를 유지하다 / 나는 정말 여름 전에 좋은 몸 상태를 유지하고 싶다.

04 ① 나는 그것을 아직 볼 기회가 없었다. ② Keith는 공학 학위를 가지고 있지만 그의 분야에서 직장을 찾지 못했다. ③ 우리의 문제는 형편없는 경영과 경험의 부족이 결합된 것 때문이었다. ④ try: 맛보다 / 만약 내가 외식하러 나간다면, 나는 다른 것을 맛보는 것을 선호한다. ⑤ 그들은 피카소가 훌륭한 색채 화가였다는 것을 잊었다.

05 inspire: 영감을 주다, 고무하다, 격려하다 / 우리는 그 팀을 고무시킬 수 있는 누군가가 필요하다. 그들은 그의 음악이 사람들에게 영감을 주고 사람들을 감동시킨다고 생각한다.

06 (A) find out: 발견하다, 알아보다 / 하지만 학부모들과 교사들은 그 경기에 문제점이 있다는 것을 발견했다. (B) make plans (for): (~의) 계획을 세우다 / 너는 여름 방학 계획을 세웠니?

서술형 시험대비

p.63

01 Whenever

02 insight

03 ⓐ lone → alone

04 come

05 to

06 (1) aurora's (2) is caused by (3) ecologists
   (4) stand in for

07 (1) keep (2) turned (3) cut (4) filled

01 whenever+주어+동사: ~할 때마다 / 내가 세차를 할 때마다 그 다음 날 비가 온다.

02 insight: 통찰력 / 그 연구는 우리가 언어를 처리하는 방식에 대한 새로운 통찰력을 제공한다.

03 ⓐ lone은 보통 한정적 용법으로 사용되고, alone은 서술적 용법으로만 사용된다.

04 come back from ~: ~에서 돌아오다 / 언제 미국에서 돌아왔어요? come true: 실현되다, 사실이 되다 / 이곳은 꿈이 실현되는 장소이다.

05 from A to B: A에서 B로 / 나는 단지 집에서 역으로 나를 데려다 줄 차가 필요하다. due to 명사: ~ 때문에 / 이 기획은 자금의 부족 때문에 내년에 계속되지 않을 것이다.

06 (1) aurora: 오로라 (2) be caused by ~: ~에 의해 야기되다 (3) ecologist: 생태학자 (4) stand in for: ~을 대신하다

07 (1) keep ~ on one's toes: ~을 계속 긴장하게 하다 / 그들은 일하는 사람들이 긴장을 늦추지 않게 하기 위해 무작위로 검사한다. (2) turn out: (일·진행·결과가 특정 방식으로) 되다 / 힘든 시기였지만 결국 상황이 모두 좋게 되었다. (3) cut down: 자르다 / 사람들은 너무 많은 나무를 잘라내고 야생 동물의 서식지를 파괴한다. (4) be filled with: ~로 가득 차다 / 공기가 장미의 향기로 가득 찼다.

[교과서]

Conversation

핵심 Check

p.64~65

1 I can't wait to go to the party.
2 I'm looking forward to trying them out on my friends.
3 that having[eating] a tomato is good for eyes
2 (C) → (A) → (B)

교과서 대화문 익히기

Check(√) True or False

p.66~67

1 F 2 T 3 F 4 T 5 F 6 T 7 F 8 T

Listen & Talk 1 Get Ready

view, amazing / wait to, run up

Listen & Talk 1 A-1

what's, plan / going, wait to visit / are, that, like / sounds, Take

Listen & Talk 1 A-2

want to watch / about adventures, was shot / heard, has / can't wait to watch, go and get

Listen & Talk 1 B

is going, in / What, plan to / study, caves, go, watching / like, interesting / I've only read about, wait to actually visit / hope, enjoy

Listen & Talk 2 Get Ready

is, high / I've heard that, travels from, to

Listen & Talk 2 A-1

weather report, able, shooting stars / When, to see them / heard that, shooting starts / between, and / special night

Listen & Talk 2 A-2

are / They are, I've heard that, made by, sticky / like / like, actually

Listen & Talk 2 B

that, sets / that, How / heard that, cycling, because / love, in, of / too, chance to try

Communication

winner / for inviting, honored / talk, heard that, was taken, true / caused by / amazing / can't wait to take / wish, best

01 ②, ⑤   02 ②   03 ①

01 'can't wait to+동사원형'은 '~하기를 몹시 바라다.' 또는 '어서 ~하고 싶다.'라는 의미로 기대를 나타낼 때 사용하는 표현이다. 'can't wait to+동사원형' 대신에 'can't wait for+(동)명사'나 'look forward to+(동)명사', 'expect to 동사원형'을 사용할 수 있다.

02 일기예보를 봤느냐고 질문하며 오늘 밤에 많은 유성을 볼 수 있을 거라고 언급하며 (B) 놀랍다고 얘기하며 언제 보는 것이 좋은지 질문하자 (A) 오전 12시에서 2시 사이에 가장 절정이라고 대답한다. (C) 다시 감탄하며, 특별한 밤이 될 것이라고 말한다.

03 남자가 새로 나온 3D 영화 중 하나가 바다 밑의 모험에 관한 것이며 호주의 Great Barrier Reef에서 찍은 거라고 말하자 여자는 그곳에 아름다운 해양 생물이 있다고 대답하고 있으므로, 남자가 말하는 사실에 대해 알고 있는 것을 표현하는 'I've heard of ~.(나는 ~에 대해 들었다)'를 쓰는 것이 적절하다.

01 ②	02 ①	03 ③	04 for
05 ④	06 ④	07 ④	08 ⑤
09 ④	10 going, Uyuni Salt Flats, bike riding		
11 ③			

01 주어진 문장은 거기서 무엇을 할 건지 계획을 묻는 것이므로 'We are going to study the caves on the island and go bird watching.(섬에 있는 동굴을 연구하고 새 관찰을 하러 갈 거예요.)'의 질문으로 적절하므로 ②번이 어울린다.

02 ① 소녀의 아빠는 독도를 가 본 적이 있는가? ② 언제 소녀의 과학 클럽은 독도에 가는가?(7월) ③ 소녀는 독도에서 무엇을 할 예정인가? (동굴을 연구하고 새 관찰을 하러 갈 것이다.) ④ 소녀의 과학 클럽은 7월에 어디를 가는가?(독도) ⑤ 소녀는 독도를 가는 것을 기대하고 있는가?(네)

03 주어진 문장은 사진이 몰디브에서 찍혔다는 것을 들었다는 것으로 ③ 다음에 나온 문장에서 몰디브에서 찍은 것이 사실인지 물어보는 것과 어울리므로 ③에 들어가는 것이 알맞다.

04 thank you는 감사를 표현하는 말로 뒤에 for를 붙여 감사하는 이유를 적는다.

05 ① 몰디브의 해변은 왜 반짝이는가?(플랑크톤 때문에) ② 그들은 무엇에 관해 이야기하고 있는가?(Ms. Scarlett Lee가 찍은 사진) ③ 누가 금년의 사진 대회의 우승자인가?(Ms. Scarlett Lee) ④ Ms. Scarlett Lee는 어느 나라로 사진을 찍으러 갈 것인가?(멋진 해변의 사진을 찍을 것을 기대한다고 말했지 특정한 나라에 대한 언급은 없었다.) ⑤ Ms. Scarlett Lee가 수상한 사진을 어디에서 찍었는가?(몰디브)

06 ⓓ를 제외한 것은 'snow rollers(두루마기 눈)'를 가리킨다. ⓓ는 snow rollers가 snow rings(눈 반지)처럼 생겼다고 말하는 것이지 snow rollers를 의미하는 것은 아니다.

07 ④ 록 콘서트를 가기를 원하는지 묻는 말에 아니라고 대답하고 기대된다고 말하는 것은 어색하다.

08 노르웨이에서는 여름 동안 해가 지지 않는 것을 알고 있느냐고 질문하니, (C) 알지 못했다고 대답하며, 흥미롭다고 감탄한다. (D) 밤에 어둡지 않기 때문에 밤에 하이킹을 가고 자전거를 타러 간다고 들은 것에 대해 말을 하자 (B) 지수도 한밤중에 하이킹과 자전거를 타러 가고 싶다고 말하며 자신의 바람을 얘기한다. (A) 남자도 역시 그렇게 하고 싶다고 말하면서 언젠가 우리가 그런 기회를 가지기를 희망한다고 말한다.

09 can't wait to+동사원형: 빨리 ~하고 싶다, ~하기를 몹시 바라다

10 be going to 동사원형: ~할 예정이다 go to 장소: ~에 가다 this vacation: 이번 방학에

11 'I've heard ~.' 이후에는 완전한 문장이 나오므로 접속사 that

을 사용한다. 'I've heard that ~.'은 '~에 대해 들었다.'나 '~에 대해 알고 있다.'는 뜻으로 알고 있거나 들은 것에 대해 말할 때 쓰는 표현이다.

01 and
02 ⓓ Where is the best place → When is the best time
03 I can't wait to visit the Rainbow Mountains.
04 like
05 was shot
06 I have heard of it.
07 I've heard that they are made by strong wind and sticky snow.

01 between A and B: A와 B 사이에서
02 유성이 자정에서 새벽 2시 사이에 가장 최고조가 된다는 말이 이어지고 있으므로 유성을 보기 좋은 장소를 묻는 질문이 아니라 언제 보기 좋은지 시간에 관해서 묻는 질문이 어울린다.
03 can't wait to+동사원형: 빨리 ~하고 싶다, ~하기를 몹시 바라다 visit: 방문하다
04 look like 명사: ~처럼 보이다
05 shoot: 촬영하다 / 주어진 It은 새로 나온 3D 영화 중 하나를 의미하므로, 동사는 수동태인 'be shot'으로 사용되며 과거에 촬영된 것이므로 'was shot'이 적절하다.
06 I have heard about[of] (동)명사 ~: 나는 ~에 대해 들었다 / have heard 다음에 완전한 문장이 나오면 that절을 이어 쓰고, 명사가 오면 전치사 of나 about을 사용한다.
07 I've heard that ~: ~에 대해 들었다, ~에 대해 알고 있다 be made by ~: ~에 의해 만들어지다 sticky: 끈적거리는, 달라붙는

교과서
Grammar

핵심 Check   p.76~77

1 (1) to (2) for (3) of
2 (1) playing (2) playing (3) doing

01 ④   02 ③
03 (1) suggesting (2) have been living (3) of (4) for
04 It is important for students to do their homework.

01 it을 가주어로 하고 to부정사를 진주어로 하며 의미상의 주어로 'for you'를 쓰고 있는 ④번이 적절하다.
02 오래 전에 괴롭히기 시작하여 현재까지 계속 진행되고 있으므로 현재완료진행형이 적절하다.
03 (1) 연구 결과가 밝히고 있는 것이므로 현재완료진행형이 적절하다. (2) 6년 동안 살아오고 있는 것이므로 현재완료진행형이 적절하다. (3) 문장에 쓰인 형용사가 nice, kind, smart, wise 등과 같이 사람의 성향, 성격을 나타내는 말일 때는 'of+명사 또는 대명사의 목적격'으로 쓴다. (4) to부정사의 의미상의 주어는 to부정사 바로 앞에 'for+목적격'으로 나타낸다.
04 it을 가주어로 하고 to부정사를 진주어로 하는 구문을 이용한다. 의미상의 주어로 'for+목적격'을 쓴다.

01 ④   02 ③   03 ⑤
04 (1) been collecting (2) for (3) since (4) for (5) of
05 ②   06 ①   07 ②
08 for me to
09 He has been working in various fields at NASA since 2001.   10 ④   11 ⑤
12 ③
13 (1) have been interviewing actors for
    (2) has been knitting a sweater since
14 (1) Mr. Lee has been teaching math for more than 30 years.
    (2) Mariel learned Korean at the school 5 years ago. 또는 Mariel has been learning Korean at the school since 5 years ago.
    (3) I have been climbing the mountain since Monday.
    (4) We have been waiting for her for 2 hours.
    (5) What time would be best for me to talk to you?
    (6) I think it is very polite of her to ask permission.
    (7) It will be difficult for the children to swim across this river.   15 It, for her to cry
16 ⑤   17 ①, ③, ④
18 As winter is coming, it is necessary for us to prepare for the winter.

15

01 ① It has been raining all day long. ② The argument has been going on for years. ③ Rana has been planting trees in the valleys for the last 31 years. ⑤ I've been visiting the forest to study animals for 20 years.

02 문장에 쓰인 형용사가 사람의 성향, 성격을 나타내는 말이 아니므로 to부정사의 의미상의 주어로 'for+목적격'을 써야 한다. insurance 보험

03 첫 번째 문장에서는 2년 동안 계속 한국어를 공부해 오고 있는 것이므로 현재완료진행형이 적절하다. 두 번째 문장에서는 to부정사의 의미상의 주어로 'for+목적격'이 적절하다.

04 (1) 현재완료진행형은 'have[has] been+동사원형-ing'의 형태이다. (2), (3) 현재완료진행형에서 since는 '시간'을 나타내는 명사(구)와 함께 쓰이고 for는 '기간'을 나타내는 명사(구)와 함께 쓰인다. (4), (5) to부정사의 의미상의 주어는 'for+목적격'으로 나타낸다. 이때 문장에 쓰인 형용사가 사람의 성향, 성격을 나타내는 말일 때는 'of+목적격'으로 쓴다.

05 to부정사의 의미상의 주어로 'for+목적격'이 적절하다.

06 현재완료진행형에서 since는 '시간'을 나타내는 명사(구)와 함께 쓰이고 for는 '기간'을 나타내는 명사(구)와 함께 쓰인다.

07 현재완료진행형은 'have[has] been+동사원형-ing'의 형태이며 과거를 나타내는 어구와 함께 쓰이지 않는다. ①번은 know가 진행형으로 쓰이지 않는 동사임에 유의한다.

08 to부정사의 의미상의 주어로 'for+목적격'이 적절하다.

09 현재완료진행형을 이용하여 쓴다.

10 문장에 사람의 성격을 나타내는 형용사가 있는 경우 의미상의 주어로 'of+목적격'을 쓴다.

11 과거 어느 때부터 시작되어 현재까지 계속 진행되고 있음을 나타내는 현재완료진행형이 적절하다.

12 ③번은 사람의 성향, 성격을 나타내는 형용사 nice가 있으므로 of를 써야 한다. 나머지는 모두 for를 써야 한다.

13 현재완료진행형은 'have[has] been+동사원형-ing'의 형태이다. since는 '시간'을 나타내는 명사(구)와 함께 쓰이고 for는 '기간'을 나타내는 명사(구)와 함께 쓰인다.

14 (1) 현재완료진행형은 'have[has] been+동사원형-ing'의 형태이다. (2) 현재완료진행형은 과거를 나타내는 어구와 함께 쓰이지 않는다. (3), (4) 현재완료진행형에서 since는 '시간'을 나타내는 명사(구)와 함께 쓰이고 for는 '기간'을 나타내는 명사(구)와 함께 쓰인다. (5), (6) to부정사의 의미상의 주어는 'for+목적격'으로 나타낸다. 이때 문장에 쓰인 형용사가 사람의 성향, 성격을 나타내는 말일 때는 'of+목적격'으로 쓴다. (7) 의미상의 주어로 'for+목적격'이 나왔으므로 진주어로 to부정사를 쓴다.

15 to부정사와 의미상의 주어로 'for her'가 나왔으므로 가주어로 It을 쓰고 진주어로 to부정사를 쓴다.

16 5시부터 도착하기 시작하여 아직도 도착하고 있는 것이므로 현재완료진행형을 이용하여 나타낸다.

17 ① 현재완료진행은 '상태'가 아닌, '동작'만을 나타낸다. ③ 현재완료진행형은 과거를 나타내는 어구와 함께 쓰이지 않는다. ④ 사람의 성향, 성격을 나타내는 형용사(rude)가 나왔으므로 'of you'가 적절하다.

18 이유를 이끄는 as와, 'It(가주어) ~ for ...(의미상의 주어) to부정사(진주어)' 구문을 이용하여 쓴다.

서술형 시험대비

p.82~83

01 (1) Naomi has been waiting for her train since two o'clock.
   (2) It has been raining for three hours.
   (3) Women have been making important contributions to sports for centuries.

02 (1) This book is too difficult for you to read.
   (2) It was very smart of him not to miss the chance.
   (3) I have been taking my parents' love for granted.

03 (1) have been enjoying, for two hours
   (2) careless of her to leave

04 (1) for   (2) since

05 (1) too difficult for you to   (2) big enough for us to
   (3) nice of her to

06 (1) for you to listen carefully to the advice
   (2) of Abigail to help me to stand on my own feet

07 (1) thought → thinking   (2) since → for
   (3) for → since
   (4) has been possessing → has possessed
   (5) 5 years ago → for 5 years, 또는 have been living→ lived
   (6) of → for   (7) finding → to find

08 (1) Everyone has been studying hard for the last few months.
   (2) He has been writing the book for long.
   (3) She has been working there since May.
   (4) It was nice of her to offer me a ride.
   (5) There are still two more chores for me to do.

01 과거에 시작하여 지금까지 계속되고 있는 것이므로 현재완료진행형을 이용한다.

02 (1)~(2) to부정사의 의미상의 주어는 'for+목적격'으로 나타내지만 문장에 쓰인 형용사가 사람의 성향, 성격을 나타내는 말일 때는 'of+목적격'으로 쓴다. (3) 과거 어느 때부터 시작되어 현재까지 계속 진행되고 있음을 나타내는 현재완료진행형 구문을 이용한다. take A for granted: A를 당연한 것으로 여기다

03 (1) enjoying이 있으므로 현재완료진행형을 이용한다. two hours라는 기간을 나타내는 명사구가 있으므로 for를 사용한다. (2) 진주어로 to부정사를 쓰고 careless가 사람의 성격을

나타내는 말이므로 'of+목적격'으로 쓴다.

04 현재완료진행형에서 since는 '시간'을 나타내는 명사(구)와 함께 쓰이고 for는 '기간'을 나타내는 명사(구)와 함께 쓰인다.

05 to부정사의 의미상의 주어는 'for+목적격'으로 나타내지만, 문장에 쓰인 형용사가 사람의 성향, 성격을 나타내는 말일 때는 'of+목적격'으로 쓴다.

06 to부정사의 의미상의 주어는 'for+목적격'으로 나타내지만, 문장에 쓰인 형용사가 사람의 성향, 성격을 나타내는 말일 때는 'of+목적격'으로 쓴다.

07 (1) 계속 생각해 오고 있는 것이므로 현재완료진행형으로 나타낸다. (2), (3) 현재완료진행형에서 since는 '시간'을 나타내는 명사(구)와 함께 쓰이고 for는 '기간'을 나타내는 명사(구)와 함께 쓰인다. (4) possess는 소유를 나타내는 동사로 진행형을 쓸 수 없으므로 has been possessing을 has possessed로 고친다. (5) 현재완료진행형은 과거를 나타내는 어구와 함께 쓰이지 않는다. (6) necessary는 사람의 성질을 나타내는 형용사가 아니므로 of를 for로 고친다. (7) 의미상의 주어로 'for me'가 나와 있으므로 finding을 to find로 고친다.

08 (1)~(3) 과거 어느 때부터 시작되어 현재까지 계속 진행되고 있음을 나타내는 현재완료진행형을 이용한다. (4) it을 가주어로 하고 nice가 있으므로 'of her'를 의미상의 주어로 쓴다. (5) 'to do'가 있으므로 'for me'를 의미상의 주어로 쓰고 'There are ~'로 '~이 있다'를 나타낸다.

교과서 Reading

확인문제 p.84

1 T 2 F 3 T 4 F 5 T 6 F

확인문제 p.85

1 T 2 F 3 T 4 F 5 T

교과서 확인학습 A p.86~87

01 Through 02 beauty, inspires
03 find out, fields of work get inspired
04 Ecologist 05 Stone Forest
06 I've been visiting, for over
07 spiky, true miracles
08 amazing, has been created
09 sharp, spiky over
10 for animals to live in, to survive

11 which, frog-like, that, from, to
12 is like, jack-in-the-box
13 keeps me on my toes
14 Fashion Colorist
15 River of Five Colors 16 is filled with
17 create colors
18 I've been gaining
19 mixed colors, anywhere else
20 combination, makes, more alive, bright
21 Whenever, countless, waiting to be created
22 Location Scout 23 Frozen Beauty
24 to shoot movies
25 for many location scouts, due to, unusual beauty
26 My personal favorite
27 stand in for any place
28 In fact, we shot here, without using
29 help make, come true

교과서 확인학습 B p.88~89

1 The World Through My Eyes
2 "The beauty of nature inspires us all.
3 Let's find out how people from different fields of work get inspired by nature."
4 Lin Wang, Ecologist
5 Tsingy, the Stone Forest of Madagascar
6 I've been visiting the stone forest of Madagascar to study plants and animals for over 20 years.
7 The spiky stones of this place are true miracles of nature.
8 This amazing shape has been created by rainfall.
9 Rain has cut down the stones and made them sharp and spiky over a long period of time.
10 The environment is harsh for animals to live in, but they have found ways to survive.
11 For example, lemurs, which only live in Madagascar, have frog-like legs that help them jump from one stone tower to another.
12 For me, the stone forest is like a jack-in-the-box.
13 It always surprises me and keeps me on my toes!
14 Amber Smith, Fashion Colorist
15 Caño Cristales, the River of Five Colors of Colombia
16 The world is filled with millions of different colors.
17 It is my job to mix, develop, and create colors for clothing.
18 Over the years, I've been gaining insights from the

beautiful colors of Caño Cristales.

19 You cannot see the wonderful mixed colors of this river anywhere else in the world.

20 The combination of colorful plants under the water and sunlight makes the colors more alive and bright.

21 Whenever I visit the Caño Cristales, it makes me think that maybe there are still countless colors that are waiting to be created.

22 Danny Mehta, Location Scout

23 Vatnajökull National Park, Frozen Beauty of Iceland

24 I'm a location scout and my job is finding perfect places to shoot movies.

25 Iceland is the best place for many location scouts to visit due to its unusual beauty.

26 My personal favorite is the Vatnajökull National Park.

27 The sharp cliffs, blue glacier caves, and long mountain ranges can stand in for any place in the world or the universe.

28 In fact, the recent sci-fi movie we shot here was produced without using computer graphics!

29 Iceland can help make our wildest dreams come true on the movie screen.

시험대비 실력평가
p.90~93

01 ②　　　02 ②, ⑤　　　03 by → without
04 ⓐ inspired　ⓑ visiting　ⓒ created
05 ④　　　06 the stone forest　　　07 full of
08 (A) mixed　(B) alive　(C) think
09 ③　　　10 ①　　　11 ⑤
12 ③　　　13 ④　　　14 ②
15 (A) the stones　(C) animals
16 The environment is harsh for animals to live in
17 gaining　　18 ③, ⑤　　19 ②, ④　　20 ④
21 ②, ④　　22 ②, ③
23 the recent sci-fi movie that[which] we shot here was produced　　24 common → unusual

01 ⓐ와 ①, ②는 형용사적 용법, ③, ⑤는 명사적 용법, ④는 부사적 용법

02 ⓑ와 ②, ⑤: 대신하다, ③ 제거하다, ④ 교환하다

03 컴퓨터 그래픽을 사용하지 '않고'라고 하는 것이 적절하다.

04 ⓐ 동작 수동태가 되도록 과거분사를, ⓑ 현재완료진행형이 되도록 현재분사를 ⓒ 현재완료수동태가 되도록 과거분사를 쓰는

것이 적절하다.

05 ④번 다음 문장의 For example에 주목한다. 주어진 문장의 예를 들고 있으므로 ④번이 적절하다.

06 '석림'을 가리킨다.

07 be filled with = be full of: ~로 가득 차다

08 (A) '혼합된'이라고 해야 하므로 mixed가 적절하다. (B) 목적격보어 자리이므로 alive가 적절하다. alive: 보어로만 쓰인다. live: 살아 있는, 생방송의(형용사: 주로 명사 앞에 씀), (C) 사역동사 makes의 목적격보어에 해당하므로 think가 적절하다.

09 ③ a great deal of: 다량의, ⓑ와 나머지는 모두 '수'가 많을 때 사용, countless: 무수한, 셀 수 없이 많은

10 ⓐ 'for+숫자', 'during+기간을 나타내는 명사', ⓑ keep ~ on one's toes: ~을 긴장을 늦추지 않게 하다

11 (A)와 ⑤: 분야, ① 들판, ② 싸움터, 전장(battlefield), ③ [보통 합성어에서 특정한 것으로 덮여 있거나 무엇이 많이 나는] 지역, ice fields: 빙원, ④ (어떤 용도에 쓰는) 지면(地面)

12 이 글은 생태학자인 Lin Wang이 어떻게 자연에 의해 영감을 받았는지에 대한 글이므로, 제목으로는 'Lin Wang은 어떻게 자연에 의해 영감을 받았는가?'가 적절하다.

13 Tsingy는 '뾰족한' 돌로 이루어진 숲이다.

14 앞의 내용의 예가 나오고 있으므로 For example이 가장 적절하다. ① 그 결과, ④ 즉, 다시 말해, ⑤ 그러므로

15 (A)는 '돌', (C)는 '동물들'을 가리킨다.

16 to부정사의 의미상의 주어를 'for+목적격'으로 쓰는 것이 적절하다.

17 현재완료진행형으로 써야 하므로 gaining이 적절하다.

18 (A)와 ③, ⑤: 가주어, ①, ④: 비인칭주어, ② 가목적어

19 (B)와 ②, ④: 아직(도), 여전히, ① (비교급을 강조하여) 더욱, 훨씬, ③ 가만히 있는, 고요한(형용사), ⑤ 그럼에도 불구하고 (부사)

20 Amber Smith가 의류를 위해 무슨 색을 만들었는지는 대답할 수 없다. ① It is the river of five colors of Colombia. ② In Colombia. ③ She is a fashion colorist and her job is to mix, develop, and create colors for clothing. ⑤ The combination of colorful plants under the water and sunlight.

21 ⓐ와 ②, ④: 동명사, ①, ③, ⑤: 현재분사

22 ⓑ와 ②, ③: 사실, ① 그러므로, ⑤ 그 결과

23 목적격 관계대명사 'that[which]'이 생략되어 있다.

24 Iceland의 '비범한' 아름다움이 그곳을 많은 장소 섭외가들이 방문하기에 최고의 장소가 되도록 만든다고 하는 것이 적절하다. common: 흔한, 보통의, 평범한거운

01 how people from different fields of work get inspired by nature

02 to visit, ago, visiting

03 mild → harsh   04 surprises

05 ④

06 make our wildest dreams come true

07 (A) sharp cliffs   (B) stand in for

08 can → cannot   09 always

10 that are

11 (A) are   (B) live in   (C) jump

12 Rainfall has created this amazing shape.

13 (A) ecologist   (B) the stone forest

---

01 'how'를 보충하면 된다.

02 for over 20 years를 over 20 years ago로 바꿔 쓰는 것이 적절하다.

03 동물들이 살기에는 환경이 '가혹하지만', 그들은 생존할 방법들을 찾아내 왔다고 해야 하므로 harsh와 같은 '가혹한'이란 의미의 단어로 고치는 것이 적절하다.

04 석림은 항상 Lin Wang을 '놀라게' 하기 때문이다. jack-in-the-box: 열면 인형이 튀어나오는 상자

05 ⓐ to부정사의 의미상의 주어로 'for+목적격'이 적절하다. ⓑ in fact: 사실

06 come true: 실현되다

07 Vatnajökull 국립 공원은 아이슬란드에 있고, 그곳의 '가파른 절벽', 푸른 빙하 동굴, 그리고 긴 산맥들은 세계나 우주의 어느 장소도 대신할 수 있다.

08 세상 다른 어느 곳에서도 이 강의 아름답게 혼합된 색깔을 '볼 수 없다'고 하는 것이 적절하다.

09 Whenever = When+always

10 '주격 관계대명사+ be동사'를 생략할 수 있다.

11 (A) 주어가 'The spiky stones'이므로 are가 적절하다. (B) It is harsh for animals to live in the environment에서 the environment를 주어로 바꾼 것이므로 live in이 적절하다. (C) 'help+목적어+원형부정사 또는 to부정사'이므로 jump가 적절하다.

12 rainfall을 주어로 해서 고치는 것이 적절하다.

13 Lin Wang은 '생태학자'이고, 식물과 동물을 연구하기 위해 마다가스카르의 '석림'인 Tsingy를 20년 이상 동안 방문해 오고 있다.

01 ④   02 (1) unusual   (2) combination

03 (1) (w)henever, yellow dust   (2) research

    (3) (c)ountless, near

04 (1) out   (2) to   (3) by   (4) of   05 ③

---

06 ④   07 like

08 I can't wait to actually visit there.

09 research   10 ④   11 ⑤

12 I hope we get the chance to try it someday.

13 ②   14 ③, ④

15 careless of Mike to break   16 ⑤

17 ①, ④

18 (1) of him to give her that money

    (2) for her to read the book   19 ②, ⑤

20 ④   21 keeps me on my toes

22 (A) clothing   (B) anywhere   (C) makes

23 ⑤   24 such as   25 shot   26 ③

27 ④   28 ④

---

01 ④ 이외의 단어들에서 접두어 in-은 '안에'의 의미로 사용되었다. ④는 반대, 부정의 의미이다. dependent: 의존하는 independent: 독립적인

02 (1) usual: 흔히 있는 unusual: 특이한, 흔치 않은 (2) combine: 결합하다 combination: 조합, 복합

03 (1) whenever+주어+동사: ~할 때마다 yellow dust: 황사 (2) research: 조사하다, 연구하다 (3) countless: 많은, 셀 수 없는 near: ~ 가까이에

04 (1) turn out: (일·진행·결과가 특정 방식으로) 되다 / 모든 사람들이 놀랍게도 템플 스테이는 인기 있는 여행 프로그램이 되었다. (2) due to: ~ 때문에 / 그의 죽음은 심장병 때문이었다. (3) be made by ~: ~에 의해 만들어지다 / 그 노래들은 세계 최고의 음악가들이 만들었다. (4) most of: 대부분의 ~ / 대부분의 폐암은 흡연에 기인한다.

05 새로 나온 3D 영화 중에서 'Which one?(어느 것)'인지 묻고 있는 질문에 바다 밑의 모험에 관한 것이 대답으로 어울리므로 ③이 적절하다.

06 ④ 영화의 내용은 'Australia's Great Barrier Reef'의 바다 생물에 관한 내용이 아니라 바다 속의 모험에 관한 내용이다.

07 sound like 명사/명사절: ~처럼 들리다, ~일 것 같다

08 can't wait to+동사원형: 빨리 ~하고 싶다, ~하기를 몹시 바라다 actually: 실제로 visit: 방문하다

09 research: 조사하다, 연구하다 / 특히 새로운 사실을 발견하거나 새로운 생각을 검사하기 위해 자세히 어떤 대상을 연구하다

10 ① 언제 남자는 그의 삼촌과 저녁을 먹을 것인가? (이번 주 토요일) ② John은 어디에서 오는가? (남아메리카) ③ 얼마나 John은 떠나 있었는가? (2년) ④ John은 정글에서 무엇을 연구하는가? ⑤ 남자는 John을 만나는 것을 기대하는가? (네)

11 (A) set: (해·달 등이) 지다. 한밤중에 하이킹을 가고 자전거를 타러 나갈 수 있으려면 해가 지지 않아야 하므로 set이 어울린다. (B) 어둡지 않기 때문에 한밤중에 하이킹 하러 간다는 내용이 어울리므로 이유의 접속사 because가 적절하다.

12 hope 희망하다 get the chance: 기회를 가지다 chance+to부

정사: ~할 기회

13 현재완료진행형에서 since는 '시간'을 나타내는 명사(구)와 함께 쓰이고 for는 '기간'을 나타내는 명사(구)와 함께 쓰인다.

14 ③ How silly of her to tell him such a thing! ④ Emma has been teaching English for three years.

15 진주어로 to부정사를 쓰고 careless가 사람의 성격을 나타내는 말이므로 'of+목적격'으로 쓴다.

16 현재완료진행형에서 since는 '시간'을 나타내는 명사(구)와 함께 쓰이고 for는 '기간'을 나타내는 명사(구)와 함께 쓰인다. ⑤번은 since가 들어가야 하고 나머지는 모두 for가 적절하다.

17 ② since → for ③ two days ago → for two days 또는 has been raining → rained ⑤ of → for

18 to부정사의 의미상의 주어는 'for+목적격'으로 나타내지만, 문장에 쓰인 형용사가 사람의 성향, 성격을 나타내는 말일 때는 'of+목적격'으로 쓴다.

19 ⓐ와 ②, ⑤: 계속 용법, ① 결과 용법, ③ 경험 용법, ④ 완료 용법

20 선행사가 동물이고 계속적 용법이므로 which가 알맞다.

21 keep ~ on one's toes: ~에게 정신을 바짝 차리게 하다

22 (A) clothing은 '의류'라는 뜻의 집합명사이고 복수형으로 쓸 수 없으므로 clothing, (B) 부정문이므로 anywhere, (C) 'The combination'이 주어이므로 makes가 적절하다.

23 Amber Smith는 아마도 여전히 만들어지기를 기다리고 있는 '셀 수 없이 많은 색깔이 있을 것'이라고 생각한다.

24 like = such as: ~와 같은

25 수동태이므로 과거분사로 쓰는 것이 적절하다.

26 생태학자가 무엇을 하는지는 대답할 수 없다. ① An ecologist. ② By rainfall[rain]. ④ Because the river has wonderful mixed colors. ⑤ In Vatnajökull National Park, Iceland.

27 앞의 내용을 추가해서 설명할 때 사용하는 In fact가 주어진 문장에 쓰인 것을 주목한다. ④번 앞 문장의 내용을 추가해서 설명하는 말이므로 ④번이 적절하다.

28 ⓐ와 ④: ~ 때문에, ① ~에 대해서 말하자면, ② ~ 대신에, ③ ~을 대신하여, ⑤ ~에도 불구하고

단원별 예상문제
p.102~105

01 ③ 02 for 03 (d)ue to
04 ④ 05 ① 06 shooting star
07 I've heard that the shooting stars will peak between 12 a.m. and 2 a.m.
08 ③ 09 (A) that (B) during (C) How
10 ① 11 out 12 ① 13 ①
14 ④ 15 ④ 16 ②
17 has been waiting, for 18 ⓐ ①, ④, ⑤, ⓑ ②, ③
19 that → which 20 ②
21 (A) colorful plants (B) colors
22 that[which] are waiting to be created

01 ① personal: 개인적인 / 직원들은 그들의 직업이 개인적인 성장에 도움이 된다고 말했다. ② unique: 독특한, 특별한 / 모든 사람은 특별하고 사람들은 자신의 정체성을 표현하는 것을 격려받아야 한다. ③ bright: 밝은, 빛나는 / 여기의 불은 읽기에 충분히 밝지 않다. ④ countless: 많은, 셀 수 없는 / 그들은 서로 말하는 데 많은 시간을 썼다. ⑤ recent: 최근의 / 최근 몇 주간 무슨 일이 일어난 것일까요?

02 stand in for: ~을 대신하다 thank you for ~: ~해서 감사합니다

03 due to 명사: ~ 때문에 / 그는 좋지 못한 건강 때문에 은퇴를 해야 했다.

04 (A) ⓑ glacier: 빙하 / 매우 느리게 움직이는 아주 큰 얼음 덩어리 / 이러한 기온의 증가는 얼음층과 빙하를 녹일 수 있다. (B) ⓒ period: 기간 / 처음과 끝을 가진 특정한 시간의 길이 / 그의 경기는 아주 짧은 시간에 향상되었다. (C) ⓓ cliff: 절벽 / 높은 땅이 있는 지역의 가파른 면 / 그는 절벽 가장자리에서 바로 다이빙한다. (D) ⓐ combination: 조합 / 몇몇 개의 것들을 결합시킨 것 / 바나나, 오렌지 주스와 크림은 이상한 조합처럼 들리지만, 함께 섞으면 맛있는 음료가 된다.

05 'When is the best time to see them?'에서 them이 shooting stars를 의미하기 때문에 ①이 적절하다.

06 shooting star: 유성, 별똥별 / 지구로 떨어질 때 밝은 빛을 내며 타는 우주로부터 온 돌이나 금속 조각

07 I've heard that ~: ~에 대해 들었다, ~에 대해 알고 있다 between A and B: A와 B 사이에서

08 남자가 노르웨이에서는 여름 동안 해가 지지 않는다고 말했을 때 여자는 몰랐다고 대답했으므로 ①과 ②는 어울리지 않고, 이어서 남자가 노르웨이 사람들이 밤에 어둡지 않아서 하이킹이나 자전거 타러 간다는 것을 들었다고 얘기하는 것이 적절하다.

09 (A) 'Did you know that 주어 동사 ~?'로 상대방에게 무언가에 대해 알고 있는지 물어볼 수 있다. that은 접속사이므로 뒤에 주어와 동사로 이루어진 완전한 문장이 온다. (B) 내용상 '여름 동안'의 의미이므로 during이 어울린다. while은 접속사이기 때문에 주어와 동사가 뒤에 나와야 한다. (C) 감탄문은 느낌이나 감탄을 나타내는 것으로 how 또는 what으로 시작하며 '정말 ~하구나!'로 해석한다. how로 시작할 때는 'How+형용사/부사(+주어+동사)!'로, what으로 시작하는 감탄문은 'What+(a/an)+형용사+명사(+주어+동사)!'이다. 그러므로 여기서는 How가 어울린다.

10 흥미로워 보인다와 너무 어려워 보인다는 두 문장은 '그러나, 하지만'의 의미를 지닌 접속사 but으로 연결될 수 있다.

11 (B) find out: 발견하다, 알아보다 (C) turn out: (일·진행·결과가 특정 방식으로) 되다

12 ① few: 거의 없는, 지역문화회관에는 다른 레벨의 코스들이 있다고 언급되고 있다. / 지역문화회관에는 실내 암벽등반 수업이

거의 없다. ② 남자는 실내 암벽등반에 관심이 있다. ③ 남자는 실내 암벽등반에 관한 것을 조사하기 위해 지역문화회관을 방문할 것이다. ④ Jake의 블로그에 그가 실내 암벽등반을 하러 간 사진이 있다. ⑤ 여자는 지역문화회관에 실내 암벽등반 수업이 있다는 것을 알고 있다.

13 첫 번째 문장에서는 foolish가 사람의 성향, 성격을 나타내는 말이므로 'of+목적격'이 적절하다. 두 번째 문장에서는 noon이라는 시간을 나타내는 명사가 있으므로 since가 적절하다.

14 의미상의 주어 앞에 전치사 for가 있으므로 빈칸에는 사람의 성격을 나타내는 형용사인 wise는 알맞지 않다.

15 ① My dad has been working in New York for a year. ② Brian has been painting his house for two hours. ③ She cleaned her house then. ⑤ What's been happening in recent weeks?

16 ②에는 사람의 성격이나 성질을 나타내는 형용사(thoughtful)가 왔으므로 의미상의 주어로 'of+목적격'이 적절하다. 나머지는 모두 'for+목적격'이 적절하다.

17 과거 어느 때부터 시작되어 현재까지 계속 진행되고 있음을 나타내는 현재완료진행형을 이용한다. '기간'을 나타내는 an hour가 있으므로 for를 쓴다.

18 ⓐ와 ①, ④, ⑤: 부사적 용법, ⓑ와 ②, ③: 형용사적 용법

19 관계대명사 that은 계속적 용법으로 쓸 수 없기 때문에, which로 고치는 것이 적절하다.

20 Lin Wang이 Tsingy를 몇 번 방문했는지는 알 수 없다. ① In Madagascar. ③ By rainfall. ④ No. ⑤ Yes.

21 햇빛이 Caño Cristales 아래의 '화려한 식물'에 비칠 때, Caño Cristales의 '색깔'은 더 생생하고 밝게 될 수 있다.

22 주격 관계대명사 that[which]을 사용하는 것이 적절하다.

서술형 실전문제
p.106~107

01 (1) thank you for invite me → thank you for inviting me
(2) I've heard that this photo took in the Maldives. → I've heard that this photo was taken in the Maldives.
(3) I can't wait taking more pictures of amazing beaches. → I can't wait to take more pictures of amazing beaches.

02 I can't wait to see him and listen to his stories.

03 ⓔ I will → I won't

04 (1) I have been visiting the Wimbledon tennis tournament since I was in high school.
(2) Phil has been repairing mobile phones for ten years.
(3) I have been staying at the hotel for a few days.

05 (1) It is fun for me to read the comic book.
(2) It is necessary for people here to eat well to stay warm and healthy.
(3) It is too difficult for me to understand this book.

06 (1) The airplane has been flying since an hour ago.
(2) The government has been stealing our public funds for a long time.
(3) I have known him ever since he was a boy.
(4) The room is large enough for all of us to stay in.
(5) I think it is nice of you to give books to your brother.
(6) The bands played music for many people to dance to.

07 (A) amazing　(B) sharp　(C) like

08 ⓐ For　ⓑ on

09 frog-like legs

01 (1) thank you for ~: ~해서 감사합니다 / 전치사 for 다음에는 명사나 동명사가 올 수 있다. (2) take a picture: 사진을 찍다 / 사진은 찍혀지는 대상이므로 수동태로 써야 한다. (3) can't wait to+동사원형: 빨리 ~하고 싶다, ~하기를 몹시 바라다

02 can't wait to+동사원형: 빨리 ~하고 싶다, ~하기를 몹시 바라다

03 이번 주 토요일에 그의 삼촌과 저녁을 할 예정이라고 다른 계획을 잡지 말라는 말에 남자는 'Okay'라고 대답했으므로 '계획을 안 잡을 게요.'란 말이 내용상 적절하므로 will이 아닌 won't가 어울린다. won't 다음에 make other plans가 생략되었다.

04 과거에 시작해서 현재도 진행 중이므로 현재완료진행형으로 쓴다. since는 '시간'을 나타내는 명사(구)와 함께 쓰이고 for는 '기간'을 나타내는 명사(구)와 함께 쓰인다.

05 가주어 it을 사용하고 to부정사를 진주어로 쓴다. 의미상의 주어를 빠뜨리지 말아야 한다.

06 (1) 현재완료진행형은 과거를 나타내는 어구와 함께 쓰이지 않는다. (2) 현재완료진행형에서 since는 '시간'을 나타내는 명사(구)와 함께 쓰이고 for는 '기간'을 나타내는 명사(구)와 함께 쓰인다. (3) know는 진행형으로 쓸 수 없는 동사이므로 현재완료시제로 나타낸다. (4), (5) to부정사의 의미상의 주어는 'for+목적격'으로 나타낸다. 이때 문장에 쓰인 형용사가 사람의 성향, 성격을 나타내는 말일 때는 'of+목적격'으로 쓴다. (6) 의미상의 주어 'for+목적격'이 있으므로 to부정사를 쓴다.

07 (A) 감정을 나타내는 동사는 감정을 유발할 때 현재분사를 쓰는 것이 적절하다. (B) 'make+목적어+목적격보어' 구문이므로, 목

적격보어로 형용사 sharp를 쓰는 것이 적절하다. (C) A is like B: ~와 같다, alike 뒤에는 목적어를 쓸 수 없다.

08 ⓐ for example: 예를 들면 ⓑ keep ~ on one's toes: ~을 계속 긴장하게 하다

09 그들이 한 개의 돌탑에서 다른 돌탑으로 뛸 수 있도록 도와주는 '개구리 같은 다리'를 가지고 있기 때문에 그곳에서 살 수 있다.

창의사고력 서술형 문제
p.108

|모범답안|

01 I can't wait to see a new film and meet a director and actors.

02 (1) |모범답안| They have been playing basketball for two hours.

(2) |모범답안| He has been playing the cello since 3 o'clock.

03 (A) hiking　(B) Mt. Jiri and Mt. Seorak
(C) hiking routes　(D) get in shape
(E) keep fit

01 preview: 시사회 can't wait to+동사원형: 빨리 ~하고 싶다, ~하기를 몹시 바라다 director: 감독 actor: 배우

단원별 모의고사
p.109~112

01 (c)ountless

02 (1) walk　(2) get　(3) cut　(4) keeps　　03 ③

04 (1) (w)henever　(2) (h)onored　(3) (h)igh

05 I've heard that there are different levels of courses at the community center.

06 ⓔ Let me to know how does it turn out. → Let me know how it turns out.

07 adventure

08 I can't wait to watch the movie.　　09 ③

10 hiking and cycling in the middle of, it isn't dark

11 ②　　　　12 rainbow　13 ③　　　14 ③

15 ②, ⑤

16 (1) for us to have a sense of belonging
(2) for employees to be properly paid

17 (1) have been living together for 5 years
(2) has been reading the book since yesterday

18 (1) The greenhouse in the Ice Cube is warm enough for Mathew to grow fresh vegetables.
(2) It was wise of Solomon to make such a careful decision.
(3) Jason has been taking horse-riding lessons for three months.
(4) Ashley has been learning to play the flute for 5

months. 또는 Ashley learned to play the flute 5 months ago.

(5) Lily has liked Gino since she first met him.

19 ①

20 비가 오랜 기간 동안 돌을 침식해서 날카롭고 뾰족하게 만들었기 때문이다.

21 ③, ④　　　22 ③　　　　23 to make

24 ⑤　　　　25 ③　　　26 trip　　　27 ②

28 ②　　　　29 ④

30 The combination of colorful plants under the water and sunlight makes the colors more alive and bright.

31 (A) fashion colorist　(B) Caño Cristales

32 Iceland is the best place for many location scouts to visit due to its unusual beauty.　　33 ①

34 (A) glacier caves　(B) mountain ranges

01 countless: 많은, 셀 수 없이 많은 / 매우 많은, 특히 당신이 생각하기에 합당한 것보다 더 많은

02 (1) walk along: ~을 따라 산책하다 / 그녀는 해변을 산책하기 위해 매일 아침 6시에 일어난다. (2) get in shape: 좋은 몸 상태를 유지하다 / 네가 좋은 몸 상태를 유지하기를 원한다면, 더 많은 운동을 해야 한다. (3) cut down: 자르다 / 나무를 베어서 종이를 만들 필요가 없습니다. (4) keep ~ on one's toes: ~에게 긴장을 늦추지 않게 하다 / 매주 금요일마다 보는 시험으로 그녀는 학생들이 긴장을 늦추지 않게 한다.

03 insight: 통찰력

04 (1) whenever+주어+동사: ~할 때마다 (2) honor: 영광으로 생각하다 (3) high: 많은

05 I've heard that ~: ~에 대해 들었다, ~에 대해 알고 있다 community center: 지역문화회관

06 let는 '~에게 …하게 하다'라는 의미를 가지는 사역동사로, 목적어와 목적격보어가 능동의 관계이면 목적격보어 자리에 동사원형을 쓴다. know의 목적어로 의문사 how가 들어간 의문문을 사용할 때는 '의문사+주어+동사'의 순서로 쓴다.

07 adventure: 모험 / 위험하고 흔치 않은 일이 발생하는 신나는 경험

08 can't wait to+동사원형: 빨리 ~하고 싶다, ~하기를 몹시 바라다

09 (A) 여름 동안 해가 안 진다는 것을 알고 있는지 물어보고 있다. (B) 사람들이 밤에 하이킹과 자전거를 타러 간다는 사실을 들어서 알고 있음을 표현하고 있다. (B) 다음에 주어와 동사가 들어간 문장이 나오므로 전치사가 아닌 접속사 that이 적절하다.

10 in the middle of the night: 한밤중에

11 여자가 남자에게 여름방학 계획에 대해 묻고, 남자가 중국에 간다는 대답을 한다. 이후에 여자가 'The Rainbow

Mountains?'라고 묻고 있으므로 'The Rainbow Mountains'에 대한 언급을 남자가 먼저 했어야 하므로 ②가 적절하다.

12 rainbow: 무지개 / 태양과 비 둘 다 있을 때 하늘에 나타날 수 있는 여러 가지의 색깔을 가진 큰 곡선

13 대화에서 that은 주격 관계대명사로 사용하였다. ③ 이외의 보기는 타동사의 목적어 자리에 들어가는 명사절을 이끄는 접속사로 사용했다.

14 과거 어느 때부터 시작되어 현재까지 계속 진행되고 있음을 나타내는 현재완료진행형을 이용한다.

15 ① Isn't it necessary for us to help them? ③ She has been listening to the music for two hours. ④ Alex has had his father's watch since his father passed away.

17 현재완료진행형에서 since는 '시간'을 나타내는 명사(구)와 함께 쓰이고 for는 '기간'을 나타내는 명사(구)와 함께 쓰인다.

18 (1), (2) to부정사의 의미상의 주어는 to부정사 바로 앞에 'for+명사의 목적격'으로 나타내지만 문장에 쓰인 형용사가 nice, kind, smart, wise 등과 같이 사람의 성향, 성격을 나타내는 말일 때는 'of+목적격'으로 쓴다. (3) 현재완료진행형에서 since는 '시간'을 나타내는 명사(구)와 함께 쓰이고 for는 '기간'을 나타내는 명사(구)와 함께 쓰인다. (4) 현재완료진행형은 과거를 나타내는 어구인 5 months ago와 함께 쓰이지 않는다. (5) 진행형으로 쓸 수 없는 동사인 like는 현재완료형으로 상태의 계속을 표현한다.

19 수동태로 고치면 We all are inspired by the beauty of nature.가 된다.

20 앞 문장의 내용을 쓰는 것이 적절하다.

21 ⓑ와 ③, ④: 관계대명사, ①, ⑤: 접속사, ② 그렇게(지시부사)

22 ⓐ와 ③: 촬영하다, ① [빛 등을] 갑자기 발하다, ②, ⑤: [총·대포를] 발사[발포]하다, ④ 던지다

23 help 뒤에 원형부정사나 to부정사를 쓸 수 있다.

24 Vatnajökull 국립 공원에서 몇 편의 sci-fi 영화가 만들어졌는지는 대답할 수 없다. ① He is a location scout and his job is finding perfect places to shoot movies. ② In Iceland. ③ Due to its unusual beauty. ④ The Vatnajökull National Park.

25 ③ 위 글은 '홍보 포스터'이다. ① (신문·잡지의) 글, 기사, ② 수필, ④ (책·연극·영화 등에 대한) 논평[비평], 감상문, ⑤ 독후감

26 '여행'을 가리킨다.

27 하이킹하는 데 시간이 얼마 걸릴지는 알 수 없다. ① For people who are interested in hiking. ③ Mt. Jiri and Mt. Seorak. ④ They will be able to walk along beautiful hiking routes and will also learn how to get

in shape and keep fit. ⑤ Yes. unforgettable: 잊지 못할[잊을 수 없는], memorable: 기억할 만한

28 앞의 내용을 추가해서 설명하고 있으므로 In fact가 가장 적절하다. ① 게다가, 더욱이, ③ 그러므로, ⑤ 즉, 다시 말해

29 Danny Mehta의 팀이 컴퓨터 그래픽을 사용하지 않고 최근에 촬영한 영화는 'action' 영화가 아니라 'sci-fi' 영화였다.

30 'combination'을 보충하면 된다.

31 Amber Smith는 'Caño Cristales'의 아름다운 색으로부터 영감을 얻어온 '패션 색채 전문가'이다.

32 scouts를 보충하면 된다.

33 stand in for: ~을 대신하다

34 그곳의 가파른 절벽, 푸른 '빙하 동굴', 그리고 긴 '산맥들'은 세계나 우주의 어느 장소도 대신할 수 있다.

Lesson 3

For the Love of Our Country

시험대비 실력평가
p.118

| 01 ③ | 02 ④ | 03 ⑤ | 04 ④ |
| 05 ② | 06 (s)ince | 07 ① | |

01 rescue: 구하다, 구조[구출/구제]하다 save: 구하다 / 우리는 지나가는 낚싯배에 의해서 가라앉는 배에서부터 구조되었다.

02 fortune: 재산 / 버핏은 영리한 투자를 통해서 큰 돈을 벌었다.

03 ① 그는 학자라기보다는 오히려 작가이다. ② 그녀는 분명히 진실을 말하고 있었다. ③ 병사들은 요새를 방어할 준비가 되어 있었다. ④ 너는 한국 전쟁 기념관에 가 본 적이 있니? ⑤ general: 장군 / 그는 최근에 장군으로 진급했다.

04 horrible: 끔찍한 / 우리의 모든 돈이 도난당했다는 것을 알았을 때 정말로 끔찍했다.

05 ① make, make an arrangement: ~을 결정하다 / 우리의 목적지를 결정하자. ② devote, devote one's life to 명사: ~에 일생을 바치다 / 그녀는 공직에 일생을 바칠 것이라고 말했습니다. ③ try. try on: 입어 보다, 신어 보다 / 입어 볼 만한 재킷 좀 있나요? ④ take, take a look around ~: ~ 주위를 둘러보다 / 이곳은 재미있는 곳이에요. 한번 둘러보시겠어요? ⑤ heard, hear of[about] ~: ~에 대해 듣다 / 너는 차고 세일에 대해 들어 본 적 있니?

06 since: ~이기 때문에

07 movement: (정치적·사회적) 운동 / 태도, 의견 또는 정책의 점진적인 발전 또는 변화

서술형 시험대비
p.119

01 (1) trying to be used to new glasses
　(2) It is said that she has been all over the world.
　(3) I hate talking like this behind his back.
　(4) Is it okay if I take a picture?
02 independence
03 so, that he could
04 (i)nclude　(r)uin　(s)ave
　(1) ruin　(2) save　(3) include
05 by
06 (1) article　(2) would

01 (1) be used to (동)명사: ~하는 데 익숙하다 (2) It is said that 주어+동사 ~: (사람들이) ~라고 한다 (3) behind one's

back: 등 뒤에서 (4) Is it okay if I ~?: 제가 ~해도 될까요? take a picture: 사진을 찍다

02 depend: 의존하다 independence: 독립 / 그녀는 대한민국 독립을 위한 3.1 운동에 참여했다.

03 so+형용사/부사+that 주어+동사: 너무 ~해서 …하다

04 include: ~을 포함하다 / 사람이나 사물을 어떤 것의 일부로 내포하다 ruin: 망치다, 파산시키다 / 누군가로 하여금 그들의 돈이나 권력을 모두 잃게 만들다 save: 구하다 / 위험, 해로움, 또는 파괴로부터 사람이나 사물을 안전하게 만들다 (1) 어떤 사람들은 스포일러가 이야기를 망친다고 말한다. (2) 안전띠를 매는 것은 너의 생명을 구할 수 있다. (3) 호텔비는 아침식사를 포함한다.

05 be+p.p+by 행위자(수동태) / 그 빌딩은 2004년 화재에 의해 파괴되었다. by 동사ing: ~함으로써 / 그녀는 아이들을 돌봄으로써 여분의 돈을 번다.

06 (1) article: 기사 (2) would: (과거에 있어서의 습관·습성·반복적 동작) ~하곤 했다

교과서
Conversation

핵심 Check
p.120~121

1 It is said that there will be a big festival
2 It is said that he is a liar.
3 It is said that purple was
4 Is it okay if I practice the guitar?
5 Is it okay if I sit next to you?

교과서 대화문 익히기

Check(√) True or False
p.122~123

1 F　2 T　3 T　4 F　5 F　6 F　7 F　8 T　9 T

Listen & Talk 1 Get Ready

was / read, it is said / both

Listen & Talk 1 A-1

what, reading / biography / haven't heard / the first female, It is said that, over

Listen & Talk 1 A-2

interesting, detective / scholar / but it is said that he was also, solved / didn't know that

Listen & Talk 1 B

know about / heard / Take a look at, to be included / helped, by building a clinic, that such stories, be included in / to, such

Listen & Talk 2 A-1

can't take, museum / Is it okay / leave, in

Listen & Talk 2 A-2

to, How / is it okay if I take pictures in / don't

Listen & Talk 2 B

How was / were / get the chance to, okay if I / remember that, at / on / Let me know if

Communication Step A

are moving onto, As you can see, many, inventions, is called / musical instrument / It is said that it is, largest / How, Is it okay if

Wrap Up 1

what / watching / Isn't he / It is said that he won / how, possible / general who made creative

Wrap Up 2

Would you like to / I'd like to / Here / is it okay if / if, on, stay

01 ⑤   02 ②   03 ②, ④, ⑤
04 Is it okay if I open the window?

01 무엇을 읽고 있는지 물어보는 질문에, (C) 권기옥의 자서전을 읽고 있다고 대답한다. (D) 그녀(권기옥)에 대해 들어본 적이 없다고 말하며, 그녀가 누구인지 질문한다. (B) 그녀는 한국 최초의 여자 비행 조종사라고 얘기하며 비행시간이 7,000시간 이상이었다는 사실을 추가해서 말한다. (A) 놀라움을 표현하며, 그러한 사실을 몰랐다고 반응한다.

02 'Is it okay if I ~?'는 '제가 ~해도 될까요?'라는 뜻으로 어떤 행동을 하기 전에 허가를 요청할 때 사용하는 표현이다.

03 빈칸 다음에 접속사 but(하지만)이 나오고 플래시를 사용하지 말라는 내용이 나오는 것으로 보아 미술관 안에서 사진을 찍는 것을 허락하고 당부하는 말을 덧붙인 것으로 볼 수 있다.

04 Is it okay if I ~?: 제가 ~해도 될까요? open: 열다

01 ③   02 ②   03 ③   04 ③, ④
05 ④   06 ③   07 ⑤   08 ①, ③
09 ①   10 ②, ④

01 주어진 문장은 조선 시대에 그가 학자가 아니었는지 묻는 것으로 여기서 그는 정약용을 말한다. 남자가 정약용이 학자이지만, 또한 형사였다고 말하는 것이 주어진 문장에 대한 대답이 될 수 있으므로 ③에 들어가는 것이 적절하다.

02 밑줄 친 부분은 대략 90개의 사건을 해결했다는 의미이므로, 사건을 해결할 수 있는 detective(형사, 탐정)가 가장 어울린다. ① diplomat: 외교관 ③ reporter: 기자 ④ victim: 피해자 ⑤ painter: 화가

03 주어진 문장에서 she는 여자가 읽고 있는 자서전의 주인공인 권기옥을 의미한다. 남자는 그녀(권기옥)에 대해 들어 본 적이 없다고 말하며 이어서 그녀가 누구인지 여자에게 묻는 것이 어울리므로 ③이 적절하다.

04 ① Lisa는 어떤 종류의 책을 읽고 있는가? (자서전) ② 얼마나 많은 비행 시간을 권기옥은 가지고 있었는가? (7,000시간 이상) ③ 누가 한국에서 최초의 남성 비행사였는가? (최초의 여성 비행사에 대한 정보만 있으므로 알 수 없다.) ④ Lisa는 왜 권기옥에 관한 책을 읽고 있는가? (책을 읽는 이유에 대해서는 언급되어 있지 않다.) ⑤ 남자는 권기옥에 대해서 들어본 적이 있는가? (아니요)

05 ④ 상대방의 핸드폰을 사용할 수 있는지 허락을 묻는 질문에 긍정으로 대답하고 핸드폰을 안 가져왔다고 말하는 것은 어울리지 않는다.

06 한옥 마을이 어땠는지 감상을 묻는 질문에 (C) 좋았다고 대답하며 집들이 예뻤다고 대답한다. (A) 잘 되었다고 말한다. (B) 여자가 저녁을 먹을 기회가 없었다고 하면서, 부엌을 이 시간에 쓰는 것에 대해 허락을 요청하자 (D) 괜찮다고 대답하며, 하지만 부엌이 10시에 닫는다는 사실을 상기시켜 준다.

07 주어진 문장에서 such stories는 여자가 말한 이태석 신부가 병원과 학교를 지음으로써 아이들을 도왔다는 이야기를 의미하므로 그 문장 다음에 나와야 적절하다.

08 남자가 이태석 신부에 대해서 들어 본 적이 있다고 대답하고 있으므로, 이태석 신부에 대해서 들어 본 적이 있는지 아니면 이태석 신부에 대해서 알고 있는지 물어보는 것이 적절하다.

09 take a look at ~: ~을 보다

10 알고 있는 내용을 진술할 때 'It is said that 주어+동사 ~.(~라고 한다)', 'It is believed that 주어+동사 ~. (~라고 믿어진다.)', 'It is thought that 주어+동사 ~. (~라고 생각된다.)'라고 말할 수 있다.

01 who Shin Saimdang is

02 it is said that her paintings were so realistic that birds gathered around the painted tree

03 if

04 Sure / Of course / Certainly / No problem

05 by

06 such

07 built, will be included, South Sudan

08 Is it okay if I try on your hat?

01 간접의문문의 어순은 '의문사+주어+동사'이다.

02 It is said that 주어+동사 ~: (사람들이) ~라고 한다 so+형용사/부사+that 주어+동사: 너무 ~해서 …하다 realistic: 진짜 같은, 사실적인 gather: 모이다

03 Is it okay if I ~?: 제가 ~해도 될까요?

04 사진을 찍어도 되는지 허가를 묻는 말에 허락의 말이 나오고 접속사 but 다음에 카메라의 플래시를 터뜨리지 말라는 말이 나오는 것이 어울린다.

05 by 동사ing: ~함으로써

06 such: (형) 이러한, 그러한 such (a(n))+형용사+명사: 너무 ~한 명사

07 build: 짓다(built-built) include: ~을 포함하다 social studies: 사회 Sudan: 수단 (민주 공화국) / 이태석 신부가 아이들을 돕기 위해서 병원과 학교를 지은 이야기는 남수단의 사회 교과서에 포함될 것이다.

08 Is it okay if I ~?: 제가 ~해도 될까요? try on: 입어[써] 보다, 신어 보다

 교과서

Grammar

1 (1) if[whether]   (2) whether   (3) if[whether]

2 (1) had just heard   (2) had lost   (3) heard

01 ⑤

02 (1) had already left   (2) had broken   (3) if
   (4) whether   03 ④

04 (1) My daughter had never been sick until then.

(2) I had just fallen asleep when someone knocked at the door.

(3) She is not sure if she will return in the future.

01 주절의 동사가 remembered로 과거이고 그것들을 탁자 위에 던져 놓은 것은 그 이전의 사실이므로 과거완료(대과거)를 써야 한다.

02 (1) 도착한 것보다 기차가 떠난 것이 앞서는 것이므로 과거완료가 적절하다. (2) 꽃병을 깼음(앞선 사실)을 고백하는 것이므로 과거완료가 적절하다. (3) 내용상 '올 수 있다는 것을 모른다'는 어색하다. 사실의 여부를 확인하거나 불확실함을 나타내는 if가 적절하다. (4) 바로 뒤에 or not이 이어지고 있으므로 whether가 적절하다.

03 asked의 직접목적어가 나와야 하는데 '~인지 (아닌지)'라는 의미로 명사절을 이끄는 접속사 if가 적절하다.

04 (1) 경험을 나타내는 과거완료를 이용한다. (2) 노크하기 전에 잠이 막 들은 것이므로 과거완료로 나타낸다. (3) '~인지 (아닌지)'라는 의미의 접속사로 어떠한 사실의 여부를 확인하거나 불확실함을 나타낼 때 쓰이는 if를 이용한다.

01 ②   02 ④   03 ①

04 (1) encountered   (2) had bought   (3) had practiced
   (4) whether   (5) if   (6) whether

05 ③   06 ①   07 ⑤

08 (1) unless   (2) if   (3) though   (4) when   (5) whether

09 ⑤   10 ③   11 ②

12 had played   13 ③

14 (1) Please tell me if[whether] your sister is in her room.

(2) Whether he wants or not isn't that important.

(3) I suddenly remembered that I had left the windows open.

(4) I had never been to the big city before.

(5) I found out that someone had broken the lamp.

15 ④   16 ⑤   17 ①, ②

01 When she arrived at the station, the first train had already left.

02 He asked her nicely if he could see her license.

03 첫 번째 빈칸에는 '~인지 (아닌지)'라는 의미의 접속사 if가 적절하다. 두 번째 빈칸에는 잃어버린 것이 우연히 찾은 것보다 앞서므로 과거완료가 적절하다.

04 (1) 과거완료는 'had+과거분사'의 형태이므로 encountered가 적절하다. (2) 산책시킨 시점보다 아빠가 사주신 시점이 앞서므로 had bought가 적절하다. (3) since(~ 이래로)가 있으므로 had practiced가 적절하다. (4) 내용상 '~인지 (아닌지)'라는 의미의 접속사 whether가 적절하다. (5) 내용상 '~인지 (아닌지)'라는 의미의 접속사 if가 적절하다. (6) 뒤에 or not이 바로 이어서 나오고 있으므로 whether가 적절하다.

05 도착했을 때(과거) 이미 극장에 들어간 것이므로 과거완료로 써야 한다.

06 I thought보다 앞선 시제이므로 ⓐ의 have been은 had been으로 고쳐야 한다.

07 뒤에 or not이 있고 내용상 '~인지 (아닌지)'라는 의미가 자연스러우므로 if나 whether가 적절하고, 알고 싶어 하는 것보다 가방이 버려진 시점이 앞선 시제이므로 과거완료가 적절하다.

08 (1) 조건의 unless가 적절하다. (2) 조건의 부사절을 이끄는 if가 적절하다. (3) 서로 상반되는 내용이 나오므로 though가 적절하다. (4) 뒤에 '주어+be동사'가 생략된 형태로 when이 적절하다. (5) or not이 바로 뒤에 이어지므로 whether가 적절하다.

09 집에 도착한 것보다 산책을 나간 것이 앞서므로 과거완료가 적절하다.

10 '~인지 (아닌지)'라는 의미의 명사절을 이끄는 if가 적절하다.

11 ask의 목적어로 '~인지 (아닌지)'라는 의미의 명사절을 이끄는 if가 적절하다.

12 6살에 연주하기 시작했으므로 6살 이래로 연주해 왔다고 과거완료로 나타낼 수 있다.

13 <보기>는 계속적 용법이다. ① 완료, ② 경험, ③ 계속, ④ 결과, ⑤ 대과거

14 (1) what이 문장 내에서 하는 역할이 없으므로 '~인지 (아닌지)'라는 의미의 접속사로 쓰이는 if나 whether로 고치는 것이 적절하다. (2) if가 이끄는 명사절은 주어 역할을 할 수 없으므로 whether로 고치는 것이 적절하다. (3) 창문을 열어 놓은 것이 기억하는 시점보다 앞서므로 과거완료로 고치는 것이 적절하다. (4) 완료시제와 어울리는 것은 ago가 아니라 before이다. (5) 누군가 램프를 깨뜨린 것이 발견한 것보다 앞서므로 과거완료가 적절하다.

15 '~인지 (아닌지)'라는 의미의 접속사 if가 적절하며 if 다음에는 or not을 바로 붙여 쓰지 않는다.

16 사기 전에 말했던 것이므로 과거완료로 나타내는 것이 적절하다. 전치사 about을 빠뜨리지 않도록 주의한다.

17 ① He asked me whether or not the book was boring. ② I remembered that I had turned the stove on.

01 (1) had bought for me　(2) she had received

02 (1) had not locked　(2) he had already gone

03 (1) I wonder if these dishes will suit your taste.
　(2) I don't know whether he is at home or at the office.
　(3) We found out that we had been at the same school.
　(4) She seemed astonished that I had never been to Paris.

04 (1) If → Whether　(2) if → whether　(3) if → whether

05 (1) had never learned　(2) if[whether] she forgot

06 (1) The man isn't sure if[whether] he can help her.
　(2) They don't know if[whether] he will be promoted.
　(3) Would you tell me if[whether] he needs surgery or not?

07 (1) He won the contest because he had practiced a lot for the contest.
　(2) I couldn't take the class because it had been canceled.

08 (1) He told me that he had stolen the money the other day.
　(2) No computer had won even one game against a human player until then.
　(3) I found my bag that I had lost on the bus.
　(4) I asked the lady if[whether] I could use the bathroom.
　(5) I'm not sure if Santa will give me a nice gift or not.
　(6) I couldn't decide whether to buy it.

01 각각 과거보다 앞선 시제에 행한 것을 나타내는 과거완료를 이용한다.

02 (1) 과거완료의 대과거 용법을 이용한다. (2) 과거완료의 결과 용법을 이용한다.

03 (1) if가 명사절을 이끌도록 한다. (2) whether가 명사절을 이끌도록 한다. (3), (4) 하나 앞서는 시제에 과거완료를 이용한다.

04 (1) 문두에서 주어를 이끄는 역할을 하고 있으므로 If를 Whether로 고치는 것이 적절하다. (2) 뒤에 or not이 바로 이어서 나오고 있으므로 if를 whether로 고치는 것이 적절하다. (3) whether 다음에 to부정사를 쓸 수 있지만 if는 to부정사와 함께 쓰이지 않는다.

05 (1) 과거보다 앞서는 일이나 상태를 나타내는 과거완료(대과거)를 이용한다. (2) 명사절을 이끄는 if[whether]를 이용한다.

06 명사절을 이끄는 if나 whether를 이용하여 두 문장을 연결한다.

07 시간차가 드러나도록 하라고 했으므로 앞서는 사건을 과거완료 시제로 나타낸다.

08 (1) 말했을 때보다 그가 훔친 시점이 앞서므로 과거완료가 적절하다. (2) until then으로 보아 그때까지의 경험을 나타내는 과거완료가 적절하다. (3) 잃어버린 후에 발견한 것이므로 잃어버린 것을 과거완료로 쓰는 것이 적절하다. (4) 명사절을 이끄는 if나 whether를 쓰는 것이 적절하다. (5) if가 이끄는 절이 명사절이므로 미래는 미래시제로 나타내야 한다. (6) whether 다음에 to부정사를 쓸 수 있지만 if는 to부정사와 함께 쓰이지 않는다.

Reading

확인문제 p.140

1 T 2 F 3 F

확인문제 p.141

1 T 2 T 3 F

교과서 확인학습 A p.142~143

01 Secret
02 a strange man
03 an odd question, was more used to being called
04 your father's friend
05 wonder if
06 disappointing, good memories
07 Back, whenever, There goes
08 from   09 Instead of living
10 That is why, which, ruins
11 has gambled away
12 have no more money left, would, whenever
13 would yell at, empty-handed
14 Bring
15 had already made an arrangement
16 As part of, a new chest for clothes
17 Right before, has taken the money
18 such a horrible thing
19 What   20 no choice
21 You'll have to take
22 How embarrassing, behind my back
23 had been difficult for me
24 continued his story
25 a gambler   26 independence fighters
27 made himself, keep this a secret from
28 if
29 afterwards, had been wrong
30 had devoted his life to

교과서 확인학습 B p.144~145

1 The Secret of My Father
2 In 1946, a strange man visited me and asked, "Are you Mr. Kim Yonghwan's daughter?"
3 For me, this was an odd question because I was more used to being called the daughter of a *parakho*.
4 "I'm your father's friend.
5 You may wonder if it is true, but your father....," the man said.
6 At that moment, I was expecting disappointing news since I did not have good memories of my father.
7 Back in the 1920's, whenever people saw me in the village, they would say, "There goes the *parakho's* daughter."
8 My father was a son from a very rich family.
9 Instead of living the life of a seonbi, he was always at the gambling house.
10 That is why he was called a *parakho*, which means someone who ruins his family's fortune.
11 "Your father has gambled away all of the money, and now he's asking for more.
12 Go and tell him that we have no more money left," my mother would tell me whenever she sent me to the gambling house.
13 Then, my father would yell at me angrily, "Why did you come empty-handed?
14 Bring me more money!"
15 When I was sixteen years old, my family had already made an arrangement for me to marry Mr. Seo.
16 As part of the wedding tradition, Mr. Seo's family sent my family some money to buy a new chest for clothes.
17 Right before the wedding day, my mother came into my room and said, "Your father has taken the money for the chest."
18 I asked angrily, "How could he do such a horrible thing?
19 What should we do now?"
20 "We have no choice.

21 You'll have to take your aunt's old chest," my mother said.

22 "How embarrassing for the family," people would whisper behind my back.

23 Since the first day of marriage, life at my husband's house had been difficult for me.

24 "Your father, my dear friend....," my father's friend continued his story.

25 "He was not a gambler.

26 Your father sent the family money to the independence fighters in Manchuria.

27 He made himself look like a gambler to keep this a secret from the Japanese officers."

28 At first, I was not sure if he was telling the truth.

29 But afterwards, I found out the truth about my father and I realized that I had been wrong about him.

30 Ever since that moment, I have been proud to be the daughter of a *parakho* who had devoted his life to the independence movement.

시험대비 실력평가

p.146~149

01 Are you Mr. Kim Yonghwan's daughter?
02 (A) odd   (B) being   (C) if
03 ②, ⑤   04 ③, ④   05 ④   06 ①
07 ②   08 ②   09 ①
10 (A) already   (B) What   (C) Since   11 ⑤
12 ④   13 ④   14 ③   15 ④
16 I was not sure if[whether] he was telling the truth
17 ②   18 ②, ③
19 (A) would   (B) ruins   (C) empty-handed
20 and it
21 we have no more money left

01 낯선 남자가 물어본 내용을 가리킨다.

02 (A) 나는 파락호의 딸이라고 불리는 것이 더 익숙했기 때문에 이것은 나에게 '이상한' 질문이었다고 해야 하므로 odd가 적절하다. familiar: 익숙한, 친숙한, odd: 이상한, 특이한, (B) 나는 파락호의 딸이라고 불리는 것에 더 '익숙했다'고 해야 하므로 being이 적절하다. be used to ~ing: ~하는 데 익숙하다, be used to 동사원형: ~하기 위해 사용되다, (C) wonder if: ~ 여부를 궁금해 하다, that은 목적어의 내용이 확실할 때 사용한다.

03 ⓑ와 ②, ⑤: [이유를 나타내어] …이므로, …이니까, ①, ③, ④: …부터[이후]

04 ⓐ와 ③, ④: ~인지 아닌지, ①, ②, ⑤: 만약

05 필자의 아버지가 독립운동가들에게 얼마나 많은 돈을 보냈는지는 알 수 없다. ① No. ② To the independence fighters in Manchuria. ③ To keep the fact that he sent the family money to the independence fighters in Manchuria a secret from the Japanese officers. ⑤ Her father's friend told her the truth.

06 ⓐ ask for: 요청하다, ⓑ yell at: ~에게 소리를 지르다

07 ②번 다음 문장의 That에 주목한다. 주어진 문장의 내용을 받고 있으므로 ②번이 적절하다.

08 글쓴이의 아버지는 '선비'의 삶을 사는 대신 항상 도박장에 계셨다.

09 ① (C)의 첫 부분은 (A)의 내용을 가리키므로 (A) 다음에 (C)가 이어지고 (B)의 that moment가 (C)에서 아버지에 대한 사실을 알게 된 다음을 가리키므로 (C) 다음에 (B)가 와야 한다. 그러므로 (A)-(C)-(B)의 순서가 적절하다.

10 (A) 긍정문이므로 already를 쓰는 것이 적절하다. yet: 부정문(아직), 의문문(벌써), (B) do의 목적어를 써야 하므로 What이 적절하다. (C) 결혼 첫날 '이래'라고 해야 하므로 Since가 적절하다. for+기간(~ 동안), since+기점(~부터[이후])

11 ⓐ와 ⑤: [역할·자격·기능·성질 따위를 나타내어] …으로서(전치사), ① …할 때(접속사), ② [비례] …함에 따라(접속사) ③ [보통 as ~ as …로 형용사·부사 앞에서] …와 같은 정도로(앞의 as는 지시부사, 뒤의 as는 접속사), ④ [상태] …한 대로(접속사)

12 글쓴이의 아버지가 장롱을 살 돈을 어디에 썼는지는 대답할 수 없다. ① Mr. Seo. ② To buy a new chest for clothes. ③ No. ⑤ No.

13 선비의 삶을 사는 '대신에'라고 해야 하므로 instead of가 적절하다. instead of: ~ 대신에, ① ~에도 (불구하고), ② ~ 때문에, ③ ~에 더하여, 게다가, ⑤ ~에 더하여

14 ③의 his는 글쓴이의 아버지가 아니라 일반적인 '파락호'를 지칭한다.

15 ⓑ와 ④: ~하곤 했다(과거의 불규칙적 습관), ① 시제 일치에 의해 will(…일[할] 것이다)을 과거형 would로 쓴 것임. ② 정중히 요청을 할 때 씀, ③ would rather 동사원형(~했으면 좋겠다), ⑤ 정중한 제의·초대를 할 때 씀

16 if[whether]를 보충하면 된다.

17 이 글은 필자의 아버지가 파락호로 신분을 숨기고 독립 운동 자금을 대었다는 내용의 글이므로, 제목으로는 ②번 '파락호가 아니라 비밀 독립운동가'가 적절하다.

18 the reason why는 선행사와 관계부사 중에서 the reason이나 why 어느 한 쪽만 써도 된다.

19 (A) '말하곤 했다'라고 해야 하므로 과거의 불규칙적 습관을 나타내는 would가 적절하다. (B) 집안의 '재산을 탕진하는' 사람

29

이라고 해야 하므로 ruins가 적절하다. ruin one's fortune: 재산을 탕진하다, (C) 명사에 ed를 붙인 유사분사가 주격보어로 쓰인 것이므로 empty-handed가 적절하다. empty-handed: 빈손인

20 계속적 용법의 관계대명사는 '접속사+인칭대명사'로 바꿔 쓸 수 있다.

21 have no more money left: 남은 돈이 없다

🦉 서술형 시험대비   p.150~151

01 left

02 every time 또는 each time

03 Instead of living the life of a *seonbi*, he was always at the gambling house.

04 had devoted

05 Your father sent the independence fighters in Manchuria the family money.

06 whether

07 (A) independence fighters   (B) a secret

08 (A) some money   (B) new chest

09 (A) clothes   (B) horrible   (C) embarrassing

10 chest

11 There goes the *parakho's* daughter

12 that → which

13 (A) *parakho*   (B) gambled

---

01 have no more money left: 더 이상 남은 돈이 없다

02 whenever = every time = each time: …할 때 언제든지

03 앞 문장의 내용('선비의 삶을 사는 대신 그는 항상 도박장에 계셨다.')을 가리킨다.

04 독립 운동에 생애를 바친 것이 먼저 일어난 일이므로 과거완료로 쓰는 것이 적절하다.

05 to를 생략하고 '간접목적어+직접목적어' 순서로 쓰는 것이 적절하다.

06 if = whether: ~인지 아닌지

07 필자는 아버지를 파락호라고 오해했지만, 사실 그의 아버지는 가족의 돈을 만주에 있는 독립운동가들에게 보냈고 그 사실을 일본 순사들에게 비밀로 하기 위해 도박꾼처럼 보이게 했다.

08 신랑측 가족이 신부측 가족에게 옷을 넣을 새 장롱을 살 약간의 돈을 보내 주었다.

09 (A) '옷'을 넣을 장롱이라고 해야 하므로 clothes가 적절하다. cloths: cloth(옷감, 천)의 복수 clothes: 옷, 의복, (B) 그런 '끔찍한' 일이라고 해야 하므로 horrible이 적절하다. horrible: 끔찍한, terrific: 아주 좋은, 멋진, (C) 감정을 나타내는 동사는 감정을 유발할 때 현재분사를 쓰는 것이 적절하므로

로 embarrassing이 적절하다.

10 chest: (보통 나무로 만든) 상자, 장롱, 물건을 보관하기 위해 사용되는 크고 무거운 상자

11 There+동사+명사 주어

12 관계대명사 that은 계속적 용법으로 쓸 수 없기 때문에, which로 고치는 것이 적절하다.

13 gamble away one's fortune: 노름으로 가산을 탕진하다

🦉 영역별 핵심문제   p.153~157

01 ③, ④   02 marriage   03 of

04 keeping   05 (A) is called   (B) if   06 fortress

07 ④   08 ①   09 ①

10 wooden   11 (A) Right.   (B) who   (C) made

12 general   13 ⑤   14 ④

15 if[whether] he would forgive his fault

16 ⓑ, ⓓ, ⓔ   17 ③

18 (1) I was not sure if[whether] he was telling the truth.

   (2) Rob wants to know if[whether] more men than women like gardening.

   (3) I asked her if[whether] I could have a drink.

19 ⑤   20 ⑤

21 because → why   22 ①   23 ②

24 (A) her father   (B) new chest

25 (A) himself   (B) keep   (C) At first

26 ②, ④, ⑤   27 ④   28 had been 또는 was

29 ②   30 ④

---

01 ① 이상한 것은 그가 나를 못 알아본다는 점이었다. ② 이 나라는 독립 이후로 많은 발전을 이룩했다. ③ movement: (정치적·사회적) 운동 / 그는 인상주의 운동을 추종했다. ④ leave: 맡기다, 남기다 / 너는 아이들을 토요일에 할머니한테 맡겼니? ⑤ 옆 사람과 속삭이지 마세요.

02 주어진 단어는 동사와 명사의 관계이다. marry는 뒤에 −age를 붙여 명사형을 만든다. solve: 해결하다, 풀다 solution: 해결 marry: 결혼하다 marriage: 결혼

03 hear of ~: ~에 대해 듣다 / Big Star라고 불리는 밴드에 대해 들어 본 적 있니? instead of: ~ 대신에 / 내가 햄 대신에 참치를 먹어도 되나요?

04 keep a secret: 비밀을 지키다 / 대부분의 사람들은 비밀을 지키는 것을 잘하지 못한다. keep: (~한 상태를) 유지하다 awake: 깨어 있는 / Paul은 강한 블랙 커피를 많이 마심으로써 깨어 있었다.

05 (A) call이 5형식으로 사용하여 '[사람·물건을] (어떤 이름으로) 부르다, 이름을 붙이다'로 쓰일 수 있다. 원래는 'People call this the Geojunggi.'인 문장을 수동태로 바꿨으므로 is

called가 적절하다. (B) 어떤 일을 하기 전에 해도 되는지 허가 여부를 물을 때 'Is it okay if I ~?(제가 ~해도 될까요?)'라고 질문한다.

06 fortress: 요새 / 중요한 장소를 방어하기 위해 사용되는 크고 튼튼한 건물

07 ⓐ 거중기는 화성 요새를 지을 때 사용되었다.(○) ⓑ B는 화성 요새를 더 가까이 보기를 원했다. (화성 요새가 아닌 거중기를 더 가까이 보고 싶어 했다.) ⓒ 화성 요새는 28개월 동안에 지어졌다.(○) ⓓ 거중기는 기계의 일종이다. (○) ⓔ A는 거중기가 무엇인지 알고 있다.(○)

08 'How was ~?'는 상대방의 경험에 대해 묻는 표현으로, 대답 'It was wonderful.(좋았어요.)'과 어울리므로 ①이 적절하다.

09 ⓐ to, the chance to 동사원형: ~할 기회, to부정사가 the chance를 꾸며주고 있다. ⓑ if, Is it okay if I ~?: 제가 ~해도 될까요? ⓒ that, that은 remember의 목적어 자리에 들어가는 명사절을 이끄는 접속사로 사용됐다. ⓓ at, 시간 앞에는 전치사 at을 사용한다. ⓔ if, if: (접) ~한다면

10 ships를 수식하는 형용사가 들어갈 자리이다. wood: 나무, 목재 wooden: 나무로 된, 목재의

11 (A) (사람들이) 그가 12척의 나무 배로(목선으로) 전쟁을 이겼다고 말했으므로, 긍정의 대답이 나와야 한다. (B) 여기서 general은 '장군'이므로 사람을 선행사로 하는 주격 관계대명사 who[that]가 적절하다. (C) 목적어 creative plans가 있으므로 능동이 어울린다.

12 general: 장군 / 육군이나 공군에서 높은 계급을 가진 장교

13 명사절을 이끄는 접속사 if는 whether로 바꿔 쓸 수 있다.

14 When Megan arrived at the station, the train had already left for London. 도착하기 전에 이미 출발한 것이므로 도착한 것은 과거로, 출발한 것은 과거완료로 써야 한다.

15 명사절을 이끄는 접속사 if나 whether를 이용하고 주절이 과거시제이므로 will을 would로 써야 하는 것에 유의한다.

16 ⓐ has → had ⓒ had eaten → ate, made → had made ⓕ which → if[whether] ⓖ that → if[whether]

17 already로 보아 had already eaten과 같은 과거완료가 나와야 한다.

18 명사절을 이끄는 접속사 if[whether]를 이용한다.

19 ⑤번은 believe의 목적어를 이끄는 접속사 that이 적절하고 나머지는 모두 '~인지 (아닌지)'라는 의미의 명사절을 이끄는 접속사 if[whether]가 적절하다.

20 win a lot of money by gambling: 노름으로 돈을 많이 따다

21 '그것이 그가 파락호라고 불린 이유이다'라고 해야 하므로, because를 why로 고치는 것이 적절하다.

22 ①번 다음 문장의 the money에 주목한다. 주어진 문장의 some money를 받고 있으므로 ①번이 적절하다.

23 ⓐ와 ② 꼭, 바로(부사), ① 권리(명사), ③ 옳은(형용사) ④ 제

대로 된(형용사), ⑤ (상태가) 좋은(형용사)

24 글쓴이는 Mr. Seo와 결혼하게 되었지만, '그녀의 아버지' 때문에 옷을 넣을 '새 장롱'을 살 수 없었다.

25 (A) 주어와 목적어가 같으므로 재귀대명사 himself가 적절하다. (B) '일본 경찰들로부터 이것을 비밀로 지키려고'라고 해야 하므로 keep이 적절하다. keep+O.C.+from A: A로부터 ~을 …로 지키다, stop A from B: A가 B하는 것을 막다, (C) '처음에는'이라고 해야 하므로 At first가 적절하다. for the first time: 처음으로

26 ⓐ와 ①, ③: 계속 용법, ② 경험 용법, ④ 결과 용법, ⑤ 완료 용법

27 'I realized that I had been wrong about him'을 통해 'ashamed'를, 'I have been proud'를 통해 'respectful'을 찾을 수 있다. ① ashamed: 부끄러운, ② respectful: 존경심을 보이는, ③ disappointed: 실망한

28 after가 있을 때는 시간의 전후관계가 분명하므로, 과거완료를 과거로 쓸 수 있다.

29 ② 위 글은 '전기'이다. ④ (신문•잡지의) 글, 기사, ⑤ 자서전

30 석방된 직후에 죽었다.

단원별 예상문제 p.158~161

01 ②   02 (1) so (2) such   03 ④
04 (1) (g)eneral (2) marriages (3) (o)bject (4) (s)ince
05 ①   06 ④
07 is it okay if I use the bathroom now?
08 (A) What are you reading? (B) Who is she?
09 ⓐ female ⓑ is said ⓒ that
10 biography 11 ⑤   12 inventions
13 if[whether] she could go out   14 ④
15 ④   16 ③, ⑤   17 gambling house
18 ⓑ such a horrible thing ⓒ behind my back
19 has → had   20 ④   21 ⑤
22 ①, ④   23 (A) look like (B) Japanese officers
24 to look → look like
25 He sent the family money to the independence
   fighters in Manchuria.

---

01 ②번을 제외한 보기들은 뒤에 –ward(s)를 붙여 부사를 만들 수 있다. ① inward: 안으로 ③ afterwards: 후에, 나중에 ④ backwards: 뒤로 ⑤ forwards: 앞으로

02 (1) so+형용사/부사+that 주어 동사: 너무 ~해서 …하다 / 모든 것이 너무 변해서 나는 그 장소를 알아차리지 못했다. (2) such (a(n))+형용사+명사: 너무 ~한 명사 / 그는 너무 갑작스럽게 멈춰서 우리가 거의 그를 칠 뻔했다.

03 (A) unwilling: 꺼려하는, 싫어하는 ask for: 청구하다, 청

하다 / 그는 항상 다른 사람에게 부탁하기를 꺼려한다. (B) devote one's life to 명사: ~에 일생을 바치다 / 그녀는 예술에 자신의 일생을 바치겠다고 발표했다.

04 (1) general: 장군 (2) marriage: 결혼, 혼인 (3) object: 물체, 물건 (4) since: ~이기 때문에

05 주어진 문장은 카레랑 비빔밥 중 무엇을 먹을지 묻는 질문이다. 이에 대한 대답으로 'I'd like to have *bibimbap*, please.'가 어울리므로 ①이 적절하다.

06 마지막 부분에서 여자가 좌석 불이 켜지면 좌석에 앉아야 한다고 말하는 것을 볼 때 대화는 항공기 안에서 이뤄지고 있다.

07 Is it okay if I ~?: 제가 ~해도 될까요? if 다음에는 주어와 동사 순으로 나온다. use: 사용하다 bathroom: 화장실

08 (A) Lisa가 권기옥에 대한 책을 읽고 있는 중이라고 대답하였으므로 무엇을 하고 있는지 묻는 질문이 어울린다. (B) Lisa가 권기옥에 대한 설명을 하고 있으므로, 그녀(권기옥)가 누구인지 물어보는 질문이 적절하다

09 ⓐ She가 주어이므로 female이 어울린다. male: 남성; 남성의 female: 여자, 여자의, 여성의 ⓑ, ⓒ It is said that 주어+동사 ~: (사람들이) ~라고 한다.

10 biography: 전기 / 누군가가 다른 누군가의 삶에 대해 쓴 책

11 남자는 조선 시대로 넘어가자고 얘기하면서 조선 시대의 유물들을 보여주며 그 중 하나인 자격루를 소개하고 있는 상황이다. As you can see: 보시다시피

12 invent: 발명하다 invention: 발명품, 발명

13 명사절을 이끄는 접속사 if나 whether를 이용하고 주절이 과거 시제이므로 will을 would로 써야 하는 것에 유의한다.

14 ④번은 '만약 ~한다면'의 의미로 부사절을 이끄는 접속사로 쓰였지만 나머지는 모두 '~인지 아닌지'라는 의미로 명사절을 이끄는 접속사로 쓰였다.

15 ① I told the story that I had read in the book. ② I couldn't find the pen which Dad had given to me. ③ After she had been[was] in prison for 6 months, she was released and died short after. ⑤ It was proved that the officials had taken bribes from him months before. bribe: 뇌물

16 ⓐ와 ①, ②, ④: 동명사, ③, ⑤: 현재분사

17 선비의 삶을 사는 대신 항상 '도박장'에 계셨기 때문이다.

18 ⓑ 'such a 형용사+명사'의 순서로 쓰는 것이 적절하다. ⓒ behind one's back: ~ 몰래

19 기준 시점보다 더 이전에 일어난 일이므로, 과거완료로 쓰는 것이 적절하다.

20 '결혼식 직전'에 돈을 가져갔다.

21 ⓐ keep+O+O.C.+from A: A로부터 ~을 …로 지키다, ⓑ devote A to B: A를 B에 바치다

22 (A)와 ②, ③, ⑤: 부사적 용법, ① 형용사적 용법, ④ 명사적

용법

23 필자의 아버지는 파락호가 아니라 가족의 돈을 만주에 있는 독립운동가들에게 보내는 사실을 '일본 순사들'에게 비밀로 하기 위해 그 자신을 도박꾼처럼 보이게 했다.

24 사역동사(made)+목적어+원형부사, look like+명사: ~처럼 보이다

25 '그가 가족의 돈을 만주에 있는 독립 운동가들에게 보냈다.'는 것을 가리킨다.

🦉 서술형 실전문제 p.162~163

01 ⓐ Why? ⓒ He is going to be included in the social studies textbook in South Sudan.
ⓔ It is good to hear that students will learn about such a great person.

02 It is said that such stories will be included in the textbook. / People say that such stories will be included in the textbook.

03 (1) had left (2) had been closed

04 Is it okay if I bring in my water bottle? /
Can I bring in my water bottle?

05 (1) It was the most interesting game that I had ever played.
(2) His wife was surprised to learn that he had already been fired without any warning.
(3) He could not decide if[whether] this was a fairy tale or a nightmare.
(4) I'm considering whether to accept his offer.

06 (1) I want to know if[whether] he can give her a recommendation.
(2) She could not open the door because she had left the key at school.

07 not, but

08 Bring more money to me!

09 marry with → marry

10 글쓴이의 아버지가 장롱을 살 돈을 가지고 간 것

11 her father, money

---

01 ⓐ 남자가 그 사람에 대해서 들어본 적이 있다고 했는데, 그 사람이 누구인지 묻는 것은 앞뒤가 맞지 않는다. 여자가 이태석 신부의 이야기가 교과서에 실린다는 말을 하고 있으므로 남자는 이태석 신부를 아는지 물어본 이유에 대해서 질문하는 것이 적절하다. ⓒ 그의 이야기가 교과서에 포함되어지는 것이므로 수동태로 써야 한다. ⓔ 학생들이 훌륭한 사람에 대해서 배우는 일은 듣기 좋은 것이므로 bad를 good으로 바꿔야 한다.

02 알고 있는 내용을 진술할 때 'It is said that 주어+동사 ~.'나

'They[People] say (that) 주어+동사 ~.'을 쓸 수 있다.

03 (1) 기억하는 시점보다 앞선 시점에 문을 열어 놓은 것이므로 과 거완료를 이용한다. (2) 도착한 시점보다 앞선 시점에 문이 닫힌 것이므로 과거완료를 이용한다. 수동태로 써야 하는 것에 주의 한다.

04 'Is it okay if I ~?'는 '제가 ~해도 될까요?'라는 뜻으로 어떤 행 동을 하기 전에 허가를 요청할 때 사용하는 표현이다. 이외의 허 가를 구하는 다른 표현으로 'Can I ~?'가 있다.

05 (1) 과거의 어느 시점까지 게임을 해 본 것이므로 과거완료로 나 타내는 것이 적절하다. (2) 해고된 것이 앞선 일이고 already 가 있으므로 과거완료로 나타내는 것이 적절하다. (3) 뒤에 or a nightmare가 나오므로 that을 if나 whether로 고치는 것 이 적절하다. (4) if는 to부정사와 함께 쓰이지 않으므로 if를 whether로 고치는 것이 적절하다. nightmare: 악몽

06 (1) '~인지 (아닌지)'라는 의미의 명사절을 이끄는 접속사 if[whether]를 이용한다. (2) 열쇠를 두고 온 것이 문을 열지 못 하는 시점보다 앞서므로 과거완료로 써야 한다.

07 not A but B = instead of A, B = B instead of A

08 bring은 to를 사용하여 3형식으로 고친다.

09 marry는 타동사이므로 전치사 with 없이 목적어를 쓰는 것이 적 절하다.

10 글쓴이의 어머니가 말한 "Your father has taken the money for the chest."를 가리킨다.

11 '그녀의 아버지'가 장롱을 살 '돈'을 가져갔기 때문이다.

창의사고력 서술형 문제
p.164

|모범답안|

01 A: Is it okay if I borrow your bicycle? / Can[May] I borrow your bicycle? / I'm wondering if I can borrow your bicycle.
B: I'm sorry. It's broken.

02 (1) if[whether] she is reading
(2) had memorized

03 (A) female independence fighter
(B) to fight for independence
(C) built schools and educated women
(D) six months   (E) an award

01 'Is it okay if I ~?'는 '제가 ~해도 될까요?'라는 뜻으로 어떤 행 동을 하기 전에 허가를 요청할 때 사용하는 표현이다. if 다음에는 허락을 구하는 내용을 쓴다. 허가를 묻는 다른 표현으로는 'Can I ~?' 등이 있다. borrow: 빌리다 broken: 고장 난

단원별 모의고사
p.165~169

01 ⓑ to spend → to spending   02 at
03 (1) biography   (2) female   (3) locker   (4) detective
04 (1) movement   (2) inventions   (3) getting
05 ②   06 ④
07 (A) is called   (B) it   08 ③
09 It is said that it is the oldest and the largest water clock in Korea.
10 ①   11 scholar
12 It is said that he was also a detective.
13 ④   14 ③
15 (1) if[whether] the school lunch is delicious
(2) if[whether] it's all right to sit next to her
(3) had already eaten
16 (1) Would you please check if[whether] I filled out this card right?
(2) I don't know if[whether] my mom likes potato pizza.
(3) I am not sure if[whether] Mike will meet Judy at 3 o'clock.
(4) He insisted that he had never heard a girl crying that night.
(5) I decided to come home earlier than I had planned.   17 ⑤
18 (1) had been sold out   (2) had never met
19 ①, ②, ③   20 good memories
21 they called him a parakho   22 ①
23 ④   24 ②, ④   25 himself   26 ②
27 who[that] had devoted his life to the independence movement   28 ③

01 ⓐ so+형용사/부사+that 주어+동사: 너무 ~해서 …하다 / 땅 의 표면이 너무 뜨거워서 녹았다. ⓑ be used to 동명사: ~하는 데 익숙하다 / 아이들은 그들의 많은 자유 시간을 TV 보는 데 쓰는 것에 익숙하다. ⓒ by 동사ing: ~함으로써 / 나는 내 집을 팔아서 새 차를 사기를 바랐다.

02 at that moment: 그 순간에 / 바로 그 순간, 당신은 나에게 다 가와서 내게 설명할 기회도 주지 않고 딱지를 끊었어요. yell at: ~에게 고함치다 / 나에게 그렇게 소리치지 마.

03 (1) biography: 전기 / 나는 아브라함 링컨의 전기를 읽었다. (2) female: 여자; 여자의, 여성의 / 오은선은 한국의 여성 등반 가이다. (3) locker: 사물함 / 제 사물함 열쇠를 어디서 받을 수 있나요? (4) detective: 형사, 탐정 / 그 탐정은 약간의 증거를 찾았다.

04 (1) movement: (정치적·사회적) 운동 (2) invention: 발명 품, 발명 (3) be used to 동명사 ~하는 데 익숙하다

05 ⓐ take ⓑ know ⓒ bring ⓓ leave

33

06 ① 남자가 물병을 박물관 안에 가지고 들어갈 수 있나요? (네) ② 남자는 지금 어디에 있는가? (박물관) ③ 박물관에 사물함이 있나요? (네) ④ 박물관 안에서 사진을 찍을 수 있나요?(답할 수 없음) ⑤ 남자가 가방을 박물관 안에 가지고 들어갈 수 있나요? (아니요)

07 (A) 이것이 '자격루'라고 불리는 것이므로 수동태를 사용해야 한다. (B) *Jagyeongnu*를 가리키고 있으므로 'it'으로 받아야 한다.

08 actually: 사실은, 실제로 in fact: 사실은

10 주어진 문장의 it은 남자가 본 영화를 의미이므로 ①번이 적절하다.

11 scholar: 학자 / 특히 과학적인 주제가 아닌 특정한 주제에 대해 공부하고 많이 아는 사람

12 It is said that 주어+동사 ~: (사람들이) ~라고 한다 also: 또한 detective: 형사, 탐정

13 동사 know 뒤에 목적어 자리로 명사절을 이끄는 접속사 that이 어울린다.

14 if는 'if or not'의 형태로 쓰이지 않으므로 if만 쓰거나 or not을 '~ it or not.'의 형태로 문장의 뒷부분에 써야 한다.

15 (1) 의문사가 없는 간접의문문에 쓰인 if[whether]이다. (2) 명사절을 이끄는 접속사 if[whether]를 이용한다. (3) 점심을 먹은 것이 앞선 시점이고 already가 있으므로 과거완료로 쓰는 것이 적절하다.

16 (1) 명사절을 이끄는 접속사 if[whether]를 이용한다. (2) 의문사가 없는 간접의문문에 쓰인 if[whether]이다. (3) I am not sure의 목적어로는 접속사 if[whether]를 이용하는 것이 적절하다. (4) 주장하는 시점보다 듣지 못한 시점이 앞서므로 과거완료로 쓰는 것이 적절하다. (5) 결정하는 시점보다 계획한 시점이 앞서므로 과거완료로 쓰는 것이 적절하다.

17 ⑤ I'm not sure if she made a mistake or not.

18 과거의 어느 시점보다 먼저 일어난 일이나 상태를 나타낼 때 과거완료를 사용한다.

19 ⓐ와 ①, ②, ③: 동명사, ④, ⑤: 현재분사

20 아버지에 대한 '좋은 기억'을 가지고 있지 않았기 때문이다.

21 they를 주어로 하여 능동태로 고치는 것이 적절하다.

22 ⓐ와 ①, ②, ③, ⑤: 관계대명사, ④: 의문대명사

23 신랑 집에서 장롱을 사라고 준 돈을 신부의 아버지가 결혼식 전에 가져가 버렸기 때문에, '난처한'이 적절하다. ② 만족스러운, ⑤ (감탄스럽도록) 놀라운

24 ⓐ와 ②, ④: 완료 용법, ① 결과 용법, ③ 계속 용법, ⑤ 경험 용법

25 주어와 목적어가 같은 사람이므로 재귀대명사를 써야 한다.

26 at first: 처음에

27 devote A to B: A를 B에 바치다

28 필자의 아버지는 '일본 순사들'로부터 자신의 신분을 비밀로 지키려고 도박꾼처럼 보이기를 원했다.

교과서 파헤치기

Lesson 1

01 막다, 예방하다　02 요구
03 구체적 내용, 자세한 내용　　04 주장, 논쟁
05 부주의한, 조심성 없는　　06 집중하다
07 사실은　08 딱 부러지는, 단도직입적인
09 불편한　10 효과적으로
11 말다툼하다, 언쟁하다　　12 표현하다, 나타내다
13 준비하다　14 숨기다, 감추다　15 해결하다
16 화난　17 못된, 심술궂은; 의미하다
18 배려하다, 고려하다　　19 아마도
20 요청　21 실망한, 낙담한　22 이유
23 관계　24 단순히　25 고민, 문제
26 그 대신에　27 우울한 얼굴　28 화난, 기분 나쁜
29 어딘가에　30 도움이 되는, 유용한
31 선택하다, 고르다　32 (~처럼) 보이다, ~인 듯하다
33 집중하다　34 크게, 큰 소리로　35 해결하다
36 ~을 중단시키다, ~을 잘라내다
37 ~을 명심하다, 마음에 담아 두다
38 ~할 준비가 되다　39 긴장하다, 겁을 먹다
40 ~이 없는　41 ~에 대해서 화가 나다
42 비밀을 누설하다　43 ~을 비난하다

01 argument　02 careless　03 direct
04 somewhere　05 probably
06 focus[concentrate]　07 helpful
08 upset　09 hide　10 instead
11 argue　12 uncomfortable 13 exam
14 mean　15 consider　16 disappointed
17 solve　18 effectively　19 long face
20 pick　21 prepare　22 simply
23 actually　24 prevent　25 demand
26 request　27 detail　28 reason
29 relationship　30 scared　31 express
32 feeling　33 seem　34 trouble
35 order+사람+around
36 make a demand　37 first of all
38 be ready to 동사원형　39 keep ~ in mind
40 on time　41 in the middle of
42 end up 동사ing 43 cut ~ off

1 mean, 못된, 심술궂은　2 scared, 두려워하는, 겁먹은
3 unhappy, 불만스러운, 불행한
4 helpful, 도움이 되는, 유용한
5 argument, 주장, 논쟁　6 upset, 화난, 기분 나쁜
7 concentrate, 집중하다　8 long face, 우울한 얼굴
9 consider, 배려하다, 고려하다　10 hide, 숨기다, 감추다
11 solve, 해결하다　12 prevent, 막다, 예방하다
13 express, 표현하다, 나타내다
14 detail, 구체적 내용, 자세한 내용
15 disappointed, 실망한, 낙담한　16 reason, 이유

Listen & Talk 1 Get Ready

Why, look. unhappy / about, copies / take it, hard

Listen & Talk 1 A-1

how come, with, these days / upset about an argument / Why, upset / cutting me off in / mad, stopped talking to / sorry to hear

Listen & Talk 1 A-2

How, going / I'm upset about / wrong / I don't think that, on time / too bad

Listen & Talk 1 B

Why, long face / angry at, said some mean / why, angry / to sleep, But, talking loudly on the phone / upset / haven't worked it out / that, mean, but I don't know how / Why don't, send

Listen & Talk 2 Get Ready

let the cat out of the bag, surprise party / That's not what, Keep, a secret

Listen & Talk 2 A-1

get, grade in, What should / concentrate, first of all, have your head in the clouds / see the sky / That's not what I meant, meant, focus

Listen & Talk 2 A-2

go diving / Actually, got cold feet / get a cold / what, I meant that, scared

Listen & Talk 2 B

stressed out about / two more to go / finishing, go on a, hair down / hair style / what I meant, feel free from, troubles

Communication

seem, wrong / keep telling me that, direct, upset / what they're talking about / What, mean / tend to say what's on, strongly / Should, keep quiet / That's not what I meant, try to consider, feelings / try

Listen & Talk 1 Get Ready

A: Why do you look so unhappy?

B: I'm upset about Roy. He always copies me.

A: Don't take it so hard.

Listen & Talk 1 A-1

M: Sally, how come you don't talk much with Anna these days?

W: Well, I'm upset about an argument we had.

M: Why are you upset?

W: She kept cutting me off in the middle of my sentences, so I got mad. We argued and I stopped talking to her.

M: Oh, I'm sorry to hear that.

Listen & Talk 1 A-2

W: How is your science homework going?

M: Not good. I'm upset about my science group.

W: What's wrong?

M: The group members only speak and never listen. I don't think that we can finish the homework on time.

W: That's too bad.

Listen & Talk 1 B

M: Why the long face, Julie?

W: I got angry at my sister yesterday and said some mean things to her.

M: Oh, why were you angry?

W: I was really tired and I wanted to sleep. But she was talking loudly on the phone. I was really upset about that.

M: I see. And you two haven't worked it out yet?

W: No, not yet. I want to say I'm sorry that I was mean to her, but I don't know how.

M: Why don't you write her a note or send her a text message?

W: Hmm, that's a good idea. Thanks.

Listen & Talk 2 Get Ready

A: Don't let the cat out of the bag about Clara's surprise party.

B: A cat? I don't have a cat.

A: That's not what I meant. Keep her party a secret.

Listen & Talk 2 A-1

W: Mr. Brown, I want to get a good grade in English. What should I do?

M: Well, Sujin, you should concentrate in class, first of all. I see you often have your head in the clouds.

W: Clouds? I can't see the sky from inside the classroom.

M: That's not what I meant. I meant you don't focus in class.

Listen & Talk 2 A-2

W: Did you finally go diving yesterday, Nick?

M: Actually, I got cold feet, Mina.

W: That's too bad. How did you get a cold?

M: No, Mina. That's not what I meant. I meant that I got scared, so I didn't dive.

Listen & Talk 2 B

W: I'm so stressed out about my exams, Jinsu.

M: Yeah, me, too. We have two more to go.

W: After finishing my exams, I want to go on a trip and just let my hair down.

M: You want to change your hair style?

W: No, that's not what I meant. I want to go somewhere and feel free from all my troubles.

Communication

W: Hey, Jason. You seem upset. Anything wrong?

M: People keep telling me that I'm too direct. I'm upset about that.

W: Hmm.... I kind of know what they're talking about.

M: What do you mean?

W: Well, somet imes you tend to say what's on your mind too strongly.

M: Should I just keep quiet, then?

W: That's not what I meant. You can try to consider others' feelings.

M: I see. I'll try that.

01 Speak, Mind Effectively

02 Welcome to, Teens   03 Dr. Carter

04 using, skills, express, effectively

05 Let's, with. clip

06 tries, ends up arguing

07 find out, reason why

08 *lost, Why, so careless*

09 sentence with, express, feelings

10 Instead, use, I-message

11 focus on, rather than

12 *upset because, favorite, lost*   13 Next, Calli

14 trying, busy preparing, work

15 have a look

16 *Could, talk, something*

17 needs, find, right time

18 wanted, to what, going

19 enough time to, with

20 pick, ready to listen

21 *Could, about something*   22 *Mom, Sure*

23 take, look at 24 often hurts, feelings

25 *Don't put, on*

26 felt uncomfortable, demand using

27 simply, taking orders   28 try to, such as

29 what, like, request, demand

30 *Could, put, on*

31 change, express, solve, prevent

32 keep, in mind

---

01 Mind Effectively

02 Welcome to, Teens   03 I'm

04 using good communication skills, ourselves, effectively

05 Let's, our first clip

06 tries to, ends up arguing

07 find out the reason why   08 *lost, careless*

09 sentence with, to express his feelings

10 Instead, I-message

11 focus on, rather than point the finger at

12 *I'm, upset, are lost*   13 Next

14 is busy preparing

15 have a look

16 *Could I*

17 needs to, the right time

18 what, going to say

19 enough time to talk

20 pick a time, is ready to listen

21 *Could I*   22 *Sure*

23 take a look at 24 hurts, feelings 25 *Don't put*

26 felt uncomfortable, made a demand

27 simply, taking orders

28 should try, such as

29 what, sound like, request, demand

30 *Could you*

31 a small change, express ourselves, prevent communication problems

32 keep, in mind

---

1 당신의 마음을 효과적으로 말하라

2 '십 대들의 모든 것'에 오신 걸 환영합니다.

3 저는 Carter 박사입니다.

4 오늘 우리는 자신을 더 효과적으로 표현하기 위해 적절한 의사소통 기술을 사용하는 것에 대해 이야기해 보겠습니다.

---

5 Brian에 대한 첫 번째 동영상으로 시작해 보죠.

6 Brian이 남동생과 이야기하려고 할 때, 그는 결국 동생과 항상 말다툼을 하게 돼요.

7 그에게 이런 문제가 있는 이유를 알아봅시다.

8 Brian: "너 또 내 이어폰 잃어버렸지. 너는 왜 그렇게 조심성이 없니?"

9 Brian은 그의 감정을 표현하기 위해 '너'로 문장을 시작하고 있군요.

10 대신에 그는 '나 메시지'를 써야 해요.

11 '나'로 시작하는 것이 그가 남동생을 비난하기보다는 자신이 느끼거나 생각하는 것에 집중하도록 도울 수 있답니다.

12 Brian: "내가 가장 좋아하는 이어폰이 없어져서 난 정말 속상해."

13 다음은 Calli입니다.

14 그녀는 어머니와 이야기하려고 하지만, 어머니는 출근 준비로 바쁘시군요.

15 한번 보시죠.

16 Calli: "저기, 엄마. 엄마랑 뭔가에 대해 이야기 좀 할 수 있을까요?"

17 Calli는 어머니와 이야기를 나눌 적절한 때를 찾아야 해요.

18 Calli의 어머니도 아마 Calli가 말하려고 했던 것을 듣고 싶어 하셨을 거예요.

19 그러나 어머니에게는 딸과 이야기할 시간이 충분하지 않았어요.

20 Calli는 어머니가 들으실 준비가 된 때를 골라야 해요.

21 Calli: "저기, 엄마. 엄마랑 뭔가에 대해 이야기 좀 할 수 있을까요?"

22 Mom: "물론이지."

23 이제 마지막 동영상을 봅시다.

24 Anna와 Julie는 가장 친한 친구 사이이지만, Anna가 종종 Julie의 마음을 상하게 합니다.

25 Anna: "네 가방을 내 책상에 놓지 마!"

26 Anna가 don't라는 단어를 써서 요구했기 때문에 Julie는 아마 불편하게 느꼈을 거예요.

27 사람들은 명령 받는 것을 전혀 좋아하지 않아요.

28 Anna는 can, could 또는 please와 같은 말을 사용하도록 노력해야 해요.

29 그러면 그녀가 하는 말이 요구보다는 요청처럼 들릴 거예요.

30 Anna: "네 가방은 네 책상에 놔두겠니?"

31 우리가 동영상에서 본 것처럼, 우리 자신을 표현하는 방식을 조금만 바꾸어도 의사소통의 문제를 해결하거나 심지어 막을 수도 있답니다.

32 이 조언들을 명심합시다!

---

1 Speak Your Mind Effectively

2 Welcome to "All about Teens."

3 I'm Dr. Carter.

4 Today, we're going to talk about using good communication skills to express ourselves more effectively.

5 Let's start with our first clip about Brian.

6 When he tries to talk to his brother, he always ends up arguing with his brother.

7 Let's find out the reason why he has this problem.

8 Brian: You lost my earphones again. Why are you so careless?

9 Brian is starting a sentence with "you" to express his feelings..

10 Instead, he should use the "I-message."

11 Starting with "I" can help him focus on what he feels or thinks rather than point the finger at his brother.

12 Brian: I'm really upset because my favorite earphones are lost.

13 Next is Calli.

14 She is trying to talk to her mother, but she is busy preparing to go to work.

15 Let's have a look.

16 Calli: Hey, Mom. Could I talk to you about something?

17 Calli needs to find the right time to talk to her mom.

18 Maybe Calli's mom wanted to listen to what Calli was going to say.

19 But she didn't have enough time to talk with her daughter.

20 Calli should pick a time when her mom is ready to listen.

21 Calli: Hey, Mom. Could I talk to you about something?

22 Mom: Sure.

23 Now, let's take a look at our last clip.

24 Anna and Julie are best friends, but Anna often hurts Julie's feelings.

25 Anna: Don't put your bag on my desk!

26 Julie probably felt uncomfortable because Anna made a demand using the word "don't."

27 People simply don't like taking orders.

28 Anna should try to use words such as "can," "could," or "please."

29 Then, what she says will sound like a request rather than a demand.

30 Anna: Could you put your bag on your desk?

31 As we saw in the video clips, a small change in the way we express ourselves can solve or even

prevent communication problems.

32 Let's keep these tips in mind!

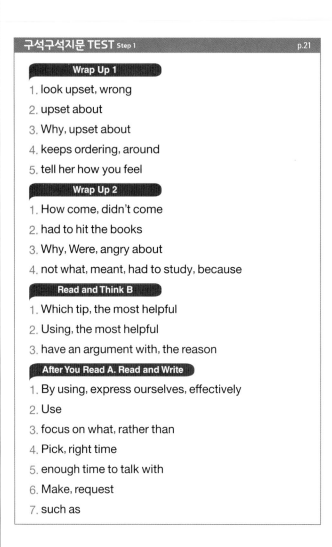

Wrap Up 1

1. look upset, wrong
2. upset about
3. Why, upset about
4. keeps ordering, around
5. tell her how you feel

Wrap Up 2

1. How come, didn't come
2. had to hit the books
3. Why, Were, angry about
4. not what, meant, had to study, because

Read and Think B

1. Which tip, the most helpful
2. Using, the most helpful
3. have an argument with, the reason

After You Read A. Read and Write

1. By using, express ourselves, effectively
2. Use
3. focus on what, rather than
4. Pick, right time
5. enough time to talk with
6. Make, request
7. such as

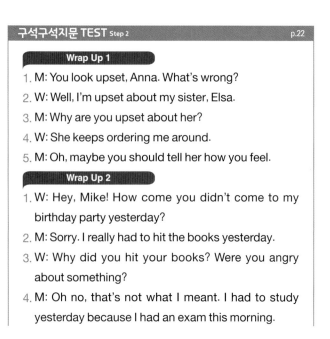

Wrap Up 1

1. M: You look upset, Anna. What's wrong?
2. W: Well, I'm upset about my sister, Elsa.
3. M: Why are you upset about her?
4. W: She keeps ordering me around.
5. M: Oh, maybe you should tell her how you feel.

Wrap Up 2

1. W: Hey, Mike! How come you didn't come to my birthday party yesterday?
2. M: Sorry. I really had to hit the books yesterday.
3. W: Why did you hit your books? Were you angry about something?
4. M: Oh no, that's not what I meant. I had to study yesterday because I had an exam this morning.

Read and Think B

1. Which tip was the most helpful to you, and why?

2. Using the "I-message" was the most helpful.

3. I often have an argument with my sister, and now I understand the reason.

After You Read A. Read and Write

1. By using good communication skills, we can express ourselves more effectively.

2. ⓐ Use the "I-message."

3. You can focus on what you feel or think rather than point the finger at others.

4. ⓑ Pick the right time.

5. Others will listen to you when they have enough time to talk with you.

6. ⓒ Make a request.

7. Use words such as "can," "could," or "please."

단어 TEST Step 1   p.23

01 모양, 형태	02 독특한, 특별한	03 끝이 뾰족한
04 특이한, 흔치 않은	05 황사	06 조사하다
07 풍경, 전망	08 끈적거리는, 달라붙는	
09 조합	10 절정[최대한도]에 이르다	
11 촬영하다	12 유성, 별똥별	13 위치, 장소
14 기간	15 살아남다, 생존하다	
16 강우	17 빙하	18 대회
19 많은, 셀 수 없는	20 만들다, 발전하다	
21 생기 넘치는, 살아 있는		22 생태학자
23 절벽	24 개선하다, 향상시키다	
25 통찰력	26 개인적인	
27 놀라운 일, 기적	28 조사하다, 연구하다	
29 빛나다	30 (날씨·생활 환경이) 혹독한, 가혹한	
31 영광으로 생각하다		
32 영감을 주다, 고무하다, 격려하다		33 의류, 옷
34 색채화가	35 ~을 대신하다	
36 ~에 의해 영감을 받다		
37 실현되다, 사실이 되다		38 ~로 가득 차다
39 좋은 몸 상태를 유지하다		
40 ~에게 정신을 바짝 차리게 하다	41 ~ 때문에	
42 ~에 의해 만들어지다	43 산책하다	

단어 TEST Step 2   p.24

01 insight	02 cliff	03 countless
04 peak	05 clothing	06 improve
07 colorist	08 location	09 combination
10 miracle	11 shape	12 develop
13 ecologist	14 glow	15 reef
16 harsh	17 shoot	18 inspire
19 glacier	20 investigate	21 spiky
22 survive	23 research	24 honor
25 rainfall	26 sticky	27 alive
28 unusual	29 view	30 adventure
31 personal	32 yellow dust	33 actually
34 recent	35 millions of	36 find out
37 be caused by ~		38 stand in for
39 be[get] inspired by		40 be filled with
41 get in shape	42 due to 명사	43 cut down

1 glow, 빛나다   2 cliff, 절벽   3 unique, 독특한, 특별한

4 peak, 절정[최대한도]에 이르다   5 cave, 동굴

6 harsh, (날씨·생활 환경이) 혹독한   7 combination, 조합

8 period, 기간   9 glacier, 빙하   10 mixed, 섞인, 혼합한

11 adventure, 모험   12 countless, 많은, 셀 수 없는

13 ecologist, 생태학자

14 inspire, 영감을 주다, 고무하다, 격려하다

15 research, 조사하다, 연구하다

16 shooting star, 유성, 별똥별

Listen & Talk 1 Get Ready

view, top, amazing / can't wait to, run up

Listen & Talk 1 A-1

what's, plan / going to, wait to visit / are, that look canvases / sounds, Take lots of

Listen & Talk 1 A-2

want to watch / Which / about adventures under, was shot / heard of, has, sea life / can't wait to watch, go and get

Listen & Talk 1 B

is going to go, in / What, plan to / going to study, caves, go, watching / like, interesting trip / I've only read about, wait to actually visit / hope, enjoy, trip

Listen & Talk 2 Get Ready

is, high / I've heard that, travels from, to

Listen & Talk 2 A-1

weather report, able, hundreds of shooting stars, When, to see them / heard that, shooting stars, between, and / special night

Listen & Talk 2 A-2

are / They are, I've heard that, made by, sticky / look like / like, actually, someday

Listen & Talk 2 B

that, sets, during summer / that, How interesting / heard that, even cycling, because / love, in the middle of / too, get, chance to try, someday

Communication

winner, competition / for inviting, honored to receive / talk, heard that, was taken, true / glowing beach, caused by / amazing / can't wait to take, amazing beaches / wish, best

Listen & Talk 1 Get Ready

A: The view of the top of the mountain is going to be amazing.

B: Yeah, I can't wait to see the view. Let's run up there!

Listen & Talk 1 A-1

W: David, what's your summer plan?

M: My family is going to China. I can't wait to visit the Rainbow Mountains.

W: The Rainbow Mountains?

M: They are some mountains that look like canvases in rainbow colors.

W: That sounds amazing! Take lots of pictures!

Listen & Talk 1 A-2

M: Do you want to watch the new 3D movie?

W: Which one?

M: The one about adventures under the sea. It was shot near Australia's Great Barrier Reef.

W: Oh, I've heard of it. It has the most beautiful sea life.

M: Right. I can't wait to watch the movie. Let's go and get the ticket.

Listen & Talk 1 B

W: Dad, my science club is going to go to Dokdo in July.

M: Oh, really? What do you plan to do there?

W: We are going to study the caves on the island and go bird watching.

M: Sounds like it will be an interesting trip.

W: Yeah. I've only read about Dokdo in books. I can't wait to actually visit there.

M: I hope you enjoy your trip!

Listen & Talk 2 Get Ready

A: The level of yellow dust is really high today.

B: Yeah. I've heard that the yellow dust travels from the deserts of Mongolia to Korea.

Listen & Talk 2 A-1

M: Mom, did you watch the weather report today? We will be able to see hundreds of shooting stars tonight!

W: Wow, fantastic! When is the best time to see them?

M: I've heard that the shooting stars will peak between 12 a.m. and 2 a.m.

W: Wow, it will be a special night!

Listen & Talk 2 A-2

M: Erica, what are the white things in the picture?

W: They are snow rollers. I've heard that they are made by strong wind and sticky snow.

M: Interesting! They look like snow rings.

W: Yeah, I'd like to actually see them someday.

M: Jisu, did you know that the sun never sets in Norway during summer?

W: No, I didn't know that. How interesting!

M: Yeah, and I've heard that people go hiking and even cycling at night because it isn't dark.

W: I'd love to go hiking and cycling in the middle of the night!

M: Me, too. I hope we get thechance to try it someday.

M: Let's welcome Ms. Scarlett Lee, the winner of this year's photo competition.

W: Hello, thank you for inviting me. I've honored to receive the award.

M: Let's talk about your photo. I've heard that this photo was taken in the Maldives. Is that true?

W: Yes, this glowing beach is caused by plankton.

M: Wow, it truly is amazing!

W: Yes, it is. I can't wait to take more pictures of amazing beaches.

M: I wish you the best of luck!

본문 TEST Step 1 p.32~33

01 World Through, Eyes

02 beauty, nature inspires

03 find out, fields, inspired

04 Lin, Ecologist 05 Stone Forest

06 been visiting, for over

07 spiky, true miracles

08 amazing, has been created

09 down, sharp, spiky over

10 environment, harsh, animals, survive

11 which, frog-like, that, another

12 For, is like   13 surprises, keeps, on, toes

14 Fashion Colorist

15 River of Five Colors

16 filled with, different

17 mix, develop, create, clothing

18 Over, been gaining, insights

19 mixed, anywhere else, world

20 combination, colorful, alive, bright

21 Whenever, countless, waiting, created

22 Location Scout

23 National, Frozen Beauty

24 location, perfect, shoot

25 for, due to, beauty

26 My personal favorite

27 glacier, ranges, stand, place

28 recent, shot, without using

29 help make, come true

본문 TEST Step 2 p.34~35

01 World Through

02 beauty, inspires us all

03 Let's find out, fields of work get inspired

04 Ecologist   05 Stone Forest

06 I've been visiting, stone forest, for over

07 spiky stones, true miracles

08 amazing, has been created buy rainfall

09 cut down, sharp, spiky over

10 harsh for animals to live in, to survive

11 which, frog-like, that help, jump from, to another

12 is like, jack-in-the-box

13 surprises, keeps me on my toes

14 Fashion Colorist

15 River of Five Colors

16 is filled with millions of

17 mix, develop, create colors

18 I've been gaining, beautiful colors

19 wonderful mixed colors, anywhere else

20 combination, colorful plants, makes, more alive, bright

21 Whenever, makes, think, countless, waiting to be created

22 Location Scout

23 Frozen Beauty

24 perfect places to shoot movies

25 for many location scouts, due to, unusual beauty

26 My personal favorite

27 cliffs, glacier caves, stand in for any place

28 In fact, we shot here, produced without using

29 help make, come true

본문 TEST Step 3 p.36~37

1 내 눈에 비친 세계

2 "자연의 아름다움은 우리 모두에게 영감을 준다.

3 서로 다른 직업 분야의 사람들이 자연에 의해 어떻게 영감을 받는지 알아보자."

4 Lin Wang, 생태학자

5 Tsingy, 마다가스카르의 석림

6 나는 20년 이상 동안 식물과 동물을 연구하기 위해서 마다가스카르의 석림을 방문하고 있다.

7 이 지역의 뾰족한 돌들은 진정한 자연의 놀라움이다.

8 이 놀라운 모양은 비에 의해서 만들어졌다.

9 비가 오랜 기간 동안 돌을 침식해서 날카롭고 뾰족하게 만들었다.

10 이런 환경은 동물들이 살기에 험난하지만, 동물들은 생존할 방법들을 찾아냈다.

11 예를 들어, 마다가스카르에서만 사는 여우원숭이는 한 개의 돌탑에서 다른 돌탑으로 뛸 수 있도록 도와주는 개구리와 같은 다리를 가지고 있다.

12 나에게 석림은 '잭인더박스(열면 인형이 튀어나오는 상자)'와 같다.

13 그것은 늘 나를 놀라게 하고 정신을 바짝 차리게 한다!

14 Amber Smith, 패션 색채 전문가

15 Caño Cristales, 콜롬비아의 다섯 색깔의 강

16 세계는 수백만의 다양한 색깔로 가득 차 있다.

17 의류를 위해서 색을 섞고, 발전시키고, 만들어 내는 것이 나의 일이다.

18 수년 동안, 나는 카뇨 크리스탈레스의 아름다운 색으로부터 영감을 얻어 오고 있다.

19 이 강의 아름답게 혼합된 색깔은 세상 어느 다른 곳에서도 볼 수 없다.

20 물속의 화려한 식물들과 햇빛의 결합은 그 색깔을 더 생생하고 밝게 만든다.

21 내가 카뇨 크리스탈레스를 방문할 때마다 그 강은 나로 하여금 아마도 여전히 만들어지기를 기다리고 있는 셀 수 없이 많은 색깔이 있음을 생각하게 한다.

22 Danny Mehta, 장소 섭외가

23 Vatnajökull 국립 공원, 아이슬란드의 얼음으로 덮인 아름다움

24 나는 장소 섭외가이고 나의 일은 영화를 찍기에 완벽한 장소를 찾는 것이다.

25 아이슬란드는 비범한 아름다움 때문에 많은 장소 섭외가들이 방문하기에 최고의 장소이다.

26 내가 개인적으로 가장 선호하는 곳은 바트나이외쿠틀 국립 공원이다.

27 가파른 절벽, 푸른 빙하 동굴, 그리고 긴 산맥들은 세계나 혹은 우주의 어느 장소도 대신할 수 있다.

28 사실상, 우리가 여기서 찍은 최근의 공상 과학 영화는 컴퓨터 그래픽 없이 만들어졌다!

29 아이슬란드는 우리의 가장 무모한 꿈을 영화 스크린에서 실현할 수 있게 해 준다.

1 The World Through My Eyes

2 "The beauty of nature inspires us all.

3 Let's find out how people from different fields of work get inspired by nature."

4 Lin Wang, Ecologist

5 Tsingy, the Stone Forest of Madagascar

6 I've been visiting the stone forest of Madagascar to study plants and animals for over 20 years.

7 The spiky stones of this place are true miracles of nature.

8 This amazing shape has been created by rainfall.

9 Rain has cut down the stones and made them sharp and spiky over a long period of time.

10 The environment is harsh for animals to live in, but they have found ways to survive.

11 For example, lemurs, which only live in Madagascar, have frog-like legs that help them jump from one stone tower to another.

12 For me, the stone forest is like a jack-in-the-box.

13 It always surprises me and keeps me on my toes!

14 Amber Smith, Fashion Colorist

15 Caño Cristales, the River of Five Colors of Colombia

16 The world is filled with millions of different colors.

17 It is my job to mix, develop, and create colors for clothing.

18 Over the years, I've been gaining insights from the beautiful colors of Caño Cristales.

19 You cannot see the wonderful mixed colors of this river anywhere else in the world.

20 The combination of colorful plants under the water and sunlight makes the colors more alive and bright.

21 Whenever I visit the Caño Cristales, it makes me think that maybe there are still countless colors that are waiting to be created.

22 Danny Mehta, Location Scout

23 Vatnajökull National Park, Frozen Beauty of Iceland

24 I'm a location scout and my job is finding perfect places to shoot movies.

25 Iceland is the best place for many location scouts to visit due to its unusual beauty.

26 My personal favorite is the Vatnajökull National Park.

27 The sharp cliffs, blue glacier caves, and long mountain ranges can stand in for any place in the world or the universe.

28 In fact, the recent sci-fi movie we shot here was produced without using computer graphics!

29 Iceland can help make our wildest dreams come true on the movie screen.

Communication Step

1. on receiving, I've heard, was taken, true
2. is caused by, drops
3. truly is amazing
4. can't wait to take, amazing clouds
5. wish, the best of luck

Wrap Up 1

1. coming back from
2. has been away, right
3. most of the time to research
4. can't wait to see, listen to
5. having dinner, don't make other plans
6. won't

Think & Write Step A

1. Mt.
2. Trip, Hiking
3. walk along, routes
4. in shape, keep fit
5. Trip, Soccer
6. Manchester
7. famous players
8. how to improve
9. Paris
10. Trip for Art
11. famous art museums
12. how to draw, creatively

4. M: Wow, that's amazing. I can't wait to see him and listen to his stories.
5. W: Me, too. We're having dinner with him this Saturday, so don't make other plans.
6. M: Okay, I won't, Mom.

Think & Write Step A

1. Mt. Jiri and Mt. Seorak
2. Trip for Hiking Fans
3. • walk along beautiful hiking routes
4. • learn how to get in shape and keep fit
5. Trip for Soccer Fans
6. Madrid and Manchester
7. • meet famous players
8. • learn how to improve your soccer skills
9. Paris and London
10. Trip for Art Fans
11. • visit famous art museums
12. • learn how to draw pictures creatively

Communication Step

1. A: Congratulations on receiving the award. I've heard that this photo was taken in India. Is that true?
2. B: Yes, this rainbow cloud is caused by thin clouds and water drops.
3. A: Wow, it truly is amazing!
4. B: Yes, it is. I can't wait to take more photos of amazing clouds.
5. A: I wish you the best of luck!

Wrap Up 1

1. W: Your uncle, John, is coming back from South America this weekend.
2. M: That's great. He has been away for almost 2 years, right?
3. W: Yeah, he's been in the jungle most of the time to research.

단어 TEST Step 1 p.44

01 끔찍한 02 기사 03 자서전, 전기

04 망치다, 파산시키다 05 남편

06 형사, 탐정 07 요새

08 도박하다, ~을 도박으로 잃다 09 실망시키는

10 나중에, 그 뒤에 11 재산, 행운 12 장군

13 ~을 포함하다 14 사물함

15 ~할 때마다, ~하면 16 독립, 광복

17 (정치적·사회적) 운동 18 나무로 된, 목재의

19 이상한 20 경찰관, 장교 21 진짜 같은, 사실적인

22 발명품, 발명 23 부끄러운, 당황스러운

24 낯선, 모르는 25 여자; 여자의, 여성의

26 속삭이다. (사람·일에 대하여) 소곤소곤 이야기하다

27 결혼, 혼인 28 서랍장, 큰 상자, 장롱

29 ~이기 때문에, ~ 이래로 30 상인

31 병원, 진료소 32 해결하다, 풀다 33 진실, 사실

34 학자 35 ~ 대신에 36 ~에게 고함치다

37 ~하는 데 익숙하다 38 ~에 일생을 바치다

39 그 순간에 40 ~을 결정하다 41 비밀을 지키다

42 ~ 몰래, ~의 등 뒤에서

43 (사람들이) ~라고 한다

단어 TEST Step 2 p.45

01 afterwards 02 merchant 03 biography

04 chest 05 movement 06 ruin

07 disappointing 08 embarrassing 09 independence

10 odd 11 fortune 12 gamble

13 social studies 14 general 15 whisper

16 include 17 machine 18 scholar

19 invention 20 horrible 21 article

22 marriage 23 female 24 wonder

25 object 26 fortress 27 clinic

28 realistic 29 detective 30 save

31 husband 32 wooden 33 locker

34 strange 35 keep a secret 36 yell at

37 take a look at ~ 38 ask for

39 at that moment 40 instead of

41 try on 42 make an arrangement

43 be used to 동(명사)

단어 TEST Step 3 p.46

1 female, 여자의, 여성의 2 fortune, 재산

3 husband, 남편 4 chest, 서랍장, 큰 상자, 장롱

5 ruin, 망치다, 파산시키다 6 general, 장군

7 include, ~을 포함하다 8 biography, 자서전, 전기

9 merchant, 상인 10 save, 구하다 11 fortress, 요새

12 independence, 독립 13 article, 기사

14 movement, (정치적·사회적) 운동 15 locker, 사물함

16 scholar, 학자

대화문 TEST Step 1 p.47~49

Listen & Talk 1 Get Ready

was a painter / read, it is said, scholar / fight, both right

Listen & Talk 1 A-1

what, reading / reading, biography / haven't heard / the first female, It is said that, over, flying time

Listen & Talk 1 A-2

interesting, detective / scholar / but it is said that he was also, solved, cases / didn't know that, detective

Listen & Talk 1 B

know about / heard / Take a look at, to be included, social studies / helped, by building a clinic, that such stories, be included in / It, to, that, such

Listen & Talk 2 A-1

can't take, museum / Is it okay, water bottle / leave, in

Listen & Talk 2 A-2

welcome to, How / is it okay if I take pictures in / don't use

Listen & Talk 2 B

How was / were / get the chance to, okay if I / remember that, closes at / on, 5th floor / Let me know if

Communication Step A

are moving onto, As you can see, many, inventions, is called / musical instrument / water clock, It is said that it is, oldest, the largest / How, Is it okay if, picture of

Wrap Up 1

what, watching / watching / Isn't he, saved / It is said that he won, wooden ships / how, possible / wise general who made creative

Wrap Up 2

Would you like to / I'd like to / Here / is it okay if, bathroom / if, on, stay, your seat

Listen & Talk 1 Get Ready

A: Kim Deuksin was a painter.

B: No! I read a book and it is said that he was a scholar.

C: Don't fight. You are both right.

Listen & Talk 1 A-1

M: Lisa, what are you reading?

W: I'm reading a biography of Gwon Giok.

M: I haven't heard about her. Who is she?

W: She was the first female pilot in Korea. It is said that she had over 7,000 hours of flying time.

M: Wow, I didn't know that.

Listen & Talk 1 A-2

M: I watched an interesting movie yesterday. Jeong Yakyong was a detective in it.

W: Jeong Yakyong? Wasn't he a scholar in the Joseon Dynasty?

M: Yeah, but it is said that he was also a detective. He solved about 90 cases.

W: Oh, I didn't know that he was also a detective.

Listen & Talk 1 B

W: Hey, Mark, do you know about Father Lee Taeseok?

M: Yeah, I've heard of him. Why?

W: Take a look at this article. He is going to be included in the social studies textbook in South Sudan.

M: Wow, that's great.

W: Yeah, he helped the children by building a clinic and a school. It is said that such stories will be included in the textbook.

M: It is good to hear that students will learn about such a great person.

Listen & Talk 2 A-1

W: Excuse me, you can't take your backpack inside the museum.

M: Oh, I didn't know that. Is it okay if I bring in my water bottle?

W: Yes, that's fine. You can leave your bag in the locker.

M: Okay, thank you.

Listen & Talk 2 A-2

W: Hi, welcome to the National Museum. How can I help you?

M: Hi, is it okay if I take pictures in the museum?

W: Yes, but please don't use a flash.

M: Oh, I see. Thank you.

Listen & Talk 2 B

M: Hello, Ms. Jackson. How was your tour of the Hanok Village?

W: It was wonderful. The houses were really beautiful.

M: That's great.

W: Actually, I didn't get the chance to have dinner. Is it okay if I cook in the kitchen at this hour?

M: Yes, but please remember that the kitchen closes at 10 p.m.

W: Okay. The kitchen is on the 5th floor, right?

M: Yes, it is. Let me know if you need anything.

Communication Step A

M: All right, everyone! This way, please. Now, we are moving onto the Joseon Dynasty. As you can see, there were many interesting inventions. This one is called the *Jagyeongnu*.

W: Is it a musical instrument?

M: Actually, this is a water clock. It is said that it is the oldest and the largest water clock in Korea.

W: How amazing! Is it okay if I take a picture of it?

M: Sure.

Wrap Up 1

W: James, what are you watching?

M: Oh, I'm watching a video about Yi Sunsin.

W: Isn't he the one that saved Joseon from Japan?

M: Right. It is said that he won the war only with twelve wooden ships.

W: Wow, how can that be possible?

M: He was a wise general who made creative plans.

Wrap Up 2

W: Excuse me, sir. Would you like to have curry or *bibimbap*?

M: I'd like to have *bibimbap*, please.

W: Here you are.

M: Thank you. Oh, is it okay if I use the bathroom now?

W: Sure, but if the seat light is on, you should stay in your seat.

M: Okay, thank you.

01 Secret, My Father

02 strange, visited, asked, daughter

03 odd, used to being

04 your father's friend

05 wonder if, true

06 moment, expecting disappointing, memories

07 Back, whenever, There goes

08 from, rich family

09 Instead, living, always, gambling

10 why, which, ruins, fortune

11 gambled away, asking for

12 have, left, would, whenever

13 yell at, angrily, empty-handed

14 Bring, more

15 had already made, arrangement

16 part, tradition, chest, clothes

17 Right before, taken, money

18 angrily, such, horrible thing

19 What should, do

20 have no choice

21 have to take, chest

22 How embarrassing, behind, back

23 Since, marriage, been difficult

24 dear, continued, story

25 was not, gambler

26 family money, independence fighters

27 made himself, keep, secret

28 sure if, telling, truth

29 afterwards, out, realized, wrong

30 since, proud, devoted, movement

21 You'll have to take

22 How embarrassing, whisper behind my back

23 marriage, had been difficult for me

24 continued his story

25 a gambler   26 independence fighters

27 made himself, keep this a secret from, Japanese officers

28 if, telling, truth

29 afterwards, had been wrong

30 had devoted his life to, independence movement

1 아버지의 비밀

2 1946년에, 낯선 남자가 나를 찾아와 물었다. "당신이 김용환 씨의 딸입니까?

3 나는 파락호의 딸이라고 불리는 것이 더 익숙했으므로 나에게 이것은 이상한 질문이었다.

4 "나는 당신 아버지의 친구입니다.

5 당신은 이것이 사실인지 의아하겠지만, 당신의 아버지는…," 이라고 그 남자는 말했다.

6 나는 내 아버지에 대해 좋은 기억을 가지고 있지 않았으므로 그 순간에 실망스러운 소식을 예상하고 있었다.

7 1920년대에 마을에서 사람들이 나를 볼 때마다 그들은 "저기에 파락호의 딸이 가네."라고 말하곤 했다.

8 나의 아버지는 매우 부유한 집안의 아들이었다.

9 선비의 삶을 사는 대신, 아버지는 항상 도박장에 계셨다.

10 그것이 그가 집안의 재산을 탕진하는 사람이라는 뜻의 파락호로 불린 이유이다.

11 "네 아버지는 도박으로 모든 돈을 써 버리고 지금 더 요구하고 계신다.

12 가서 더 이상 남아 있는 돈이 없다고 말씀드려라."라고 나의 어머니는 나를 도박장으로 보낼 때마다 말씀하시곤 했다.

13 그러면, 아버지는 나에게 화를 내시며 소리치셨다. "왜 빈손으로 왔니?

14 돈을 더 가져와!"

15 내가 16살이 되었을 때, 나의 가족은 나를 서 씨와 결혼시키기로 이미 결정을 했었다.

16 결혼 풍습의 일부로, 서 씨네 가족은 새 장롱을 사라고 우리 가족에게 돈을 보냈다.

17 결혼식 바로 전날, 나의 어머니는 내 방에 들어오셔서 말씀하셨다. "네 아버지가 장롱을 살 돈을 가져가 버렸다."

18 나는 화가 나서 물었다 "어떻게 그리 끔찍한 일을 하실 수 있나요?

19 우린 이제 어떡해요?"

20 "우리에게 선택권은 없구나.

21 큰어머니의 옛 장롱을 가져가야겠구나."라고 어머니가 말씀하셨다.

01 Secret, Father

02 a strange man visited, asked

03 an odd question, was more used to being called

04 your father's friend

05 wonder if, true

06 expecting disappointing, since, good memories

07 Back, whenever, There goes

08 from, rich family

09 Instead of living, gambling house

10 That is why, was called, which, ruins

11 has gambled away, asking for

12 have no more money left, would, whenever, sent

13 would yell at, angrily, empty-handed

14 Bring me, money

15 had already made an arrangement, marry

16 As part of, a new chest for clothes

17 Right before, came into, has taken the money

18 angrily, such a horrible thing

19 What   20 no choice

22 "가문에 부끄러운 일이야."라고 사람들이 내 뒤에서 속삭이곤 했다.

23 결혼 첫날부터, 남편의 집에서의 생활은 나에게 힘겨웠다.

24 "당신의 아버지, 나의 친애하는 친구…," 나의 아버지의 친구분은 그의 이야기를 이어가셨다.

25 "그는 도박꾼이 아니었어요.

26 당신의 아버지는 가족의 돈을 만주에 있는 독립운동가들에게 보냈답니다.

27 그는 이것을 일본 순사들에게 비밀로 하기 위해 그 자신을 도박꾼처럼 보이게 했어요."

28 처음엔, 나는 그분이 사실을 얘기하시는 건지 확신할 수 없었다.

29 그러나 나중에, 나는 나의 아버지에 대한 진실을 알게 되었고 내가 아버지에 관해 오해하고 있었다는 것을 깨달았다.

30 그 순간부터, 나는 독립운동에 그의 인생을 헌신하신 파락호의 딸인 것이 자랑스러웠다.

본문 TEST Step 4-Step 5 p.59~62

1 The Secret of My Father

2 In 1946, a strange man visited me and asked, "Are you Mr. Kim Yonghwan's daughter?"

3 For me, this was an odd question because I was more used to being called the daughter of a *parakho*.

4 "I'm your father's friend.

5 You may wonder if it is true, but your father...," the man said.

6 At that moment, I was expecting disappointing news since I did not have good memories of my father.

7 Back in the 1920's, whenever people saw me in the village, they would say, "There goes the *parakho*'s daughter."

8 My father was a son from a very rich family.

9 Instead of living the life of a seonbi, he was always at the gambling house.

10 That is why he was called a *parakho*, which means someone who ruins his family's fortune.

11 "Your father has gambled away all of the money, and now he's asking for more.

12 Go and tell him that we have no more money left," my mother would tell me whenever she sent me to the gambling house.

13 Then, my father would yell at me angrily, "Why did you come empty-handed?

14 Bring me more money!"

15 When I was sixteen years old, my family had already made an arrangement for me to marry Mr. Seo.

16 As part of the wedding tradition, Mr. Seo's family sent my family some money to buy a new chest for clothes.

17 Right before the wedding day, my mother came into my room and said, "Your father has taken the money for the chest."

18 I asked angrily, "How could he do such a horrible thing?

19 What should we do now?"

20 "We have no choice.

21 You'll have to take your aunt's old chest," my mother said.

22 "How embarrassing for the family," people would whisper behind my back.

23 Since the first day of marriage, life at my husband's house had been difficult for me.

24 "Your father, my dear friend...," my father's friend continued his story.

25 "He was not a gambler.

26 Your father sent the family money to the independence fighters in Manchuria.

27 He made himself look like a gambler to keep this a secret from the Japanese officers."

28 At first, I was not sure if he was telling the truth.

29 But afterwards, I found out the truth about my father and I realized that I had been wrong about him.

30 Ever since that moment, I have been proud to be the daughter of a *parakho* who had devoted his life to the independence movement.

구석구석지문 TEST Step 1 p.63

Grammar in Real Life A

1. have many questions, your plans
2. Are, going to release
3. interested in various, genres
4. plans to work with other artists
5. going to go on, would tour

Grammar in Real Life B

1. got back home, had gone
2. seemed a little bit strange
3. remembered, had left
4. saw, had broken
5. found out, had eaten
6. At last, who did it
7. found small footprints

After You Read: Read and Write A

1. Secret

2. thought

3. was known as

4. was born into, gambled away

5. even took, a new chest for clothes

6. Actually

8. sent, independence fighters

9. made himself look like, keep this a secret

구석구석지문 TEST Step 2   p.64

Grammar in Real Life A

1. Mary Jane, your fans have many questions about your plans.

2. 1. Are you going to release a new song this month?

3. 2. Are you interested in various music genres?

4. 3. Do you have any plans to work with other artists?

5. 4. Are you going to go on a would tour this year?

Grammar in Real Life B

1. When I got back home, my parents had gone out for a walk.

2. The house was dark and quiet, but it seemed a little bit strange.

3. I remembered that I had left the door in my room open.

4. I saw that someone had broken the lamp.

5. I found out that someone had eaten my cookies on the table.

6. At last I knew who did it!

7. I found small footprints of my dog, Lucy, and the cat next door

After You Read: Read and Write A

1. The Secret of My Father

2. I thought my father was ...

3. My father was known as a *parakho*.

4. He was born into a rich family but he gambled away all of the money.

5. He even took the money for a new chest for clothes.

6. Actually my father was ...

7. My father was not a gambler.

8. He sent the family money to the independence fighters in Manchuria.

9. He made himself look like a gambler to keep this a secret from the Japanese officers.

적중 100

영어 기출 문제집

정답 및 해설

비상 | 김진완